Guide to Broadcasting Stations

Twentieth Edition

Edited by
Philip Darrington

Heinemann : Newnes

Heinemann Newnes
An imprint of Heinemann Professional Publishing Ltd

OXFORD LONDON MELBOURNE AUCKLAND
SINGAPORE IBADAN NAIROBI GABORONE KINGSTON

First published by Butterworth & Co. (Publishers) Ltd 1946
Nineteenth edition first published by Heinemann Professional Publishing Ltd, 1987
Twentieth edition, 1989

British Library Cataloguing in Publication Data

Guide to broadcasting stations. – 20th ed.
1. Radio stations – Directories
I. Darrington, Philip II. Wireless world guide to broadcasting stations
621.3841′6′025 TK6555

ISBN 0 434 90309 4

Typeset in Great Britain by
Scarborough Typesetting Services

Printed and bound in Great Britain by
Biddles Ltd, Guildford and King's Lynn

Contents

1 Choosing a short wave receiver

Richard Lambley
Communications Editor, *Electronics & Wireless World*

Few people in Britain have any grasp of the enormous scale and scope of world broadcasting. Like other European audiences, British radio listeners can choose from a wide variety of programmes from local and national services, and in general they enjoy reliable reception from powerful transmitters nearby. With so much information and entertainment so easy to find, there is little reason for most listeners to look further.

Only one foreign station at present attracts a sizeable audience in Britain, Radio Luxembourg's evening disc-jockey programmes on medium wave. Beyond this, foreign radio stations are unknown territory. Yet international broadcasting is one of the world's big growth industries. In Europe, where so few have access to radio with adequate short wave coverage, it mostly passes straight over our heads.

But in other parts of the world, radio listening on the short waves is often the norm. Poorer countries rarely have television or FM radio outside the main cities – nationwide networks giving full coverage of the population are simply too expensive to set up. On the other hand, in the tropics our familiar medium wave band is susceptible to static interference which makes it unattractive for broadcasting. To cover the wide-open spaces, radio stations are therefore forced to depend on the short waves for their basic output.

From an audience's point of view, a service on short wave lacks convenience. On a simple domestic receiver, the short wave station you want can be difficult to find. And even when you *have* tracked it down, its service may be unreliable because of varying reception conditions. But in countries where listeners are equipped to receive a national service on short wave, they can also pick and choose from a mass of foreign stations competing for their attention.

International radio

Nearly every country of any size runs an international service on the short waves; indeed, with many newly-emerging countries, the appearance of a pair of 250 kilowatt transmitters carrying broadcasts for foreign consumption is often the first sign of their presence on the stage of world affairs.

As a basic minimum, an international service can consist simply of an extra transmitter or two carrying a short wave relay of the home service, for the benefit of *émigrés* or citizens working abroad. This is the case with, for example, Radio Denmark, which broadcasts only in the Danish language. But having installed the necessary hardware, many countries seize with enthusiasm the opportunity to address a wider audience.

Operating an external service is by far the cheapest way for a country to make its voice heard. Radio programmes cost little to make and disseminate; and, though it may surprise us, acclimatized as we are to the domination of the small screen, experience has shown that they can be highly influential.

Several of the world's principal broadcasters transmit many hundreds of hours of programmes per week and can be heard right around the clock in scores of languages. Smaller stations may manage only a quarter of an hour per day, or even per week, in your language. But all have information and ideas to put across, and all are worth sampling.

The staple of these international services is almost always news; or, shall we say, that part of the news which the station wants you to be aware of. Most international broadcasting is run (or at least financed) by governments; and although a good deal of it consists merely of harmless image-building, some stations have a definite political message and make no secret of it. Try Albania's Tirana for an example.

Observant listeners soon notice that certain stations tend to interpret world events in different ways for different target audiences. It can be quite instructive to compare, say, a station's news bulletin for North America with those carried in its African or Asian service.

But it would not be fair to imply that international broadcasting is all political manipulation and aggression. Many stations confine their attentions exclusively to friendly countries – such as Radio New Zealand, which broadcasts principally to Australia, the East Indies and the Pacific islands. It is noticeable, though, that other governments can in exactly the same circumstances decide that a short wave service is not worth the expense. It was for this reason that the British Foreign Office ceased a few years ago to fund BBC vernacular broadcasts to countries such as Spain and Italy.

However, with the help of a short wave radio, listeners with an interest in current affairs can follow events in the world's trouble-spots at first hand: in between trading insults, the radio stations involved often provide the first signs of newsworthy developments. When you listen to the BBC's foreign news reports, note how frequently you hear phrases such as 'According to Radio XYZ . . .'. Even the professionals are forced to depend on radio monitoring in a crisis: when fighting breaks out or disaster strikes, it can take them hours to fly their correspondent in. But the local radio station is there on the spot. In a *coup d'état*, invariably the first action of the insurgents is to take over the microphones; and naturally the listener gets a ringside seat from which to follow the action.

An intriguing factor in many long-running conflicts is the emergence of clandestine broadcasting – undercover stations pressing the cause of one side or the other. These undercover stations have little in common with the unlicensed pop broadcasters we encounter at home. Some participants in the game complicate matters for the listener by flaunting misleading titles (such as the Voice of the Islamic Revolution of Iraq, which during the recent Gulf War appeared on schedules issued by the Voice of the Islamic Republic of *Iran*).

Feature programmes

In addition to news and current affairs, many stations broadcast feature programmes about their corner of the world, their history, customs, culture and way of life, giving opportunities for pleasurable armchair travelling. Besides promoting tourism, this type of material helps them to create the climate of goodwill in which an export trade can flourish. Radio also gives a nation a showcase to display the talents of its local artists to a world-wide audience. One regular example (and I could have quoted dozens of others) is the engaging country music from Switzerland on Swiss Radio International, 1000–1030 GMT and 1600–1700.

Recognizing the popularity of listening to short wave radio as a pastime, larger stations – and a good few tiny ones – feature special programmes for hobbyist listeners. Often these programmes are among their biggest audience-pullers. Tune to them for technical tips, equipment reviews, details of rare stations to listen out for, and up-to-date news of comings and goings on the wavebands. A list of programmes of special interest to short wave listeners (s.w.ls) appears at the end of this book. Several stations circulate useful information sheets and bulletins for hobbyists (among them are Radio Netherlands and, especially, Radio Sweden); and some (such as Radio Budapest and Radio Bucharest) run listeners' clubs. But all stations like to hear from their audiences, and they welcome letters. However, bear in mind that an established station will usually be more interested in learning your reaction to its programmes than in reading yet another reception report from someone who is merely trying to extend his collection of pennants and QSL cards. (QSL is jargon for a formal acknowledgement issued by a station to confirm an accurate reception report of one of its transmissions.) Note that *domestic* stations are not normally interested in reception reports from listeners abroad, since their programmes are intended solely for the local audience; but of course, if you do achieve some special feat of reception, it may just happen that your letter will land on the desk of an engineer who appreciates it and will respond.

Governments, however, do not have the international airwaves entirely to themselves. Another major group of programmers consists of religious organizations: examples are Trans World Radio broadcasting from Monaco, Radio HCJB from Ecuador, Radio ELWA from Liberia, and the World Christian Broadcasting Corporation from KNLS at Anchor Point, Alaska. Missionary broadcasters operate by direct transmission from their own sites, by buying time on transmitters operated by others, and by distributing recorded programmes for stations to schedule in their own output. Most are financed from the US.

Another development which has recently been gaining momentum is commercial short wave broadcasting from the USA. Despite the dominance of commercial programming on the domestic US airwaves, up to now it has had little success in international broadcasting. Nevertheless, commercial broadcasting from the US dates back to December 1939, shortly after the outbreak of war in Europe, when the United Fruit Company sponsored a 15-minute news bulletin from NBC.

Now things seem to be moving again, with the emergence of stations such as WRNO, KUSW, Radio Earth and others – some of them with interesting-looking programme schedules. One, NDXE Global Radio, even promises stereo reception: all you need, says the station, to enjoy its 'full spectrum stereo HF' is two receivers. Two years past its proposed starting date of July 1986, NDXE was still not on the air. But if you can wait, NDXE's programme plans include a varied mixture of news, features, stereo music and American radio classics such as Gunsmoke and Dragnet.

Sets for short wave

British listeners are placed in an exceptionally fortunate position, for English is the principal language of international broadcasting; which makes it all the more ironic that the general audience in Britain is so unaware of the wealth of programmes from abroad. This lack of interest has meant that few sets in British shops are equipped for any but the most cursory listening on the short waves. What coverage they give is unlikely to extend much beyond the 49 metre band. (Across the Channel, this band is known as the Europa band and is much used for short-haul international broadcasting; it is even included in some car radios.) Where further bands are provided, they are usually cramped together on the dial so that tuning through them can be discouragingly fiddly.

If you have a low-priced radio with a short wave band or two tacked on to it for luck, you should certainly be able to find some interesting foreign stations under good reception conditions. But do not expect to hear many of the rarities listed in this book. For more serious listening you will need a receiver with good technical performance, to cut a path through tangles where stations are tightly packed together, and a tuning mechanism which allows you to know accurately what frequency you have tuned to.

Of the sets listed in Table 3, all but one are imported: the exception is a low-frill, high-performance receiver designed by a British company, Lowe Electronics, well known to radio amateurs as UK agents for Trio (Kenwood) equipment. Other British sets do exist, bearing such distinguished names as Eddystone, Vigilant and Racal; but these are no-compromise instruments built to suit professional monitoring requirements. Their prices are likely to discourage all but the most dedicated of amateurs.

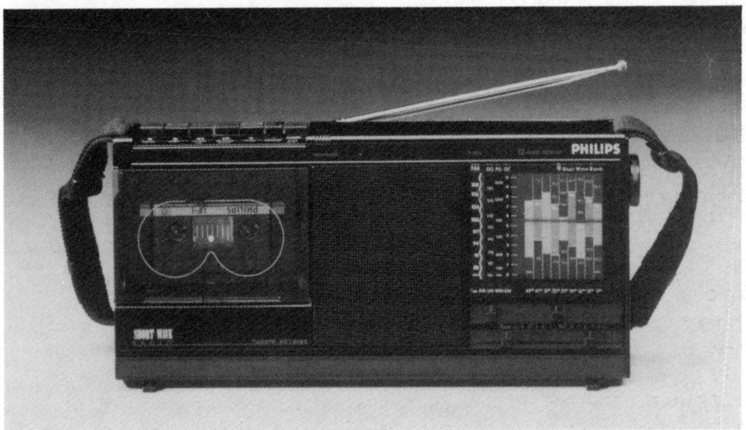

Figure 1 For recording rare finds, a radio with a built-in cassette unit could be useful. This example is the Philips D7476, which has nine short wave bands and sells for £70.

Table 1 *High frequency broadcasting bands*

Metres	*MHz*	
90	3.2–3.4	Tropical band
75	3.95–4.0	
60	4.75–5.06	Tropical band
49	5.95–6.2	
41	7.1–7.3	
31	9.5–9.7	
75	9.775–9.9	
*	11.65–11.7	
25	11.7–11.975	
*	11.975–12.05	
*22	13.6–13.8	
*19	15.1–15.45	
	15.45–15.6	
*	17.55–17.7	
*16	17.7–17.9	
13	21.45–21.75	
	21.750–21.850	
*11	25.670–26.1	

* Additional bands agreed in 1979.
Some sets also cover the 120 m tropical band, 2.3–2.49 MHz.

In recent years the more advanced short wave radios have altered almost out of recognition. Digital readouts, calculator-style keypads and often a mass of push-buttons are among the more obvious innovations. But many more subtle developments have taken place inside the casing. And so it is worth taking a little time to examine some of the features you may come across on a modern receiver.

Tuning range

One of the first points you should check when considering a set is whether it covers the frequency bands you need. The short wave range (what an engineer calls the high-frequency band) embraces all frequencies between 3 MHz and 30 MHz (100 metres to 10 metres). But broadcasters are not the only users of the radio spectrum, and all sorts of other classes of radio user use this range too. Among them are maritime radio operators, aircraft, diplomatic and military operators, news agencies and radio amateurs. So only certain sections of the short wave range are available to the broadcasters.

In principle, high-frequency broadcasting is restricted by international treaty to the bands set out in Table 1; however, it is worth noting that certain radio stations also use frequencies outside these limits. The BBC is an example: three of its principal frequencies are 9.41, 12.095 and 15.07 MHz, which lie close to but not inside the 31, 25 and 19 m bands. With the approval of the UK administration (the Radiocommunication Division of

Table 2 *HF amateur radio bands in the UK. Most speech transmissions in these bands are in single-sideband mode: you will need a set with an SSB facility to listen to them. AM, being a less efficient mode of communication, is now virtually extinct among radio amateurs*

Metres	*MHz*	*Status*
80	3.5–3.8	
40	7.0–7.1	
*	10.1–10.15	Secondary user
20 m	14.0–14.35	
*	18.068–18.168	Secondary user, morse code only
15 m	21.0–21.45	
*	24.89–24.99	Secondary user, morse code only
	10 m	28–29.7

* Additional bands agreed in 1979.

the Department of Trade and Industry) these transmissions continue, despite being within bands otherwise allocated to point-to-point transmissions.

To make room for the continuing expansion of international broadcasting, new bands marked in Table 1 by an asterisk were added in 1979 by a World Administrative Radio Conference organized by the International Telecommunications Union. In Britain, these bands have been occupied mostly by Government stations and transmitters for public telecommunications, a service which for long-haul links is increasingly moving over to satellite or cable. To give existing users time to move out, the intention was to bring the new bands into use in 1989, except for the 9 MHz band which was to become available in 1994. However, a subsequent session of the conference decided to delay matters until a satisfactory frequency-planning arrangement could be devised. Nevertheless, some stations have jumped the gun and are already occupying certain of the new frequencies.

WARC-79 also proposed extended allocations for amateur radio operators (Table 2).

Every short wave band has its own special propagation characteristics; for each one, there will be some time of the day, some season of the year, or some point in the sun's 11-year cycle at which it is the best band for the job of carrying programmes from transmitter to listener.

From the listener's point of view, some bands are more useful to have than others. Mainstream international broadcasting is to be found in the bands between 19 m and 49 m, and so you should ensure that your set covers at least these bands. Radio propagation conditions on the highest frequencies, the 11 m and 13 m bands, are unfavourable except around the peak of the solar cycle; however, at such times they can give good daytime reception over very long distances. At the other end of the scale, the 75 m band is used by broadcasters less than it ought to be because many radios cannot receive it (a chicken-and-egg situation); and the 60, 90 and 120 m tropical bands are not available to broadcasters in temperate regions such as Europe.

Take care not to confuse the bands listed in the tables with the tuning ranges selectable on your radio set. If you check carefully, you may find significant differences.

What the ranges on your set cover is a choice made by the designer, with economics in mind. Some modern receivers allow completely uninterrupted scanning of the high-frequency range; others handle it in sections, with a band selection switch for jumping from one to another. Still others may provide just the broadcast bands, with little or no coverage of the intervening ranges. Make sure that any set you are planning to buy covers the extended WARC-79 bands and, if appropriate, any out-of-band frequencies you want to use (such as the BBC frequencies mentioned above).

Despite the 1979 additions, the future of short wave broadcasting still remains somewhat uncertain. A second session of the World Administrative Radio Conference on high-frequency broadcasting in February and March 1987 failed to agree to the radically new method of allocating broadcasters' channels which the International Frequency Registration Board had put forward. This plan, which was designed to achieve the highest occupancy of each channel without creating undue interference, would have meant an end to continuous periods of broadcasting on the same frequency, and would have put listeners to the inconvenience of retuning as often as every half hour. A further WARC-HFBC will be needed to produce a more acceptable solution to the problem of overcrowding: if every country were given the allocations it has asked for, the present bands would be oversubscribed by about ten times. If no agreement can be reached, the future will bring congestion far worse than we know at present and interference will become virtually unavoidable. An increase in out-of-band broadcasting would be one of the most likely consequences. And if more than a few countries decided to step out of line and ignore the rules, a breakdown of the present system of frequency planning could become a real possibility.

It is probably unrealistic to suppose that any further HF spectrum could be turned over to broadcasting; but even if it could, the demand for frequencies would still be far too great to allow every transmitter a clear channel of its own.

Direct-broadcast satellites, which are making possible an enormous expansion in television broadcasting, seem unlikely to do the same for radio. Although the D-MAC and D2-MAC systems selected by European broadcasters for d.b.s. do carry some spare capacity suitable for radio programmes, a dish antenna (even one as small as a dinner-plate) is quite bulky compared with a radio set, and most radio listeners want something a little more portable. However, one interesting proposal being followed up by several European broadcasters is for a new radio broadcasting band in the 1000–2000 MHz region, to be used for digital broadcasting from co-ordinated groups of low-orbiting satellites. This would enable radio to upgrade to digital sound, an area where it is losing the advantage to television. And the proposed band would be suitable for car radios and portables as well as fixed hi-fi sets. But satellites, with their relatively narrow beams, are more suited to improving the coverage of domestic channels than to external broadcasting.

Direct *short wave* broadcasting from satellites has attractions. It could provide good territorial coverage and would activate the higher frequency bands which otherwise are unusable for most of the time. Unfortunately,

Figure 2 Grundig's Satellit 650 is a radio for the true enthusiast. Its microprocessor-controlled frequency synthesizer gives continuous short wave coverage from 1.6 to 30 MHz.

even the biggest satellites would not be capable of generating the amount of electrical power it would demand. At microwave frequencies, dish antennas direct a narrow beam towards a precisely-defined target zone, achieving efficient use of the few hundred watts of electricity supplied by the spacecraft's solar panels. But a space-borne dish for wavelengths numbered in tens of metres is simply too big to be practicable.

However, one decision made at the 1987 conference will have a profound effect on short wave listening, and that was the plan to abandon the use of AM.

AM, amplitude modulation, was the first method to be discovered for conveying speech and music on radio waves. In terms of efficiency and immunity to interference it is not the best one. But, where receivers are concerned it is the cheapest and least complicated; and so it is used universally for broadcasting on the long, medium and short waves. Well, perhaps not *quite* universally: one or two short wave stations have tried single-sideband modulation (SSB), the technique preferred by radio amateurs and short wave communications engineers, though with little apparent success. SSB's big advantage is that it could allow twice as many stations to be fitted into each waveband. But the penalty is that SSB receivers are more complicated to build and more expensive to buy. Tuning them accurately calls for much more precision than the average listener can be expected to muster. So in voting to drop AM in favour of SSB by the year 2015, the conference also recommended a programme of technical study aimed towards producing practical, low-cost SSB receivers.

Knobs or buttons?

Although plenty of sets still retain the familiar dial-and-pointer tuning mechanism, developments in microelectronics have made the digital frequency synthesizer a practical possibility even in portable receivers. Such sets are easily recognizable by their calculator-style digital readouts and push-button keypads for station selection.

You tune a synthesized set essentially by programming it with the frequency you want. The radio then locks on to that channel by reference to an accurate frequency source of its own, a quartz crystal oscillator inside.

Digital tuning is highly stable and repeatable; and although the principle of it may sound complicated, in practice it is ideal even for the inexperienced listener. Finding the station you want can be as easy as dialling a telephone number – provided you know the number to dial. There is no guesswork, no trial and error. And if reception is poor, you can search for an alternative frequency, secure in the knowledge that you can get back to your starting point without difficulty.

In addition, push-button sets are especially convenient for the visually handicapped user. The Kenwood R-5000 and the Icom go still further in this direction and can be fitted with a voice synthesizer option which announces the frequencies as you tune them!

For technical reasons, a digital set tends to perform slightly less well than a comparable set fitted with mechanical tuning. But most users find the convenience far outweighs any such sacrifice.

Digital sets usually give a choice of tuning methods. Often there is a keypad for direct frequency selection: you press the buttons and there you are. Favourite stations can be stored in memory for later recall; and in some sets the memory can store other data associated with each channel, such as filter or detector settings.

One model by Sony has no less than 32 memory buttons – an array which may seem excessive until you take into account the number of times a broadcaster may need to switch frequency to get through the day in some parts of the world. In general, propagation conditions at night mean lower frequencies, while daylight demands higher ones. At dawn and dusk, conditions in the ionosphere change rapidly; and so during breakfast time, always a peak listening period, the frequency for optimum reception may shift up through as many as six bands in only half an hour. The listener with all six programmed into his set can follow the ionosphere at the touch of a button.

Most synthesized receivers also offer scanning modes, which can save you the bother of re-keying a long number if you only want to adjust the tuning a little. Scanning enables you to roam up and down a band as if you were twiddling the tuning knob of a conventional set. Indeed, some models do actually have a tuning knob: this simulates electronically the action of a mechanical tuner, and for the user it is far more pleasant than fumbling with a pair of 'up' and 'down' buttons. In fact, it can be even better than a real mechanical tuning knob: with cheap sets, backlash in the string and pulley system tends to make the tuning drift off your chosen frequency when you let go of the knob.

In some models, scanning can be executed automatically. Several offer a choice of scanning modes, but usually they allow you at least to search a predefined band of frequencies for an occupied channel, or to flip through the stations you have programmed into the memories.

But automation can be developed further still. Automatic or remote-controlled operation is a common requirement in professional monitoring, where receivers are often grouped in a technical area and operated from a control position elsewhere. Today remote-control facilities are becoming available also to the private user.

The Icom, JRC and Yaesu sets, and the Kenwood R-5000, may be linked if you wish, to a personal computer, which then takes command of all major receiver functions. With a set-up like this, you could switch effortlessly from one station to another simply by picking them from a menu displayed on the computer screen. The computer would take care of all the adjustments and switch settings. Or you could automate your regular listening by storing station schedules on floppy disc and instructing the computer to retune at appropriate times. If you wanted to study ionospheric propagation, or the occupancy of particular bands, the system could scan those frequencies tirelessly for hours on end, and print its results in graphical form or as a listening log – just as professional HF scheduling engineers do.

Listeners familiar with the traditional tuning knob may be disconcerted to discover that with a synthesized set you cannot adjust the tuning smoothly and continuously. Always, the set jumps from one frequency to another in small, discrete steps defined by circuitry associated with the quartz crystal that governs it. To take an example from among the portable sets, the Sony ICF7600DS tunes the long wave band in 3 kHz steps, medium wave in 9 kHz, short wave in 5 kHz and VHF/FM in 100 kHz. These steps have been chosen to suit the channel-spacings on each band, enabling the listener to hop nimbly from one station to another as the tuning is altered.

This is fine with sets intended primarily for broadcast listening, with channels spaced several kilohertz apart. But in communications receivers designed for more demanding applications a smaller tuning interval is desirable; and on some it can be as little as 10 Hz, which for all practical purposes feels like no interval at all.

The main difficulty with synthesized sets is their tendency to be overloaded by very strong signals. Weak signals (on their own) are rarely a problem in short wave radio, since the limit to what you can receive is more often determined by interference than by the sensitivity of your set. Overloading by a strong signal will not physically damage your set (except maybe in extreme cases such as where lightning is involved!); but it may cause the electronics to misbehave, producing effects such as stations appearing on the wrong frequency, stations mixed up together, and distorted sound. Even when the signal is below the level that produces such gross symptoms of overloading, it may degrade reception of weaker signals on neighbouring frequencies. Such problems can be minimized by the set designer, though at a price.

With low-cost portables you may find you can provoke the effects of overloading by connecting an external antenna (which in other circumstances would be a desirable thing to have). If the manufacturer expected you to rely wholly on the built-in telescopic antenna, he may not have spent his resources on making the receiver proof against high signal levels.

Figure 3 Options available with this receiver by Icom include an infra-red remote control handset, an interface which enables you to control it from your computer, and a voice synthesizer which announces the frequency you're tuned to.

Susceptibility to overloading is not peculiar to synthesized sets; it is just that it is harder (and therefore more expensive) to build resistance to it into an electronically-tuned set than into an ordinary one. The more elaborate sets (of all kinds) usually have a switchable or variable attenuator (or RF gain control) to help you cope with such situations; in its simplest form this may be a two-position switch marked 'Local-Distant' or 'Local-DX'. Some sets have special circuitry to help minimize the problem.

One further difficulty with synthesizers is that their complex circuitry may draw a heavy current. Some such portables have a battery life no longer than nine or ten hours, but this may not discourage you if you intend to operate the set mostly on its mains unit.

Now that nickel-cadmium rechargeable cells are sold in most of the standard battery sizes, you may find them a money-saving alternative if you intend to use your set a lot. But bear in mind that these cells give a lower voltage than ordinary throwaway batteries, and that some radios (synthesized models especially) may not work properly with them. Check the instructions to see whether the set-maker has given any warning about this.

Some sets, especially the bigger communications receivers, can be run from a car battery. A special adapter may be necessary.

Largely for reasons of marketing strategy, digital tuning is still found mainly in the more expensive sets. Just as electronic calculators, watches and computers have fallen in price, so could electronically-tuned radio sets: a synthesizer on a chip could easily be made for less than the price of a good dual drive mechanism. The wider availability of cheap digital sets could do plenty to encourage short wave listening.

A straw in the wind was the arrival during 1988 from Toshiba and others of portable radio-cassette stereo units with digital tuners, some of them priced well below £100. Besides the usual long, medium and FM bands, some of these sets cover the useful short wave bands between 5 and 16 MHz. Although their tuning system is not ideal (the 'up' and 'down' buttons are more cumbersome than a direct-entry key-pad), the sets can store and recall a number of frequencies and are very convenient for everyday listening. An interesting model from Sony with dual cassette decks (CFS-W501L) has short wave coverage extending to 21.9 MHz, though the BBC frequencies 18.080 MHz and 15.070 MHz are not available because they fall into gaps between its bands. This set is not part of Sony's regular UK range, but seems to be available in London as a 'grey import', from dealers in Tottenham Court Road and elsewhere.

Note that not all sets with a digital display have genuine synthesized tuning: in a few, the display simply monitors the setting of a mechanical tuner.

Modulation modes

Several methods exist for impressing a sound signal on to radio waves, but in short wave broadcasting, amplitude modulation is almost universal – just as it is in the long and medium wave bands. Nevertheless, some sets are equipped to receive other modes of transmission. Commonest of these is single sideband, or SSB.

For an explanation of SSB signals, you should study a book on amateur radio; but to hear one, tune to the 7 MHz or 14 MHz amateur bands (Table 2). Speech from SSB stations emerges from ordinary AM receivers as an unintelligible squawking sound, often likened to the voice of Donald Duck. But with a suitable radio in experienced hands, all becomes clear.

Among radio amateurs and professional radio operators, SSB is much preferred because it gives better communications ability for less transmitter power. But with the decision of the 1987 World Administrative Radio Conference to switch short wave broadcasting to SSB by the year 2015, we shall have to become accustomed to it. However, the form of SSB the engineers have in mind will be a modified version which should prove as simple to tune in as present-day AM. Switching to SSB would double the capacity of the short wave spectrum, making room for many new stations; but broadcasters are well aware of the enormous number of AM only radios now in the hands of their listeners, and do not lightly contemplate making them all obsolete.

A few broadcasters have used SSB already (e.g. Radio Sweden), though mostly on out-of-band frequencies to feed programmes to overseas relay stations. These out-of-band transmissions are not intended for direct reception by the public; their frequencies are rarely published and schedules may be changed without warning.

With a feeder transmitter, it is possible to use the upper and lower sidebands simultaneously to carry separate programmes, a practice known as independent sideband working (ISB). But with the advent of cheap satellite circuits which give more consistent sound quality, SSB feeders have become a less attractive option.

The SSB setting on your receiver can also be used for listening to morse-code signals. But because morse signals take up less room in the radio spectrum than speech, they can be packed together more tightly; and so for the best results you need a set with special narrow filters which can discriminate sharply between closely-spaced transmissions.

Some of the more expensive sets have an advanced type of detector suitable for both AM and SSB. This circuit, which may be described in the brochure as a synchronous demodulator, gives noticeably lower distortion on AM reception. That alone might be enough to recommend it. But the synchronous demodulator if used properly can also help deal with back-

Figure 4 Panasonic's RF-B60 can be tuned in two ways: by the keypad, for instant direct access, or by a rotary electronic dial for easy scanning. The multi-colour liquid crystal display includes a signal strength indicator and a dual time zone clock.

ground noise. By treating an AM transmission as a double SSB signal, it enables the user to choose which sideband to listen to. And often one sideband will be much less affected by interference or monkey-chatter than the other. If you listen to short wave broadcasts regularly for information and entertainment (rather than merely for logging transmitters) you may well think this a refinement worth paying for.

Professional-style communication receivers may in addition be fitted with a detector for narrow-band FM transmissions (NBFM). This mode is a cut-down version of the technique used for VHF/FM broadcasting, and is widely used for civil radio communications. Citizen's band radio operators (the legal variety) use NBFM in Britain in their 27 MHz allocation and some radio amateurs have adopted it for local commmunications on 28–29.7 MHz. Otherwise the mode is not commonly used below 30 MHz; but a set with an NBFM detector can also be used for receiving radio-teleprinter or facsimile transmissions, which can be overheard as warbling sounds in the spaces between the HF broadcast bands.

These transmissions come from news agencies, weather bureaux, commercial operators and diplomatic sources. Many are encrypted to a greater or lesser degree; but if you can interface your set to a suitable home computer which can act as a receiving terminal, you may find a good deal of interest value in them. Note, however, that in Britain you are not normally permitted to monitor transmissions other than those from broadcasting stations, licensed amateurs and stations in the standard frequency and time service.

Selectivity

Stations in the short wave bands normally operate on frequencies which are multiples of 5 kHz (on medium and long waves in Europe a spacing of 9 kHz

Figure 5 High performance and a mass of advanced features put the NRD-525 from the Japan Radio Company firmly in the professional class. Optional extras include a demodulator for receiving radio teleprinter signals, and a computer interface. Using this, you can control the receiver from a program by entering frequency, mode, bandwidth, time and other data. Picture from S.M.C.

has been introduced). Any AM station 5 kHz away from the wanted one will give rise to a piercing 5 kHz whistle unless steps are taken to suppress it, and so manufacturers generally provide some audio filtering. Sometimes they add a speech/music switch, which, in the speech position removes the bass and emphasizes the mid-treble content to give extra punch for broadcasts such as news.

But most of a set's selectivity is achieved not in its audio department but in the intermediate frequency (IF) amplifier.

Virtually all modern radios are of the so-called supersonic heterodyne, or *superhet* type. In a superhet receiver, incoming signals of whatever frequency, are mixed with a locally-generated signal from an oscillator controlled by the tuning knob and so transposed or converted to a third frequency. Further processing of the radio signal is all carried out at this fixed intermediate frequency, because it is much easier to design highly selective filters for a single frequency than to make adjustable ones.

The filters need to be quite complex in any case, and in more expensive models it is desirable to make the selectivity switchable to suit differing listening conditions. The quality of the filter naturally has a big influence on both sound quality and susceptibility to unwanted signals.

For better performance, good-quality sets commonly convert twice, with IF amplifiers operating at different frequencies. When manufacturers have gone to the expense of dual conversion in a design aimed at a broad market, they can usually be relied to advertise the fact. However, with top-of-the-range synthesized sets it is safe to assume dual conversion even where it is not mentioned.

Good filtering in the early (radio frequency, or RF) stages of the receiver is necessary too, for controlling problems such as image interference. Despite its name, this phenomenon has nothing to do with television, but refers to phantom appearances of stations at points on the radio dial where they do not belong. Such interference often arises when a strong signal meets a cheap radio set.

Table 3 *Short wave receivers*

Maker	Model	Price £	Style	Dig. syn.	H.f. mem.	Coverage vhf	lf	mf	75	49	41	31	25	22	19	16	13	11	ssb /cw	nbfm	r.f. atten	No of conv.	Bandw. sel.	Comments
Goodmans	ATS 801[1]	70	P	■	25	■	■	■		+	+	+	+	+	+									F.m. stereo on headphones
	SG789L	35	P			■	■	■		■	+	■	■		o	+	+							F.m. stereo on headphones
Grundig	Satellit 650	450	T	■	32	■	■	■	+	+	+	+	+	+	+	+	+	+	■		■	2	■	Keypad, l.c.d., many features
	Satellit 400	200	P	■	24	■	■	■	+	+	+	+	+	+	+	+	+	+				2	■	Keypad, l.c.d., many features
	Yacht Boy 215		P			■	■	■		■	+	+	+		■	+	+							Built-in l.c.d. alarm clock
	Concert Boy 225	40	P			■	■	■		+	+	+	+	+	+	+								Four f.m. presets; mains/batt.
	Music Boy 165	30	P			■	■	■		+	+	+	+	+	+	+								Mains/battery
Icom	IC-R71E	821	T	■	32		+	+	+	+	+	+	+	+	+	+	+	+	■	opt	■	4	■	Computer interface option etc.
ITC	Roksana	35	P			■	■	■		■	■	+	■		■	+								Compact, low cost
	Sabina	49	P			■	■	■		■	■	■	■		■	■	■					2		Battery/mains operation
JRC	NRD-525	1195	T	■	200		+	+	+	+	+	+	+	+	+	+	+	+	■	■	■	2	■	Computer control option
Kenwood	R-2000	595	T	■	10		+	+	+	+	+	+	+	+	+	+	+	+	■	■	■		■	Many features
	R-5000	875	T	■	100		+	+	+	+	+	+	+	+	+	+	+	+	■	■	■		■	Many features; noise blanker
Lowe	HF-125	375	T/P	■	30		+	+	+	+	+	+	+	+	+	+	+	+	■	opt	■	2	■	Opt. sync. a.m. demodulator
Panasonic	RF B600LBE	500	T	■	9	■	■	■	+	+	+	+	+	+	+	+	+	+	■		■	2	■	Many features
	RF B60DL	170	P	■	9	■	■	■	+	+	+	+	+	+	+	+	+	+			■	2		Keypad, l.c.d., dual clock
	RF B40DL	140	P	■	27	■	■	■	+	+	+	+	+	+	+	+	+	+				2		Keypad, l.c.d.
	RF B20DL	75	P			■	■	■		■	■	■	■		■	■					■	2		Compact
	RF B10	60	P			■	■	■		■	■	■	■		■	■					■			Very compact
	RF 1680L	40	P			■	■	■		■	+	+	+	+	+	+								Basic portable
Philips	D1835 Compass		P			■	■	■		■	■	■	■	■	■	■	■	■						Compact portable
	D2935		P	■	9	■	+	+	+	+	+	+	+	+	+	+	+	+	■		■	2		Keypad, l.c.d.
	D2999		T/P	■	16	■	+	+	+	+	+	+	+	+	+	+	+	+	■		■	2	■	Many features
Saisho[3]	SW3500	50	P			■		■		■	■	■	■	■										Compact portable
Sanyo	RP8801		P			■	■	■		■	■	■	■	■	■	■	■					2		Compact portable
Sony	ICF2001D	330	P	■	32	+	+	+	+	+	+	+	+	+	+	+	+	+	■		■	2	■	Synchronous a.m. detector
	ICF5100		P			+	■	■		■	■	■	■		■	■	■					2		One-chip design
	ICF7600A		P			+	■	■		■	■	■	■		■	■	■					2		Bandspread feature
	ICF7600DA		P	■	15	■	■	■	+	+	+	+	+	+	+	+	+	+				2		Digital/analogue l.c.d. dial
	ICF7600DS	170	P	■	10	+	+	+	+	+	+	+	+	+	+	+	+	+	■			2		Keypad, four-way tuning, clock
	ICF7601L	100	P			■	■	■		■	■	■	■		■	■	■					2		Led tuning indicator
	ICF-PRO80	350	P	■	40	+	+	+	+	+	+	+	+	+	+	+	+	+	■	■			■	Covers 0.15-108MHz; 115-223 opt.
	ICF-SW1S kit	250	P	■	10	+	+	+	+	+	+	+	+	+	+	+	+	+						Tiny, but excellent performance
Supertech	WE-9	39	P			■	■	■		■	+	■	o		o	+								Compact
	SR-16DN[2]	130	P	■	9	+	+	+	+	+	+	+	+	+	+	+	+	+	■		■	2	■	F.m. stereo on headphones
Toshiba	RPF11		P			■	■	■		+	+	+	+	+	■	+	+	+						Compact
Vega	Selena 205	35	P			■	■	■		■	■	■	+		■	■								Tuning meter; very cheap
	206	25	P				+	■	+	+	+	+	+		o	o	o							Very cheap
Yaesu	FRG8800	639	T	■	12	opt	+	+	+	+	+	+	+	+	+	+	+	+	■	■	■		■	Computer control option

Style: P denotes a portable, T a tabletop model.

Frequency coverage:
■ denotes that the set covers the whole band including any WARC'79 extensions;
+ indicates that the set covers the whole WARC'79 band and significantly more;
o denotes that the set omits part of the new WARC'79 band.

Notes
1. The Sangean ATS-801 is similar.
2. Similar models include Uniden CR2021, Sangean ATS-803A, Realistic DX-440 (Tandy shops, £150), Saisho SW5000 (Dixons, £100) and Matsui MR-4099 (Curry's, £100).
3. Brand name of Dixons shops.

Some addresses
Icom: Icom (UK) Ltd, Sea Street, Herne Bay, Kent CT6 8LD.
ITC, Supertech: P.J.E. Marketing Ltd, Sporhams Farm House, Sporhams Lane, Danbury, Chelmsford, Essex CM3 4AJ.
Kenwood, Lowe: Lowe Electronics Ltd, Chesterfield Road, Matlock, Derbyshire DE4 5LE.
Vega: TOE (London) Ltd, Zenith House, The Hyde, Edgware Road, London NW9 6EE.
Yaesu, JRC: South Midlands Communications Ltd, School Close, Chandlers Ford Industrial Estate, Eastleigh, Hampshire SO5 3BY.

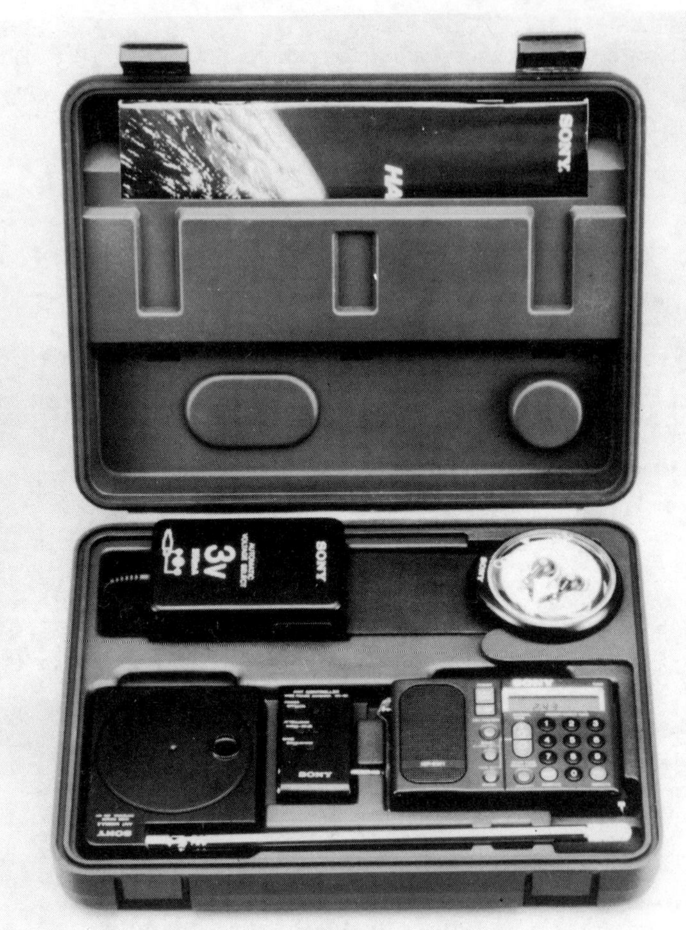

Figure 6 Sony's ICF-SW1 is scarcely larger than an audio cassette box, but its performance would do credit to much larger receivers.

Another feature desirable for listening under difficult conditions is a noise-blanker. This circuit suppresses abrupt bursts of energy, such as those caused by lightning, which might discomfort the listener. Less startling but more frustrating is repetitive noise, like the so-called Russian Woodpecker, an over-the-horizon short wave radar. Some sets have a blanker which can help suppress this too.

Sets available in the UK

Table 3 summarizes the vital statistics of most short wave receivers now available in Britain at prices below about £1000. A few other sets with some HF coverage are on the market, among them some radio-cassette recorders.

Such brief details cannot give more than a hint of the capabilities of the more expensive sets, or convey the many options that can be fitted to some of them. Among these are converters for other bands, especially for the VHF communications bands, teleprinter interfaces and additional filters. For more information you should ask for the manufacturer's literature.

2 A guide to listening

Pat Hawker
Engineering Information Officer, IBA

Many people needlessly confine listening to radio to just a few programmes from the national, regional or local transmitters serving their own locality. Yet radio waves recognize no manmade frontiers; broadcasting is, or could be, an international medium, limited primarily by different languages. It is possible to receive and enjoy programmes from all parts of the globe. The expatriate can keep in touch with his homeland; the music lover can listen to the pick of the world's concerts; foreign languages can be mastered; nations can speak peace – or spread disenchantment – across frontiers. But there is also a fascination in exploring the radio waves and identifying far off stations that others might regard as virtually impossible to receive.

In the early days of broadcasting almost every listener was an enthusiast seeking receivers that would bring in many stations 'at full loudspeaker strength'. The stations were fewer, the bands less crowded, the special properties of HF (short-waves) still largely unknown. Those days are long gone but interest in DX – the reception of far-off stations – has remained.

One reason perhaps is that short waves still offer a challenge – despite high-power transmitters and overseas relay stations one can never be quite sure what the day will bring: conditions in the form of good or poor signals, vary from day to day, season to season, affected by the mysterious 11-year-or-so 'sunspot cycle'. To listen to desired stations on short waves is not just a matter of switching on the receiver. You need to know something about the propagation of radio waves; something about antennas (aerials); something about what makes some receivers good, some poor; something about the frequency bands used by broadcasting stations; and, of course, the frequencies actually used by the stations of interest.

Broadcasting frequencies

Broadcasting is only one of many services that use the radio (electromagnetic) spectrum. Other radio communication and radio and radar navigation services all require access to the limited usable radio spectrum.

All forms of electromagnetic radiation travel at the same speed which is very nearly 300,000,000 metres per second (roughly 186,000 miles per second). Hence the time for one complete cycle of energy to pass a given place determines the wavelength (l) in the specific relationship.

$$300{,}000{,}000 = \text{frequency (Hz)} \times \text{wavelength (metres)}$$

or

$$300 = \text{frequency (MHz)} \times \text{wavelength (metres)}$$

Thus

$$\text{frequency (kHz)} = 300{,}000/l$$

$$\text{frequency (MHz)} = 300/l$$

or

$$\text{wavelength (metres)} = 300{,}000/\text{f (kHz)}$$

For historic reasons, it is still common practice in a few countries to refer to broadcasting stations in terms of wavelength but it is more convenient to use frequencies, kHz (1000 Hz), MHz (1,000,000 Hz or 1000 kHz) or even GHz (1000 MHz). Nevertheless it is still customary to refer to the long waves, the medium waves, short waves and to talk of the 19-metre band etc.

Radio waves at significantly different frequencies tend to behave differently and to be suitable for different forms of broadcasting. The detailed study of the ways in which radio waves are propagated is a complex branch of the science of radio physics. Unlike light rays (another form of electromagnetic radiation) radio signals at the frequencies used for sound broadcasting are not cut off sharply by hills or by the optical horizon. How far beyond the optical horizon that they travel is determined at medium and high frequencies by the presence or absence of ionized reflecting layers in the upper atmosphere (ionosphere). Very high frequencies are affected by atmospheric conditions existing within a few miles of the earth's surface (troposphere).

The main broadcasting bands are shown in Table 4.

Long waves (LF) are used for broadcasting only in Europe. High power transmissions have a consistent range of several hundred kilometres both day and night.

Medium waves (MF) are used for broadcasting (AM) in all parts of the world. In daylight, signals are reliably propagated by means of ground waves over distances of some tens of kilometres depending largely upon the power and size of the transmitting antenna. The sky waves are absorbed in the D-layer of the ionosphere (about 75–95 km above the earth's surface). At dusk, however, the ionization of the D-layer is much reduced, and medium-frequency signals pass through, but are reflected by the ionized E-layer about 110 km high. These reflected signals can be received up to many hundred or even a few thousand kilometres distant. However in those areas where both the ground and sky waves are received simultaneously, there can be severe fading.

Short waves (HF) are at frequencies between 3 to 30 MHz, including the broadcasting bands at roughly 3.9, 4.85, 6.1, 7.2, 9.65, 11.85, 15.3, 17.8, 21.6 and 25.85 MHz, the propagation is almost entirely by means of sky waves, the ground wave from even high power transmitters becoming rapidly attenuated. However the effect of the ionosphere becomes increasingly complex, and more liable to variations, as the frequency increases. For long periods of the night, few if any signals will be heard above 15 MHz. This will be particularly the case during sunspot minimum years; periods during which even in midday it will be rare to receive distant transmissions in the 26 MHz band.

HF transmissions below about 10 MHz may be reflected over medium distances from the E layer, but the main propagation mode depends on the F layer(s) between about 200 and 400 km above earth. In daylight there are usually two separate layers, the higher (F2) layer results in signals being reflected over distances of around 2500 km in a single hop. The lower (F1) layer reflects daytime transmissions up to about 10 MHz at distances up to about 1500 km. Unfortunately sky wave transmissions tend to suffer considerable selective fading due to the interaction of signals reflected from different layers of the ionosphere, etc. and can result in severe distortion of an amplitude modulated transmission.

Table 4 *Radio broadcasting frequency allocations*

Band	*Frequency*	*Wavelength (approx.)*	*Area and notes*
Long waveband	148.5–283.5 kHz	2020–1080 m	Region 1
Medium waveband	526.5–1606.5 kHz	570–187 m	Region 2 to extend up to 1705 kHz
120 m band	2300–2495 kHz	130–120 m	Tropical band
90 m band	3200–3400 kHz	93.7–88.2 m	Tropical band
75 m band	3950–4000 kHz	76–75 m	Regions 1 and 3 only
60 m band	4750–5060 kHz	63.2–59.3 m	Tropical band
49 m band	5950–6200 kHz	50.4–48.4 m	All regions
41 m band	7100–7300 kHz	42.3–41.1 m	Regions 1 and 3 only
31 m band	9500–9900 kHz	31.6–30.3 m	All regions
25 m band	11,650–12,050 kHz	25.8–25.9 m	All regions
22 m band	13,600–13,800 kHz	22.2–21.7 m	All regions
19 m band	15,100–15,600 kHz	19.9–19.2 m	All regions
16 m band	17,550–17,900 kHz	17.1–16.8 m	All regions
14 m band	21,450–21,850 kHz	14–13.7 m	All regions
11 m band	25,650–26,100 kHz	11.7–11.5 m	All regions
VHF/FM band	88–108 MHz	3.4–2.8 m	All regions

Notes: The frequencies listed above are those agreed under the 1982 Radio Regulations Table and include frequencies subject to delays in transfer from other radio services.

For historic reasons some broadcast services use frequencies just outside the limits shown. There are also some non-tropical areas operating broadcast transmitters in the tropical bands.

Region 1 comprises Europe, Africa, USSR and Turkey.
Region 2 comprises the Western Hemisphere: North and South America, Greenland and Pacific territories for which the FCC is the regulatory body.
Region 3 Oceania, Australasia and Asia, except some territories included in Regions 1 and 2.

HF conditions

A listener soon learns that HF propagation is subject to many changing factors that influence the state of the ionospheric layers and dramatically vary their ability to reflect or alternatively to absorb (attenuate) the signals.

The state of the ionospheric routinely varies with the time of day, the seasonal changes in the pattern of night and day, and the position within the 11-year sunspot cycle. The sunspot cycle, moreover, is far from having a regular or predictable pattern and there is still no reliable way of predicting the start or finish of a cycle. Sunspot maxima occurred around 1947, 1958, 1969 and 1979 and sunspot minima around 1953, 1964, 1974 and 1986, but the sunspot count for the different maxima vary considerably and the duration of the minima also changes in each cycle.

During sunspot maxima the higher HF bands provide strong signals over longer periods of the day.

A rather different form of ionospheric disturbance – the fadeout or sudden ionospheric disturbance (SID) – is even more spectacular but seldom lasts very long, and only during daylight. In its most extreme form, relatively rare, it results in the virtual disappearance or greatly reduced strength of all sky wave signals over much of the HF spectrum, although some signals may continue to come through on the *higher* frequencies. It occurs quite suddenly but seldom lasts more than one or two hours.

During sunspot maxima the higher HF bands provide strong signals from distant stations over quite long periods of the day and frequencies up to

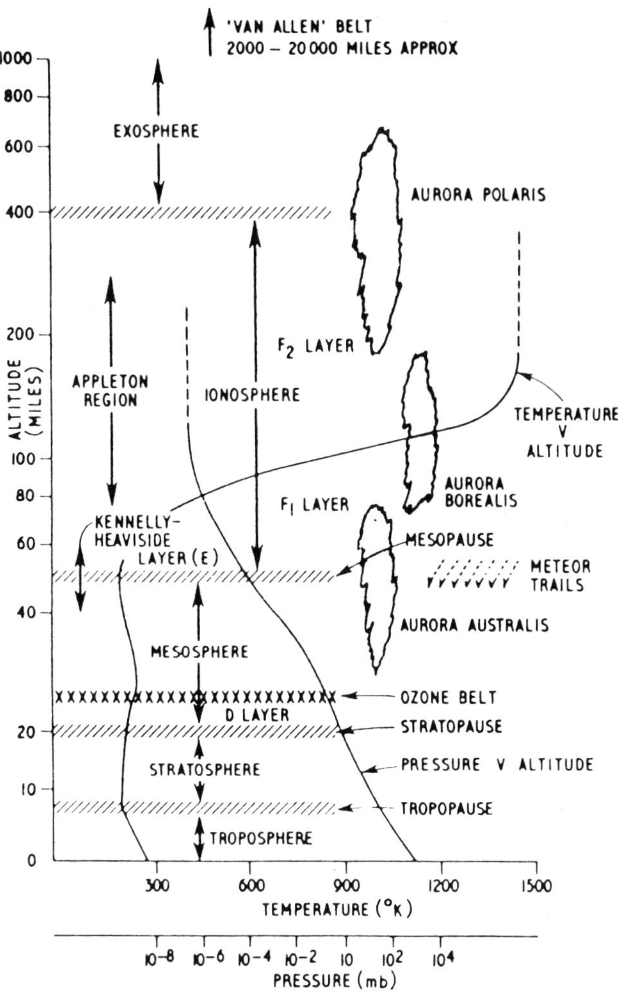

Figure 7 Earth's atmosphere and structure

15 MHz may remain 'open' throughout the night. In general transmissions over an all-daylight path (i.e. north/south paths) are heard on higher frequencies more reliably than signals arriving on east/west paths. Optimum frequencies also depend on the latitude of the listener; the listener in or near the tropics will usually hear more stations on higher frequencies than a listener in, say, Scandinavia.

The normal pattern of HF conditions can be upset by ionospheric storms that may last several days. During such storms signals deteriorate on the higher frequency bands but may continue to be reasonable on bands below about 8 MHz. The effects will be most noticeable at night.

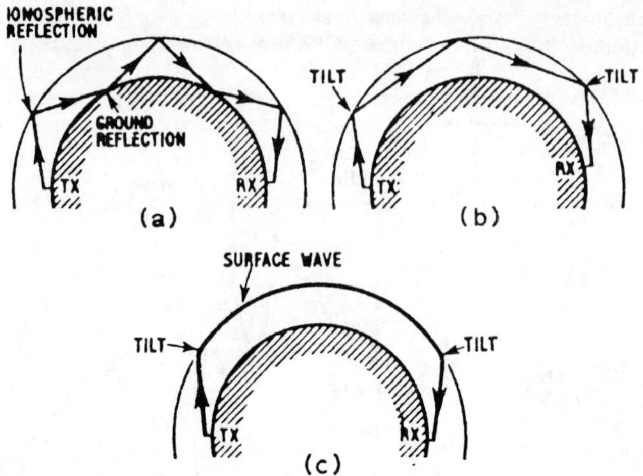

Figure 8 (a) Conventional 'HF' multihop path with two ground reflection points. (b) Chordal hop path sometimes with wave trapped between ionospheric layers. (c) Another possible form of chordal hop

HF signals reflected from the F2 layer can travel to distant parts of the globe by a series of hops each of about 4000 km (2500 miles), as they are reflected also from the surface of the earth. For many years it was assumed that, for example, signals reaching Australia or New Zealand from Europe were propagated in this multi-hop form. However it is now appreciated that a better and more reliable form of long-distance propagation occurs over paths where dawn and dusk coincide when signals are propagated over very

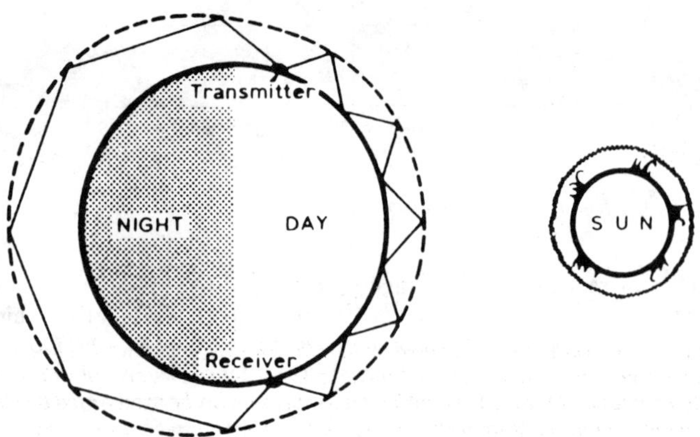

Figure 9 The change of effective height of the ionospheric reflecting layer around dusk and dawn produces the tilts that make possible chordal hop propagation for long-path transmissions, with low darkness attenuation and elimination of multiple ground-reflection losses that occur on the daylight short-path transmissions

long-distances along darkness paths without intermediate ground reflection, a mode of propagation known as chordal hop arising from ionospheric tilts that occur during the dawn and dusk periods when the F1 and F2 layers combine or separate. This mode tends to result in the signals travelling over the long path from Europe to Australasia across South America rather than the shorter path across Asia.

It should be appreciated that radio signals normally travel along the great circle path which represents the shortest route that can be measured on a

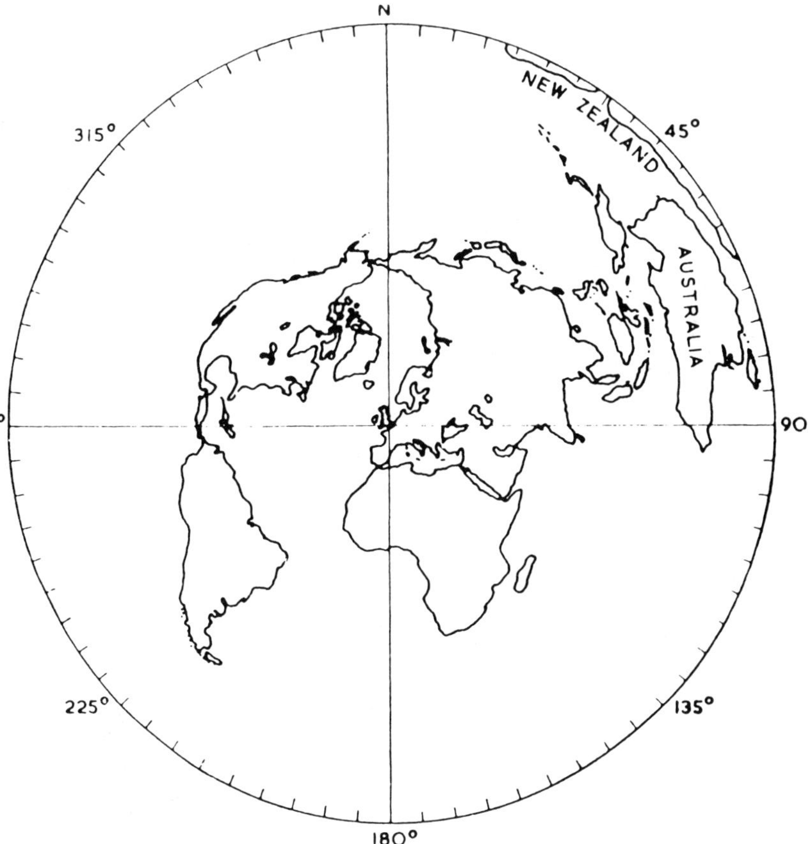

Figure 10 A great circle map, based on the UK. This is how the world appears to an amateur transmitter. Radio signals travel along great circle routes (which are the shortest routes on the globe and which on the map would be represented by straight lines radiating outwards from the centre). Such a map is essential when planning an antenna installation as it shows the directions along which signals will travel to particular countries. However, it should be noted that, in the mornings, signals to and from Australia, New Zealand and the Far East often travel the 'long way round' across South America. These directions will be exactly 180° more than those indicated on the map.

globe. This often implies a very different route direction than might be imagined from a conventional map, based for example on a map based on Mercator's projection. A great circle map applies only to a specific geographic region.

A map for UK listeners is shown in Figure 10 but to a listener in, say, India or Australia, the radio paths would look very different. A map is available from BBC External Services that enables a listener in any part of the world to estimate his radio bearing from London.

The great circle bearing becomes important where a listener decides to use a directional antenna to improve reception of a particular station. However apart from the ferrite-rod or frame antennas used on medium waves and on the low HF bands it must be appreciated that few simple or low-cost receiving antennas can be expected to show a marked directional gain. Although the half-wave dipole antenna is often regarded as broadly direction broadside to the element, this is true only of dipoles erected at least about a half-wave above ground and clear of local objects.

Interference

The very large number of broadcast transmissions in the medium and short wave bands, combined with the increasing use of extremely high power transmitters of 250, 500, 750 or even 1000 kilowatts output, has meant that interference limits rather than signal strength now defines the coverage area of many services. Since, on the medium wave band, interference levels rise substantially during the hours of darkness, the reliable coverage area at night of an MF transmitter may fall to about a quarter of its daytime area.

The spacing between MF channels is 9 kHz in Europe and 10 kHz in North America. Even with restricted audio frequencies, some radiation occurs in the adjacent channel and some degree of adjacent channel interference is inevitable at night, although either co-channel or adjacent-channel interference can often be reduced to acceptable levels by means of a directional frame or ferrite-rod antenna.

On HF the international channel spacing is only 5 kHz and adjacent-channel interference can be a serious problem.

A major problem is also the worldwide effects of deliberate interference, in the form of jamming transmissions stemming mainly from some Eastern European countries. Although intended to prevent listening in those countries to the external broadcasts directed at them, the jamming affects listeners worldwide. At peak listening times, it has been estimated that as much as 60 to 70 per cent of available spectrum is being affected by the jamming signals.

For example, the Russians currently jam, in a highly sophisticated manner, the Russian-language programmes of the Voice of America, BBC, Deutsche Welle, Radio Free Europe, Radio Liberty, Radio Israel and Radio Peking. This is done from an elaborate and costly network of ground wave jammers in the main urban areas of more than 100,000 population and powerful sky wave jammers to blanket surburban and rural areas. This network can be rapidly switched on when objectionable programmes begin.

The jamming of transmissions has also resulted in the use of a large number of transmitters on different frequencies in attempts to circumvent the jammers. This results in greatly overcrowding the broadcast spectrum and, in turn, to the use of more jammers. See Chapter 4 for an anti-jamming short wave aerial design that was first published in *Electronics & Wireless World*.

Non-deliberate mutual interference between HF transmissions also arises from poor spectrum management and lack of experience in the control of transmitters in some countries. The HF spectrum is the least well regulated of any of the broadcasting allocations and it has proved extremely difficult to obtain the necessary degree of co-operation in international planning or in compliance with the Radio Regulations of the International Telecommunication Union.

Electrical interference

Electrical disturbances from nearby electrical apparatus are among the most frequent causes of unsatisfactory reception on long, medium and short wavebands. Any electrical apparatus which includes any mechanism which generates power, however minute, at radio frequencies will tend to radiate interference unless preventative measures have been or are taken. Interference most commonly arises from small sparks caused during switching, for example by the thermostats used in central heating systems, or in the small electric motors used in many domestic and industrial appliances. More recently the generation of high-speed pulses, for example in home computers, or within television receivers, has added to the levels of electrical interference in most urban areas. Although most countries have legislation which is intended to reduce the levels of electrical interference, but this is seldom sufficiently stringent to cover weak signal reception of distant stations. Electrical interference tends to be most troublesome on the lower frequencies, particularly those below about 700 kHz (long waves and low-frequency end of the medium waves).

Most forms of electrical interference are best suppressed or reduced by the fitting of appropriate filters at the source. However this is often outside the control of the listener.

Interference is often carried along the domestic house wiring and tends to be most severe within a few metres of the house wiring, structural steelwork, tubing, etc. A receiving antenna well clear of surrounding objects will greatly reduce the amount of electrical noise, particularly if the mains supply leads to the receiver are filtered.

Spurious signals

It has been emphasized in this chapter that broadcasting is only one of a number of services that use the HF radio spectrum. The non-broadcast transmissions are mostly of a nature that is not intelligible when heard on a normal broadcast receiver. They often sound like continuous buzzes, screeches, clicks, thumps or 'Donald Duck' speech being in fact signals generated by radio teleprinters and data transmissions with frequency or phase shift keying, morse, independent and single-sideband telephony.

These communications transmissions occupy the frequencies between the broadcasting bands and do not normally interfere directly with the reception of broadcasts. Unfortunately, most domestic and portable broadcast receivers and even many of the 'communication receivers' intended specifically for short wave reception tend to receive these transmissions as 'interference' on 'spurious' frequencies that may be within segments of the spectrum reserved for broadcasting. For example, most simple superhet receivers can receive a single transmission on two or more widely-spaced frequencies, even though the transmission is on only one frequency. The most common cause of such spurious or phantom signals is 'image-frequency' reception in which the spurious signal is spaced from the real signal by twice the intermediate-frequency of the receiver. In simple terms the degree of unwanted 'image' reception is determined by the intermediate frequency of a superhet receiver and the effectiveness of the selectivity provided before the mixer stage in which frequency conversion takes place. To provide complete rejection of all image response on HF or VHF is not easy, and is unlikely to be found except on relatively high-cost receivers designed specifically with this problem in mind.

Similarly, many sets are affected by the presence of extremely strong broadcast or other signals even when these are on frequencies well away from a desired weak signal, due to what is termed the limit 'dynamic range' of most receivers. It is for this reason that the usual advice of always using the best possible outdoor antenna must be viewed with caution and why some receivers incorporate an 'attenuator' control or switch that can reduce the strength of the signals at the input to the receiver.

Fading and distortion

Broadcast transmissions on medium waves (MF) and short waves (HF) unless from local transmitting stations, may suffer severe distortion due to what is termed frequency selective fading. This is usually most pronounced on signals coming from stations hundreds rather than thousands of kilometres away. The prime cause is the arrival of signals that have travelled over more than one path (Figure 11). Such signals may alternatively increase or decrease the input to the receiver, and this can vary with the precise frequency. Long-distance (DX) HF signals, on the other hand, are normally much less severely distorted by fading, although in some conditions a very fast 'flutter' form of fading occurs.

Audio distortion owing to selective fading occurs also on medium waves (MF) and in this case one of the signals reaching the listener may be the ground wave signal. While the automatic gain circuits built into receivers can maintain the audio output from the receiver fairly constant there is little that the listener can do to reduce this form of distortion. The reason why frequency-selective fading can cause distortion is that the signal strength can vary across the 9 or 10 kHz channel and this can result in the carrier signal fading more than the sidebands carrying the information. To a receiver it then has the effect of gross overmodulation at the transmitter.

Selective fading is much less severe on single-sideband (SSB) transmissions with reduced or suppressed carrier. Tests have shown that it would be possible to broadcast a compatible form of SSB that could be received satisfactorily on conventional receivers provided that these were accurately tuned. Normally, conventional receivers are incapable of receiving SSB that has a fully suppressed carrier. Although speech transmissions on SSB can be resolved with the aid of a beat frequency oscillator (BFO) as fitted to communications-type receivers, the satisfactory reception of music requires extreme accuracy of tuning and highly-stable receivers. The extent to which compatible single-sideband transmission will be introduced during the 1990s remains uncertain, although high-power transmitters suitable for this mode of transmission are being developed.

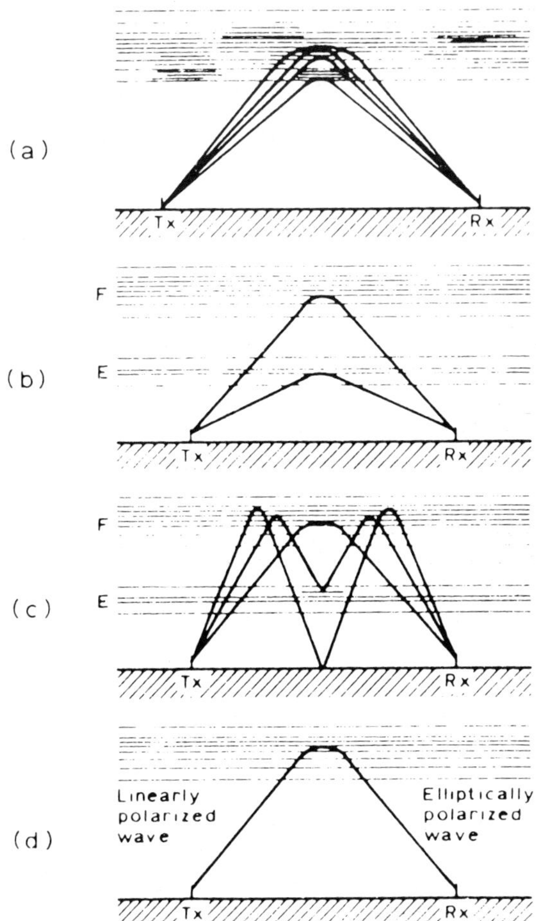

Figure 11 The modes of propagation that give rise to interference-type fading or fading due to polarization rotation. (a) Inhomogeneity of the reflecting layer providing multiple reflections of the same transmission. (b) Simultaneous arrival of signals reflected from the E and F layers. (c) Simultaneous arrival of signals propagated along different paths, including single and double hop with and without intermediate ground reflection points. (d) Polarization rotation during propagation that results in elliptical polarized wave

Home computers

A growing number of short wave enthusiasts, both listeners and transmitting amateurs, have found it possible to make effective use of home computers in pursuit of their hobby.

This can range from the use of the computer to store and retrieve useful data, building up a database gradually, to the use of special software programs, for example, to predict optimum frequencies for required stations at different times of the day or night, the various seasons and the position in the sunspot cycle. As a mathematical tool the computer can assist in the design of aerials, amplifiers, receivers etc. A computer can also be programmed to provide on request the great circle bearings, distances etc. of the principal stations. As a word processor it can be used to prepare reception reports. For those enthusiasts interested in such specialized communication modes as radio teleprinting (RTTY) or morse (CW), a computer can automatically display the incoming messages on a video screen (but remember that the deliberate interception of commercial and personal telegrams is forbidden in most countries, though this does not apply to amateur radio transmissions). Morse can thus be received without the months of practice normally required, although the human ear/brain remains superior on weak signals subject to interference.

While software programs are available for a multitude of applications, a few short wave broadcasters regularly transmit simple, non-copyright, programs that can be used in home computers – an idea pioneered by Radio Nederland. This station also publishes *InfoDutch* – a free, 22-page publication full of advice and information for those interested in using computers in pursuit of short wave radio. Copies of InfoDutch from Radio Nederland Wereldomroep, PO Box 222, 1200 JG Hilversum, The Netherlands. It includes names and addresses of firms that supply software programs for this aspect of short wave listening. Further details are given in Chapter 8 and 10.

Aerials and propagation

For medium and long wave reception most receivers have an internal ferrite-rod aerial, which enables them to receive the local stations and the stronger of the more distant stations. These aerials are directional and give very poor results when the rod points in the direction of the transmitter, so it is worthwhile checking whether the aerial is favourably orientated. Some portable receivers have a turntable built into the base to enable them to be rotated conveniently, and larger receivers sometimes have a control which rotates the aerial within the case. In searching the wavebands, it is easily possible to miss signals from transmitters in line with the aerial, and it is a good plan, therefore, to repeat the search with the aerial at right angles to its former position. Ferrite-rod aerials are not used for short wave reception and these directional effects are not present.

Many receivers have aerial and earth sockets and it is possible to effect a great improvement in reception by using an external aerial. Suitable forms of aerial are discussed later. When an external aerial is used the effect on reception of rotating the ferrite rod is much less marked and may even be absent altogether.

Short wave receivers often have telescopic aerials which can be extended to a metre or so in length and can sometimes be tilted. These, too, can provide satisfactory reception of the stronger signals.

Improved reception is often possible using an aerial external to the receiver, supported, for example, on the wall of a room or in the roof-space. Results from indoor aerials are, however, often disappointing because the aerial is screened from the wanted signals by the walls and/or roof of the building and is near the electrical wiring and domestic electrical equipment. While it may be easy to suppress noise and interference from your own

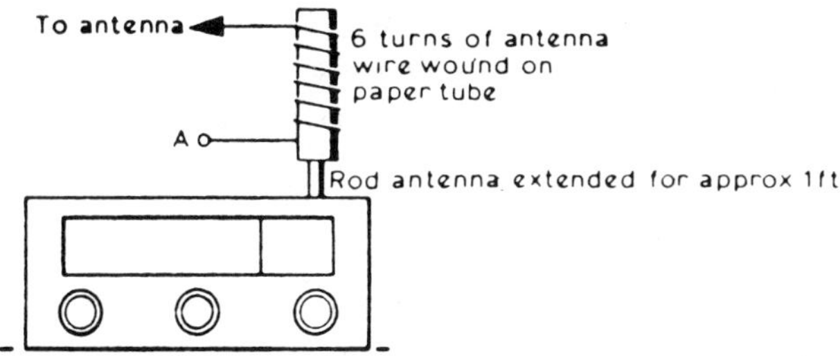

Figure 12 Using an external antenna when no socket is provided. Reception of frequencies above 15 MHz is usually enhanced by connecting point A to earth

washing machine and light dimmer, it is less easy to suppress your neighbour's, which in flats and terraces may be even nearer than your own. Indoor aerials are thus liable to pick up a high level of electrical interference.

For best results an outdoor aerial is essential and, if electrical interference is a problem, the aerial should be located in an interference-free area and special precautions taken to ensure that the cable connecting the aerial to the receiver does not pick up interference from the electrical system of the house.

The active aerial is a very compact aerial, often comprising a relatively short rod accurately matched and coupled into a broad-band, low-noise amplifier of wide dynamic range. An aerial of this type can provide the receiver with signals of similar strength to a full-size aerial with virtually the same signal-to-noise ratio. However it is important to note that such aerials should preferably be mounted outdoors away from the electrical interference radiating from the electricity mains wiring. Only if you are fortunate enough to live in an interference-free area can you expect an indoor active aerial to equal the performance of an outdoor aerial.

For reception on medium waves and on short waves below about 4 MHz (above 75 metres) a home made frame aerial can provide an effective directional aerial. This form of aerial was the fore-runner to the widely-used ferrite-rod aerial and can be made more efficient than the short ferrite rods positioned close to other components. Both the large frame-aerial and the smaller ferrite rod aerial have the useful property of providing sharp nulls (very sharp in the case of the frame aerial) to reject unwanted signals coming from a different direction to the wanted signal. This form of aerial is also less susceptible to local electrical interference than other indoor aerials that are not in the form of a closed loop.

An inverted-L aerial, Figure 14(a), is quite suitable for long and medium wave reception. Results improve as the length of the horizontal section and the height above the ground are increased. The horizontal section should be insulated from the supporting wires or ropes by several small porcelain insulators at each end. The downlead should be a continuous length of wire with the aerial and not joined separately because soldered and other kinds of joints are likely to deteriorate with weathering and eventually cause crackles and other effects in the receiver. The lead-in should be arranged to drop from the aerial well away from the building to avoid contact with gutters and to minimize pick-up of noise from the domestic electrical supply. If a tree is

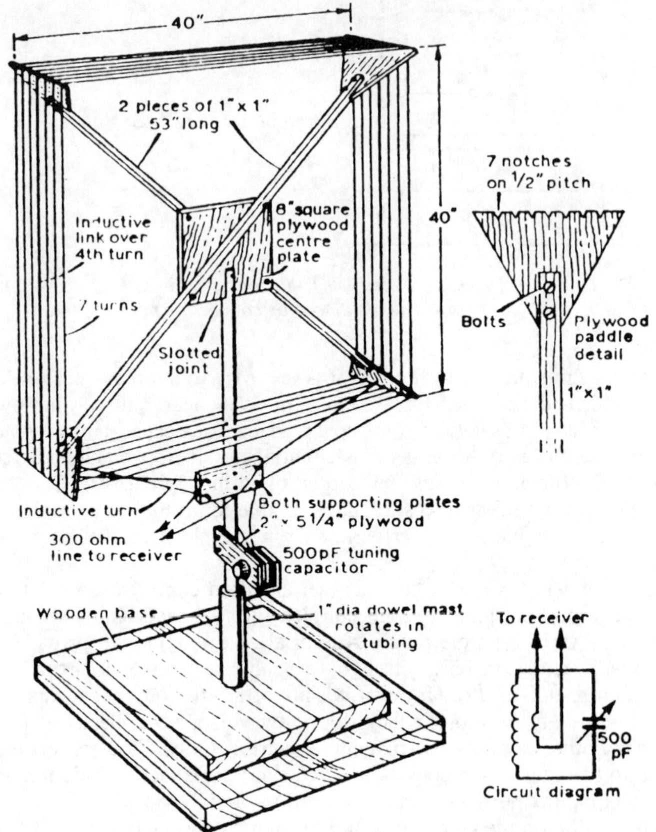

Figure 13 Constructional details of loop aerial for operation on medium waves and/or 1.8 MHz and capable of providing deep null on interfering signals

used to support the far end of the aerial, allowance must be made for the movement of the tree under windy conditions. The terminating wire or rope should be passed over a pulley and terminated with a suitable weight. In this way the tension in the aerial wire can be maintained independent of movement of the tree.

Sometimes it is convenient to take the downlead from the centre point of the horizontal section. The resulting aerial is known as a T-aerial and its performance is very similar to that of the inverted L.

As a precaution against electrical interference the downlead can take the form of a coaxial cable, the inner conductor providing the connection to the receiver and the outer conductor being earthed as shown in Figure 14(b). By this means the downlead is screened so that only signals picked up by the horizontal wire are conveyed to the receiver.

Where there is sufficient space for an inverted L or T-aerial or where electrical interference is a serious problem, a vertical rod, say, 5 m long may be

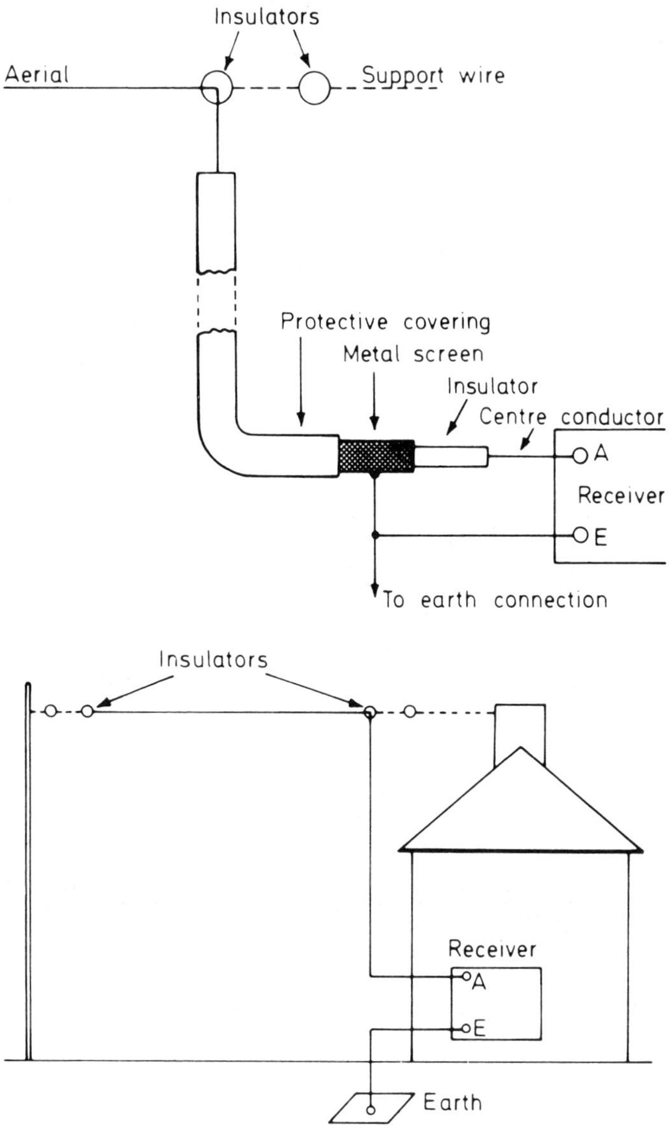

Insulators
Aerial
Support wire
Protective covering
Metal screen
Insulator
Centre conductor
A
Receiver
E
To earth connection
Insulators
Receiver
A
E
Earth

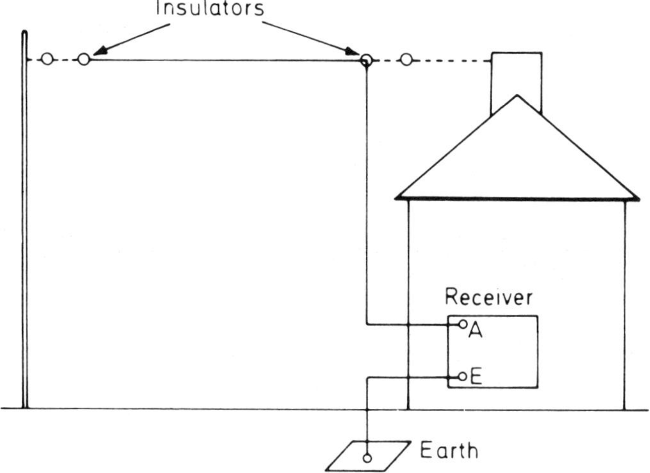

Figure 14 (a) Inverted L aerial. (b) Screened down-lead

used. This should be mounted in an area where interference is a minimum (a chimney top is often a suitable place) and connected to the receiver by a screened lead as shown in Figure 15. Aerial manufacturers market kits containing all the parts for such an installation including matching transformers for use at the aerial base and receiver input.

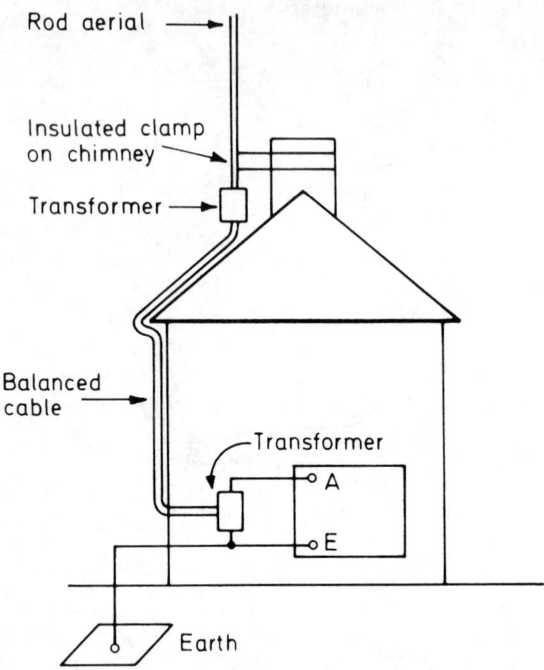

Figure 15 Vertical rod aerial

An inverted L, T-aerial or vertical rod aerial is suitable for short wave reception but where space permits there are more efficient types which can be used: these are directional aerials which should therefore be positioned to favour the direction of the transmitters it is desired to receive.

One suitable aerial is the half-wave dipole illustrated in Figure 16. It consists of two horizontal arms connected to the receiver by a balanced feeder. The dipole should be mounted as high as possible but 10 m is probably the maximum height which is convenient for most domestic situations. The length of each of the two horizontal arms should be chosen to suit the wavelength of the signals it is desired to pick up and varies between 13 m for the 49-m band to 3 m for the 11-m band. The aerial has maximum response to signals travelling at right angles to its length and has minimum response to transmissions arriving in line with the aerial.

A disadvantage of the simple dipole is that it is less effective on wavebands other than those for which it has been designed. If, however, the two leads of the feeder are connected together and to the receiver aerial terminal, the earth terminal being connected to ground, the aerial then becomes a T type which can be used for long and medium wave reception as well as for short waves. A two-pole change-over switch can be used to convert the aerial from the dipole to the T form.

A better form of directional short wave aerial is the inverted V, Figure 17. This provides a greater signal to the receiver than the simple dipole and by

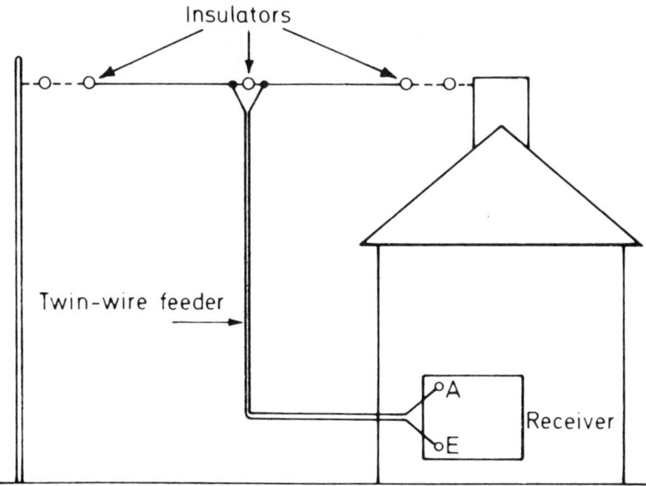

Figure 16 Simple dipole aerial

using the dimensions shown it can be effective over all the short wave bands. It requires only a single support pole, one end of the aerial being earthed via a 400 ohm terminating resistor, the other being connected to the receiver input. This aerial has maximum sensitivity to signals travelling in the plane of the aerial as indicated in the diagram.

The Beverage aerial demands length but not height and consists of a length of wire supported by a series of short poles, say 2 or 3 m high and spaced sufficiently close to prevent undue sag. Each should be surmounted with an insulator to which the wire is bound, not looped, the aerial being terminated at the far end by a 600 ohm resistor. Wire length is not critical but it should not be less than about 50 m and the lead-in should be direct to the receiver without significant deviation from the general line; if this can be achieved an RF transformer and coaxial line are not required to connect the aerial to the receiver. This aerial favours the reception of signals travelling in line with the aerial from the terminating resistor end, and is used professionally with wire lengths up to 1000 m.

When a receiver is supplied from a 3-pole main socket there is a natural temptation to use the earthed pole of the socket as an earth connection for the receiver. Such a connection is likely to be unsatisfactory because the physical connection of the main earth to ground is often at a considerable distance from the mains socket. Consequently the earth path may have appreciable resistance and can carry signals capable of causing interference to radio reception.

Where a receiver is provided with a signal earth terminal, local interference may be reduced by connecting the terminal by a short lead to a copper plate or earth rod buried in the ground. A similar connection is also required for inverted-V and some other aerials. A connection to a gas pipe is usually an unsatisfactory earth and may be extremely dangerous; most

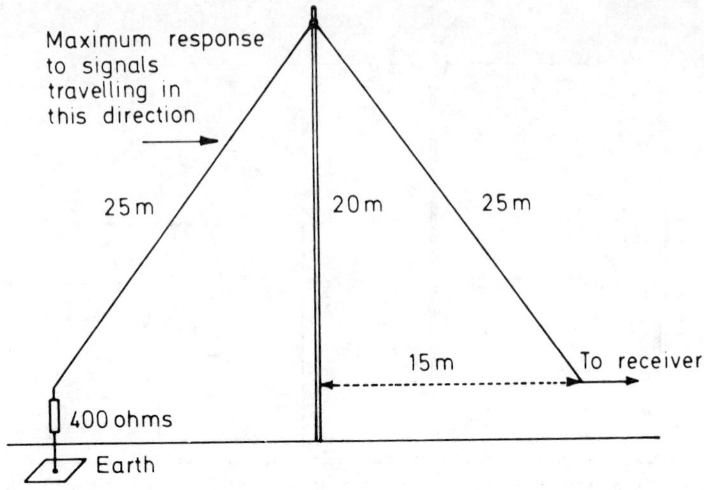

Figure 17 Inverted V aerial

underground metal gas pipes are being replaced by plastic pipes. A connection to a metal water pipe is satisfactory only if the pipe is connected directly to an underground water main: in many modern housing estates the metal pipes within the house are connected to buried polythene pipes and do not provide a satisfactory earth connection.

Propagation of radio waves is a complex subject and in this brief chapter we can give only a general description of those aspects which may interest those whose hobby is listening to broadcasts generally and who may be sufficiently enthusiastic to extend their listening to more distant and difficult signals.

A knowledge of the basic facts will ensure that listening is carried out at the right time of day for a given frequency and will certainly provide more enjoyment by enabling the listener to anticipate good reception conditions and eliminate fruitless searching when propagation is poor. Awareness of the trends in propagation will leave the listener in no doubt as to causes of changes in reception and will enable selection of the most favourable periods for searching for the weaker and seldom-heard signal.

There are good reasons why a particular broadcast may within a short period improve to a degree when programme content can be appreciated or conversely may virtually disappear. It can also happen that strong signals from a given area may suddenly disappear within a minute or two, yet are received at their former strength thirty minutes or more later. Normal fading of signals may become more rapid, accompanied by a fall in strength and a corresponding increase in noise. These are some of the effects which the listener will observe and which, if carefully considered, will enable assessment of some of the changes in the ionosphere which affect reception conditions.

The basic facts governing short wave propagation can be summarized in the following way. Short wave radio communication is achieved by waves

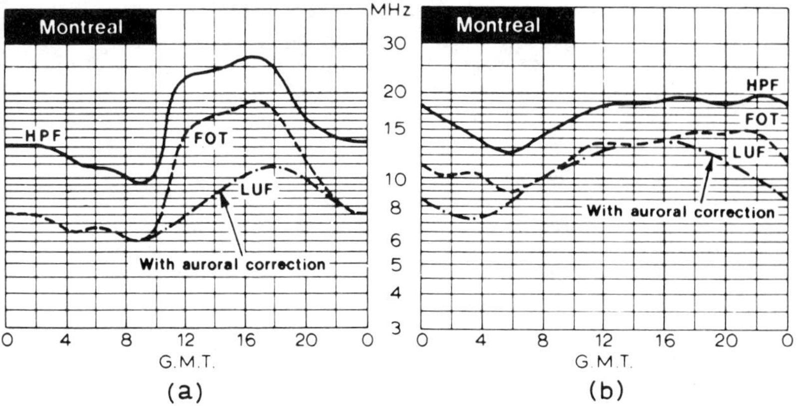

Figure 18 Examples of HF prediction curves for the UK-Montreal path for January (a) and July (b). The highest probable frequency (HPF) is the median usable frequency exceeded on 10% of the days. The LUF (lowest usable frequency) curves are for commercial telegraphy and assume the use of high-power transmitters and rhombic aerials. The path to Montreal passes through the Northern Auroral Zone and waves are subject to additional absorption: a correction is made for this in calculating the LUF. The term optimum traffic frequency (FOT) is self explanatory

which strike the ionosphere (electrified layers in the earth's upper atmosphere) at an oblique angle and are reflected back to earth to cover the receiving area. The waves may be reflected again when they strike the earth and reach other receiving areas after successive bounces from the ionosphere. However in certain areas, for example in the area between the transmitter and the first earth-reflection point, the transmission may be very difficult to receive: this is a so-called skip zone.

For satisfactory short wave communication the frequency must be chosen with care. If it is too high, the waves penetrate the ionosphere and are lost in space: if it is too low the waves are attenuated by absorption in the lower regions of the ionosphere. Best results are achieved by using the highest frequency which does not penetrate the ionosphere and the value of this, the highest probable frequency (HPF), depends on the degree of ionization of the gases in the ionosphere. This in turn depends largely on the extent to which the ionosphere over the chosen path is illuminated by the sun. Thus the HPF varies with the time of day and with the time of year.

Any changes in the degree of ionization of the reflecting layer can affect long-distance reception and such changes can be produced by increased radiation from the sun, e.g. from blemishes on its surface such as sunspots and invisible areas called M regions. As seen from the earth, the sun takes 27 days to rotate on its axis and some effects on reception, particularly those due to long-lived M regions, tend to have a 27-day periodicity. Moreover the incidence of sunspots follows an 11-year cycle; this in turn causes an 11-year periodicity in short wave reception conditions.

At any particular time, a survey of all the broadcast bands will indicate that some are very active (many stations being receivable, possibly with a fair amount of interference), while other bands may appear to be practically devoid of signals, apart from weak scattered radiation from stations some few hundred kilometres from the receiving site. These situations arise because transmissions are so arranged that programmes can be received at maximum signal strength in a desired area at local peak listening time. The choice is governed largely by HPF applicable to the required ionospheric path at that time, but the precise frequency may be somewhat lower to ensure that day-to-day variations in HPF do not seriously affect reception throughout the period of the programme or of the transmission schedule, which may be required to continue without alteration for a number of months. Two examples of prediction curves are given in Figure 18. The upper curve represents the HPF and, in general, frequencies above this value are heard infrequently. The lower curve indicates the frequency below which the signal-to-noise ratio of the received signal becomes unacceptable. If frequencies between these two boundary curves are used the transmitted wave normally propagates over the particular path and provides a service in the target zone. Frequencies which approach the HPF produce the stronger signal but their propagation is more likely to be affected by ionospheric disturbances. It is impossible to predict with accuracy the variations to which signals are likely to be subjected, although short term predictions based on daily observation of signals received can provide fair accuracy.

It is not good practice to make frequent changes of frequency in a broadcast schedule because the listener expects to find the programme at the same spot on the tuning scale. Thus to offset the variations of MUF and make best use of the transmission paths, two or more transmitters are used to radiate the same programmes on different frequencies. Thus a programme may be radiated simultaneously on, say, the 17, 15 and possibly the 11 MHz bands, so that when the HPF is high the 17 MHz signal is good and well supported by 15 MHz, whilst the low-frequency channel may suffer from some absorption. When the HPF is low, the 17 MHz signal is weak and a better service is obtained on 15 and 11 MHz.

Announcements made prior to close-down and radiated by all broadcasts in the same network mention the frequency of the broadcast band which is closing and that which is opening. For any target zone the peak listening time is evening and the schedules of transmissions to that area are arranged to provide programmes at that time. Frequency separation on the short wave bands is only 5 kHz and there may be difficulty in receiving a programme clear of interference.

The broadcast bands and their frequency limits are shown elsewhere in this book, and in general transmissions must, by international agreement, be confined to these bands. Other services are similarly restricted to certain frequencies. The highest allotted frequency used in short wave broadcasting is 26.100 MHz: thus when the HPF exceeds that figure, maximum use of propagation conditions cannot be obtained. However, most domestic receivers have an upper tuning limit as low as 21 or even 17 MHz.

Comparison of Figure 18(a) and (b) shows that under summer-time conditions the HPF curves flatten considerably, day-time frequencies being lower and night-time frequencies higher than in winter-time. In the summer more transmissions are crowded into fewer bands and interference problems increase.

At periods of minimum solar activity HPFs are generally lower throughout the year and the reduced spectrum available for broadcasting causes increased interference.

Sunspot maximum conditions occurred in 1979 and there was a gradual decrease in the HPFs until sunspot minimum conditions were reached in 1986, after which the HPFs will increase toward the next maximum.

The ionosphere is subject to disturbances which can affect radio reception. The disturbances are usually caused by sunspots and their effect is to make the reception of certain of the short wave broadcast bands difficult or even impossible. Thus, under certain conditions, signals in the high-frequency bands may be weak although the low-frequency bands are normal. Alternatively, the high-frequency bands may be normal and the low-frequency bands weak. Under more exceptional circumstances all the broadcast bands may be inaudible.

Thus, if short wave reception is found to be very poor, the most likely cause is a disturbance in the ionosphere and it is unlikely to last more than a few days. Most of the disturbances last only a few hours.

Signal identification

Tuning scales of receivers are often marked with a wealth of station names, but it does not follow that all these stations can be received, even with a good external aerial. Equally, it should not be assumed that stations, even if they can be received, will be picked up at precisely the point indicated by the name on the scale. The calibration of a receiver is not always exact, even when it is new, and it tends to drift as the receiver gets older. Calibration can be checked by tuning in certain stations which maintain their allotted frequencies with great accuracy. Most transmitters have a reasonably good frequency stability but those on 200 kHz, 5, 10, 15 and 20 MHz are particularly accurate. For further details of standard frequencies and time codes see Chapter 9.

Signal identification involves a knowledge of broadcasting organizations and their programmes, transmission schedules and target areas, rather than merely a knowledge of transmitting stations. Interval signals, clock chimes, times of operation, types of programme and signal strength also aid identification.

The large number of languages used in short wave broadcasting would be beyond the ability of one person to learn, but consistent listening to broadcasts from known countries, many radiating similar versions of the current world news, gives good practice in recognizing languages. The sound pattern of an unrecognized language can be compared with other broadcasts of languages which appear similar, remembering that a dialect may be used. Knowledge of the normal occupants of a waveband in terms of broadcasters and their programme schedules is also useful in language recognition.

Interval signals, or particular tunes, are often used to preface the start of transmissions or programmes, typical examples being the use of Bow Bells, Greenwich Time Signal and Big Ben by the BBC, the Canadian National Anthem by Sackville. The Kremlin Bells by Moscow and the Kookaburra by Melbourne. Eastern European stations often use the first few bars of a well-known melody, which may have been written by an eminent composer.

If these signals can be recorded on tape, a library of interval signals can be built up. Each recording can be annoted with the details of reception, to increase its usefulness as a reference guide. See Chapter 8 for details of some commercially available tapes.

The make-up and timing of broadcasts can often prove useful in identification. If a continuous programme is well balanced between music, speech, drama and other items, it is probably intended for home consumption and the opening and closing times of the transmission will give some idea of the time of day in the country of origin. A programme consisting of short items, with a preponderance of speech, starting or finishing at odd times, is likely to be a service for listeners outside the country. Clock chimes may narrow the choice, by fixing the time zone, and they often precede an announcement or news bulletin. Don't forget that some countries have summer or daylight saving time. The relaying of programmes can produce difficulties; for instance, London's Big Ben is heard from stations all over the world. Nevertheless, continued listening may provide a clue, which can be a change of atmosphere at the conclusion of a relay, or an announcement that follows.

Most broadcasts begin with a period of tone for technical alignment purposes, followed by an interval signal and announcement, then possibly a time check, and finally the programme. The frequency of the line-up tone differs from one organization to another; thus the BBC uses 1 kHz, Federal Germany 900 Hz, and some authorities use 440 Hz.

The close-down of a transmission is also important, because of the probability of announcements, and perhaps a national anthem or clock chime.

The type of programme may yield evidence of the nationality of the broadcasting organization and of the intended zone of reception. Domestic services can generally be recognized by the parochial nature of the news, the coverage of world events being small. Programmes for a country's nationals abroad are often a blend of domestic and world news, with commentaries in the national language; a typical example is the BBC World Service. Frequent news bulletins, almost exclusively concerned with world events and given in many languages, strongly suggest a service intended for foreign listeners.

When a programme whose source is unknown is sufficiently intelligible to be followed to a limited extent and a guess made at the language, a search for the identical programme on different frequencies may help identification. A second receiver is useful for this, because it can be tuned to known stations operating services in the supposed language. If another transmission carrying the programme is found, it may be assumed that both originate from the same source, though not necessarily from co-sited transmitters. One transmission may be a relay, and if so the quality of the unknown transmission may not be as good as the known.

It may still be difficult to determine the location of the unknown station, though listening at times of programme change for local or regional announcements can help in reaching a conclusion. At such times there may be changes in fading characteristics and background noise, indicating the conclusion of a relay and suggesting that the signal has been affected twice by ionospheric conditions. A typical example of relays is provided by the BBC World Service broadcast from the UK and relayed by bases in the Middle East, Far East and South Atlantic; other examples are provided by Deutsche Welle in Germany and its relay base in Africa, by Paris and

Brazzaville, and by the Voice of America at Greenville and its overseas stations at Tangier, Munich, Monrovia and elsewhere.

The stronger of two signals carrying the same programme may not necessarily be that of the nearer transmitter. The receiving location may be in the skip zone of this transmitter and thus obtains a weaker signal. A better signal may also be obtained from the more distant transmitters if this is beamed toward the receiver site.

Programmes which are broadcast simultaneously on a fair number of frequencies can be generally quickly identified as belonging to the same country or programme network. Even if foreign languages cause difficulty, the sound pattern of any language may indicate that the programme is originating from the same source irrespective of the number of transmitter outlets it may be heard on. With some experience, it becomes possible to identify language without understanding them; thus, if Cairo broadcasting in Arabic is positively identified, it is then feasible to recognize Arabic programmes in the external service of another country.

If a simultaneous broadcast cannot be found, but the programme pattern can be established, a search of programme schedules issued by the various countries may show details which conform closely to those of the unknown station.

A tape recorder is useful to aid identification, to give positive proof of reception, and to provide a tape library of announcements and call signs, and the interval signals and jingles which characterize so many programmes and broadcast services. The tape machine should be close to the receiver and available for immediate use with its input connected to the receiver output, the mains supply switched on and a tape ready to record.

Any announcement heard which is not readily identifiable may be recorded and later played back repeatedly to help in identifying the language or recognizing some feature. Microphone facilities are useful to enable details of the time, date and approximate frequency or wavelength to be added to the recorded announcement. Such recordings could well form the beginning of an index of station announcements, which might later be arranged in country or geographical order to facilitate further research.

Tape recordings can be made of the signature tunes which most stations use either prior to their opening announcement or before particular programmes. Signature tunes are usually repeated for some minutes before the scheduled opening time, and as indicated previously, they may consist of a well-known melody characteristic of the country, of a few tones, or of bells or clock chimes. These tunes, when memorized, can provide an instant means of identification, but while some are distinctive, others are not, and a tape recording is often useful for comparison.

Reception reports

Reports on reception are always welcomed by broadcasting organizations, whether the listener is located in the target area or not. Such reports can provide useful information on transmissions, and help the broadcaster to assess the accuracy of the assessments on which his schedule was based and the effectiveness of the service. See Chapter 3.

3 Writing useful reception reports

Jonathan Marks
Radio Nederland Wereldomroep

Since the early days of international broadcasting on short wave, listeners have sent in reports on reception to radio stations. In the beginning, when many of the broadcasts were experimental, stations relied heavily on reports from listeners, whereas in the 1980s there is now a different technique required to make your reports useful to an international broadcaster. A survey by the European DX Council in 1983 asked a number of stations about their views on reception reports, and these results have been combined together with our own recommendations here at Radio Nederland Wereldomroep.

Note: The comments that follow apply *only* to reception reports sent to international broadcasters. If you wish to report to low power stations in Africa, Asia, or Latin America, you need to use a completely different approach, as described in the chapter on Latin American DXing.

Make your report stand out – not conform!

The reception report has been fairly standard over the years. So much so, that some DX clubs now offer printed forms for their members to use. These have both advantages and disadvantages. Some are even computer generated these days. Forms are certainly easier to check, as far as the QSL department is concerned, but it might not have the desired impact in other departments, such as programming. If you live in a country where companies send unsolicited printed matter to you through the mail, you'll be aware how impersonal this type of mail can be. The use of pre-printed forms really depends then on whom you wish to address your letter to.

A 'typical' reception report as received by many international short wave stations is shown at the end of this chapter. Note that some parts of the form have been labelled with numbers. These correspond to the numbers listed below.

General hints

1 *Name and address:* So obvious and yet it is amazing how many people forget to include it. In many cases your reception report may be processed by more than one department within the radio station (i.e. the engineering and programme departments), so we advise you to include your name and address on *each* sheet that you use. Either print your name and address in block capitals or type it. Many QSLs have failed to reach their destination because it was impossible to read the name and address of the sender. Signatures are often very difficult to decipher.

2 *The station address:* Always address your letter to the correct person. Avoid the use of titles like 'Director General', 'Head of Programmes', etc.,

if you want a QSL or wish to make programme suggestions. It is very unlikely that the station director or the general management will be the people responsible for answering the letters. If a particular programme presenter made a point on the air that you wish to take further, then send the letter to her or him by name, c/o English Section, Radio XYZ, etc. This will ensure that the right person opens the letter. Alternatively, writing to the programme by name: 'Media Network', English Section, Radio Nederland, PO Box 222, 1200 JG Hilversum, Holland', increases the chances that the producer of that programme will see that letter.

3 *Date:* It is best to write this out fully (i.e. 25 July 1985) since shorthand notation, such as 12.6.86, has different meanings depending on where you live. Naturally, it is usually obvious which meaning is implied, but writing the date out in full may ensure fewer mistakes.

4 *Time:* This should be stated in Co-ordinated Universal Time (or UTC), which is the standard used by the majority of international broadcasters. The term Greenwich Mean Time (GMT) is still being announced by a few stations, e.g. BBC London. But no conversion is necessary as both terms are interchangeable 0600 GMT = 0600 UTC.

If you are in doubt as to the time difference between your own local time and UTC, simply listen on the hour or half-hour to most international broadcasters (i.e. Radio Nederland, Radio Canada International, BBC, VOA) who will announce the time in UTC. Simply work out the hours difference between your time and UTC. Use this information to make a conversion table to keep by your radio for handy reference. Alternatively, set a clock by your receiver to work on UTC. Note that UTC is always the same, and is unaffected by local changes in summer or winter time. All stations use the 24 hour clock system, so avoid the use of a.m. and p.m. which can lead to confusion, e.g. 1830 = 6.30 p.m. A world time chart is printed on page 000.

5 *Frequency:* This describes the point on the dial that the signal came in, usually indicated in kilohertz (kHz). The frequency that you quote should be accurate to within 5 kHz if possible, i.e. saying 'I heard you on about 6 MHz' is not sufficient. If, however, your set cannot give accurate frequency readout from the short wave dial, say so in your report. The term kilocycles per second (kc/s) is an older expression, but means the same as kHz. If you know that a station is using more than one frequency at the time you're listening, check as many of these as possible, and note how well each of them is received. *A report on one single frequency on one day has little value these days*, though the station will probably still send you a QSL card. The experienced listener does one, or both, of the following:

(a) Notes the reception quality of a number of frequencies carrying the same programme over a period of three to six days.
(b) When a particular channel is blocked by interference, a check is made to see whether another frequency nearby is more suitable as an alternative (but see later notes).

6 *Metre band:* Not really necessary if you have noted the frequency correctly. If you only have 'metres' marked on your set, then quote this in

your report, though few listeners quote them these days. If you need to convert metres to kilohertz, then use the following formula:

$$\frac{300{,}000}{\text{wavelength in metres}} = \text{frequency in kHz}$$

7 *Receiver:* This is a useful piece of information to the frequency department, so don't forget to include it in your report. If you are suffering bad reception, one of the first things that will be checked is the type of receiver that you're using. Remember too that the brand name and model number may not be known in the country where you send your report, so decide whether your receiver is a *domestic* type (i.e. has medium wave, or VHF/FM on it as well as short wave) or a *communications* type (i.e. made primarily for listening to short wave broadcasts between 3 and 30 MHz). If you can quote the description given in the manufacturer's brochure this is usually sufficient (e.g. 8-band SW superhet portable).

8 *Antenna:* Also a useful piece of information and frequently forgotten. Transistor portable radios usually perform adequately on a built-in antenna of the 'telescopic rod' variety. If you are using a piece of wire or a random length hung out of the window, the best description is a 'random longwire aerial'. Specially built antennas such as 'rhombics', 'inverted L' or 'dipole' should be mentioned by name if possible.

9 *Reporting code:* As soon as reception reports started flowing into radio stations, some kind of internationally recognized codes were introduced. These were needed not only to standardize report writing, but to be able to compare one report with another. The first, and most popular was the *SINPO* code, in which each letter stands for a specific item, and each is rated from 1 to 5. Full details are given below:

S – signal strength	I – interference	N – atmospheric noise	P – propagation, disturbance	O – overall merit
5 – excellent	5 – nil	5 – nil	5 – nil	5 – excellent
4 – good	4 – slight	4 – slight	4 – slight	4 – good
3 – fair	3 – moderate	3 – moderate	3 – moderate	3 – fair
2 – poor	2 – severe	2 – severe	2 – severe	2 – poor
1 – barely audible	1 – extremely strong	1 – extreme	1 – extreme	1 – unusable

While the above may look impressive and concise it will soon become evident that the SINPO code is very subjective. Somebody may rate a signal as 33232 while someone else might rate it as 44333. Likewise, although the original SINPO code did lay down technical specifications for each number (i.e. a number 3 in the P column meant a fixed number of fades per minute) these are hardly ever adhered to by reporters. Nor is it advisable to use the so called 'signal strength' meter to judge signal strength. No 'S' meter on a communications receiver under £1000 in price is anything more than a tuning indicator. The 'S' meter reading is usually dependent on the setting of the RF gain control, so use your ears, not the needle, to judge signal strength. You may also find references to the SINFO code. In this case the

‘F’ stands for fading, instead of ‘P’ for propagation, but the two codes are essentially the same.

It is also clear that many listeners cannot distinguish between the ‘I’ which stands for man-made interference, the ‘N’ which stands for natural atmospheric noise, and the rating for ‘P’ is not often understood. There are some books and periodicals that maintain the SINPO code as being the only one for DX reporters. However, from a station’s point of view we would suggest the following, simpler, code which is used by most professional monitoring stations around the world.

The SIO code

S – signal strength	I – interference (of any type)	O – overall merit
4 – good	4 – nil or very slight	4 – good
3 – fair	3 – moderate	3 – fair
2 – poor	2 – heavy	2 – unusable

You can see that the SIO code is based on the SINPO code, but in a simpler form. The two extremes (i.e. 5 and 1) are eliminated. Very few signals deserve a 55555 rating (except a local FM station), and 11111 is not much different from 22222 – both imply that reception quality is useless. The use of the SIO code, as opposed to the SINPO code, does *not* give the station the impression that you are an inferior reporter.

The backwards secret to the SIO code!

Most books that cover the subject of reception report writing have a very simple method of evaluating a signal. First, they say, judge the signal strength, then look at the level of interference. Finally, fill in the ‘O’ column by taking the average of the two numbers, and rounding down to the nearest whole number. So if the ‘S’ was 3, and the ‘I’ was 4, the ‘C’ rating would automatically be ‘3’. *This is very misleading!*

Instead, you should work backwards. First evaluate the overall rating of the signal. Is it ‘listenable’ or difficult to hear. Give it either 2, 3, or 4. Now examine the reasons for your ‘O’ rating. The signal may be weak (i.e. a 2), but if there is no interference on the signal, you simply have to turn up the volume control to enjoy the programme. Thus an SIO rating of 234 is *not impossible*.

Likewise a signal of 442 is possible. This might occur if the signal was strong, there was no interference, but the audio being broadcast was heavily distorted due to a fault in the transmitter. Listen around on the bands, and you will find a wide variation in the audio quality being broadcast. Being critical may alert a station to a problem. It is often very difficult to judge when measurements are made at the transmitter site.

If you give an ‘*Interference*’ rating of either 2 or 3 in your report, then you should explain why (as our example does in the ‘technical remarks’ column). If there is interference on the received signal, note the following details:

(a) Is the interference signal of the same frequency (so-called co-channel?) If it is, then as you move the tuning knob, both the signal you want, and the interfering signal will be tuned out. If, however, the interference gets stronger as you tune either up or down the band, the interference is probably coming from an adjacent frequency. It helps to indicate whether the interference is coming from a station on a higher or lower frequency than the one you are interested in. If you are listening on 11735 kHz and a station on 11730 is causing interference, the interference is from a station which is lower in frequency. If the interference station is a jamming signal (a buzzing sound designed to deliberately interfere with an international broadcaster) then this should be noted too.

(b) Local weather conditions *do not* generally affect short wave broadcasts, with the exception of local thunderstorms in your area. These may cause loud 'crashes' which spoil reception. If this affects your I (interference) rating, then note elsewhere that this was due to thunderstorms.

10 *Programme details:* This seems to be the most variable part of a reception report. Some people simply write 'Man spoke, woman spoke', or 'News, Newsline, Media Network' (you will find the latter details in our programme schedule) neither of which can tell the station that you have really heard the transmission. On the other hand, a verbatim script of the programme is also very undesirable. It won't be read all the way through, as secretarial staff don't usually have the time to read it. So why bother? The correct details should include the programme title, the name of the presenter (if given) and a few of the most important points raised. If the programme is musical, note the names of those performing. The reception report we have shown, has about the correct balance that most stations are looking for. Most stations need about 10 to 20 minutes of monitoring time for a verification.

11 *Programme comments:* Not the same thing as programme details. It is one thing to report what you hear in a programme, in the form of supplying programme details, but another to comment on what you heard. Although stations have set down guidelines in the past for sending in reception reports, this has rarely included advice on what to listen out for. To a certain extent this is probably the station's fault, rather than that of the listener. Suffice to say, stations are interested in your reaction to the programme. To assist you in filling the 'programme comments' sections of the report with feedback which will be of use to the station, and make your report stand out from the rest, we've listed a few questions that you might care to ask yourself while a programme is running.
Note: These are only intended to suggest points to look for. It is up to you to put the answers into a readable form. Simply writing down the answers is not sufficient, as stations won't know what the questions were!

(a) Did you tune in to the station expecting to hear a particular item or style of presentation? Did the station present the kind of information you wanted or did it seem irrelevant? (Remember though, that some stations have different specialist programmes on different days of the week. Give the stations a fair hearing before complaining that they are ignoring a particular topic of interest.)

(b) Programmes consisting of short items of up to 4 minutes each can either be very interesting or extremely boring. If you tuned in to this style of programme (a magazine format) did the whole programme interest you or did you find only a small part was relevant? Did it sound too much like short unconnected stories connected by someone saying 'Now here's something from . . .' and then, 'That was . . .', or was there a theme to the whole programme?

(c) Did music fit into the programme being broadcast, and was it of the style you enjoy? Was reception reasonable over short wave radio, or were quiet passages lost in interference. (Remember that what the producer in the studio listens to on a hi-fi speaker, and what you hear at the other end of a SW radio, 1000s of kms away, may be two entirely different things.)

(d) Did you feel that the item being presented was complete, or that you were being told only one side of the argument? Did the item change your mind on a particular topic? If so, why? If you found an item hard to believe or confusing, mention this, as the producer is being paid to get a message across! The listener judges how successful this has been done.

(e) Was the item being presented too short or too long? Did the presenter sound interested in what he/she was reading (in some cases the presenter is the author of what he/she is reading). Was the speed of presentation too fast or too slow for easy short wave reception?

(f) Will you listen again? If so, what items interest you and what topics do you suggest the station should cover. If not, why not.

Summary

Stations receive anything up to 300 letters a day per language department. Some stations have the budget to reply personally to each one that comes in, others refer to letters on the air in programmes. If you follow the guidelines set out above there is greater chance that your report will generate more than a QSL card. But please consider the following points:

- Don't give praise where praise is not due. If you sat through 15 minutes of the most boring radio you ever listened to, don't say you found it interesting, educational and fascinating to try and get a QSL. You'll get a QSL card whether your reaction to the programme was positive or negative.
- Don't over-rate a signal rating in the SIO code. If the signal is 232 don't say it was 444 to try and get a QSL. Remember there will be other listeners writing in from your area and if the engineers note that most people report 232, your report of 444 will be thrown out as being unreliable. If you do the same twice to a station, the chances are that people will remember your name!
- Don't worry about your command of English if it is your second language. Some excellent comments are received at Radio Nederlands from listeners in Japan, West Germany, Finland, India and many other countries where English is not the mother tongue. Stations do understand what you are trying to say, even if the grammar is not perfect, providing they can read your writing.
- Don't forget a bit of diplomacy. If you feel strongly about a point, by all means say so. But don't resort to personal abuse or outright demands. A

cool collected summary of why you feel something ought to be changed is a much better and effective approach. Letters which contain an alternative suggestion after criticising are always considered, those which simply criticise play far less of a role. Bear in mind too that humour and double meanings are very different from country to country. The secretary who reads your letter may or may not have the same command of English as you.

- Don't expect a station to change a frequency because you have provided them with information about a clear channel nearby. Few stations are able to hop about the band, and the use of one frequency for an hour or less is not common in international broadcasting. Stations often have to serve large target areas, and the problems of finding a clear channel are getting more difficult by the day. The low sunspot activity during the years 1985, 1986, 1987 and 1988 add to the problems. Assistance from listeners on a voluntary basis is always appreciated, though please remember that not all suggestions can be realized. It is rare that stations are able to offer payment for monitoring.
- Don't over-rate the value of a standard cassette taped reception report. Remember these recordings take much longer to process as somebody has to listen to them. They can be very misleading unless done on reasonable quality equipment. Some stations do like these reports (they are listed in the EDXC QSL Survey), though it is a *minority*. At Radio Nederland Wereldomroep we prefer written reports and cassette tapes are not generally returned.
- Don't forget to *ask* for a QSL card if you require one. Radio Nederland issues a new QSL card when stocks of the old one get low. There is a limit of one card per month per listener. Some stations have stopped sending out QSLs altogether, others do so only on request.
- Remember that reports on frequencies not intended for your target area are usually of marginal interest to the station, unless there is no service directed to your part of the world. Remember too that not all stations have a huge number of promotional items (such as pennants, books, diaries) to send out. Their primary function is to make programmes. 'I would appreciate a pennant, if you have one, please' will avoid embarrassment.

If you want details of the European DX Council QSL Survey, 2nd Edition, send one international reply coupon to European DX Council, PO Box 4, St Ives, Huntingdon, England PE17 4FE.

Sample reception report

From: (1)

Richard Jones,
Box 234, Christchurch,
New Zealand

Date: 25th September 1986

To: (2)

Media Network,
English Section,
Radio Nederland,
PO Box 222, 1200 JG Hilversum, Holland

Dear Sir,

I wish to report reception of your English language broadcasts directed to Australia and New Zealand over the past few days in the 31 and 49 metre bands.

Date	*Time UTC*	*Frequency kHz*	*S*	*I*	*Q*	*Technical remarks*
21 Sept.	0730	9630	4	3	3	Co-channel interference from an Arabic speaking station, believed to be Iraq.
21 Sept.	0733	9770	3	4	3	Weaker than 9630, but less interference.

Programme details: Welcome to REPORT programme. World news, covering items in West Beirut, Peace demonstrations in Paris. NEWSLINE programme covered relief aid to Ethiopia compiled by Tony Wilkinson, Central American political upheaval, and refugees in Cambodia.

Date	*Time UTC*	*Frequency kHz*	*S*	*I*	*Q*	*Technical remarks*
22 Sept.	0754	9630	4	3	3	Co-channel interference from an Arabic speaking station, believed to be Iraq.
22 Sept.	0755	9770	4	4	4	Good signal today.
22 Sept.	1051	9650	4	2	2	Heavy jamming splash from 9655 was serious.
22 Sept.	1058	6020	2	2	2	Very weak signal, just detectable.

Programme details: Media Network, presented by Jonathan Marks. Looked at the Amsterdam Audio and Video Fair, with news of a new shortwave receiver. Media news with Victor Goonetilleke featured an item on a new relay station for Radio Japan.

Programme Comments: My main interest is in telecommunication, so I prefer items on satellite broadcasting and shortwave receiver reviews. I don't feel your musical programmes come across very well under the present conditions. Perhaps a look at the current temperature in Hilversum, at the start of each transmission could be considered.

Receiver: Duo Museun FRG-2000. Communications type, PLL synthesised.

Antenna: 10 metre long wire out in the garden.

I hope you find my reception report to be of some use. If the details are correct, please verify with a QSL verification card. A sticker would also be appreciated, if these are available.

Yours sincerely,

RICHARD JONES.

4 New indoor short wave aerials

George Short

Three useful new aerial designs for the SWL have recently appeared. Although the impetus to evolve them was the need to combat jamming it turns out that they are very effective for general use, particularly where the listener is unable to put up an outside aerial. Each of the three types has its own special merits. All three have two additional properties: being tuned, they provide a degree of signal-frequency preselection which reduces image (second channel) interference; and they also cut down breakthrough by powerful local VHF and UHF transmitters, which can by intermodulation in the receiver come up as noise in the SW bands.

Two of these aerials can be made from domestic materials and without soldering. The third calls for only simple passive components (tuning capacitors and variable resistors) and elementary carpentry skill.

Directional reception

All of these new aerials cash in on the directional properties of a loop of conductor. If a loop is thought of as a wire run round the frame of a mirror, then the signal picked up by the loop is at a *minimum* when the mirror is looking straight at the transmitter. *Maximum* signal is produced when the transmitter is edge-on to the mirror. Since a mirror has two edges, left and right, there are two positions of maximum signal. In the same way, there are two positions for minimum signal: when the transmitter is directly in front and also when it is directly behind. In short wave reception, where scattering by the ionosphere occurs, the apparent position of the transmitter may be different from its real position, but the general behaviour of a single loop is still the same.

Twin loops can be quite different. In Villard's 'Coplanar Twin Loop' (see Figure 21), the directional pattern is distorted in a very useful fashion, to give a one-directional property, with a broad maximum to one edge of the loops and a sharp minimum to the other.

Loop aerials are inherently insensitive when small compared with the wavelength. To compensate for this, a loop can be tuned by making a gap and inserting a variable capacitor. This enables a relatively small loop (say 50 cm diameter) to deliver usable amounts of signal to a low-cost domestic receiver. Some of the loops described here can be made to work using very simple home-made capacitors.

The box loop

This aerial was originally designed as a means of reducing interference from a single local jamming transmitter. Such jammers have vertical aerials (and therefore launch vertically polarized signals). They rely for their effectiveness on the ground-wave from the aerial. At short wave frequencies this has

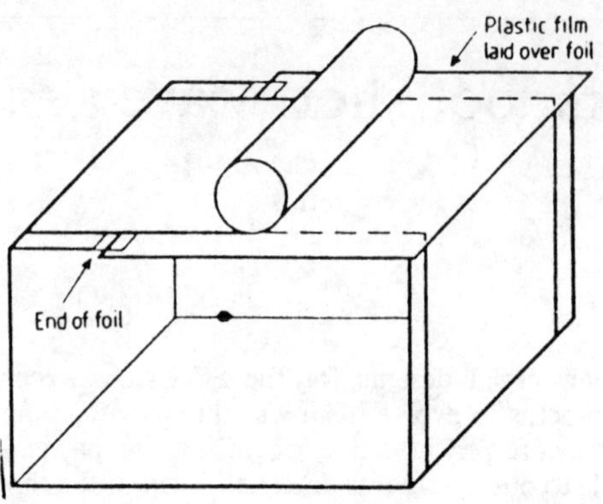

Figure 19 The box loop is made by rolling a wide strip of aluminium cooking foil round a cardboard, wooden or plastic box. Where the start and finish of the foil overlap they are prevented from shorting by inserting a sheet of plastic film. The loop can be tuned by rolling up or unrolling the foil to vary the area of overlap. The receiver is placed inside the box and coupled to it as described in the text.

only a short range (a few kilometres) but is enough to blanket a small town with interference.

A vertical loop aerial can give deep (over 40 dB) nulls when orientated to face such a jamming station. Unfortunately, the jamming can bypass the loop and get into the receiver either by direct penetration of its plastic case or by pickup on the downlead which connects loop to receiver. The standard solution is to screen the receiver against direct pickup and to use a balanced feeder. The box loop eliminates the need for a feeder and uses the loop itself as a screen. The arrangement (Figure 19) is very simple. The receiver is placed in a large (50 cm side), deep cardboard carton. A roll of aluminium cooking foil is passed round the box as shown. The beginning of the 'turn' of foil is insulated from the end by interposing a sheet of plastic film (e.g. from a shopping bag). The plastic film acts as the dielectric of a tuning capacitor, and the loop is tuned by rolling or unrolling the foil to vary the overlap region.

Since the receiver is virtually enclosed in metal (the foil), direct pickup of signals is minimized. The signal picked up by the loop can be coupled to the receiver in either of two ways. One way is to extend the usual built-in whip aerial so that its tip is close to one edge of the gap in the foil. This provides capacitive coupling through the wall of the box; if necessary, this coupling can be increased by putting a flat 'hat' of foil or metal on the tip of the whip. The second method, is very convenient when the receiver has aerial and earth terminals. These are connected to a subsidiary coupling loop in the form of a wire run the longest way round from the aerial round the receiver's cabinet and back to earth. The coupling loop can be taped to the cabinet and left permanently in position. It will not normally interfere with reception when the receiver is removed from the box for ordinary use.

To use the box loop for short wave reception, first tune the receiver to the wanted station (if necessary signal strength can be enhanced by touching the end of the whip). The hand is then removed and the loop tuned to regain signal strength. Tuning holds good for at least 100 kHz on either side of the set frequency. To reduce jamming, tune to the jammer then slowly rotate the box to find a null. Because of reflections of the signal by metal in the house, the null may occur with the loop in some other position than facing the transmitter. It pays to try various locations in the house to find the best. Also, the amount of jamming rejection may be improved by slightly tilting the box.

Tuning by rolling and unrolling foil can give a very wide frequency coverage but is not very stable. Tying a couple of strings round the box to hold down the roll of foil helps. The box loop can also be adapted so as to use the 'sliding tray' tuning method described below for the horizontal loop antenna. A conventional tuning capacitor may, of course, be used. It should be of several hundred picofarads.

General purpose loops

For the most effective anti-jamming performance, the receiver should be battery-operated, to avoid the accidental introduction of jamming into the box via the mains lead. Where jamming is not a problem but the other advantages of a tuned loop are desirable, a non-box format may be most convenient. Although a cardboard box was specified for the box loop, in fact any form of non-conducting support (wood, plastic) can be used for a loop. Also, when there is no jamming, no screening is required and instead of a broad band of foil it is possible to use a narrow band or just a simple wire.

These relaxed requirements enable a loop to be rigged up in ways convenient to the user. For example, a loop may be run unobtrusively round the back of a set of wooden bookshelves and the receiver, fitted with a coupling coil, placed on one of the shelves. If the receiver has no aerial or earth terminals and only has a pull-out whip, a coupling coil may be fitted as follows. Take a length of insulated wire and, without removing the insulation, wrap one end tightly round the base of the whip where it emerges from the cabinet. Run the wire round the cabinet (longest way round) and back underneath it. Strip off a few centimetres of insulation from the end. Tape the bare wire to a piece of foil cut to fit the base of the cabinet. Stick or tape the foil to the base. This indirect coupling works in most cases. If the signal strength is too low when the loop round the bookshelves is tuned, use more turns on the coupling coil.

The main loop may be tuned by any of the methods already described. However, a loop made from a single wire has a much higher inductance than a foil loop and needs only about a quarter of the tuning capacitance. Also, loop inductance varies with loop area. For square loops, with side 1 m in length, the inductance is about 4 μH. This tunes to 6 MHz with about 200 pF, which is a fairly tyical value for a miniature plastic foil medium wave tuning capacitor.

Large areas or loops of metal within the field of a loop aerial, impair efficiency. A loop aerial should not if possible be placed in front of a radiator, refrigerator or comparable metal artefact.

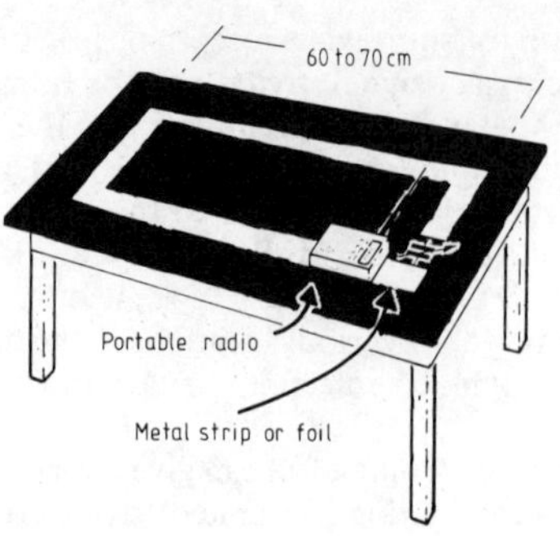

Figure 20 The horizontal loop antenna (HLA) is a wide strip of metal (sheet, aluminium foil, etc.) on an insulating support such as a table top. A gap in the loop is tuned by a variable capacitor of conventional or improvized type. The aerial is insensitive to vertically polarized signals such as local jamming but responds to long-distance ionospheric signals, which have horizontally-polarized components.

The horizontal loop antenna

If a local jamming signal is (as usual) vertically polarized it can induce no signal in a horizontal loop. The loop can, however, respond to any signals from distant transmitters if they are to some extent horizontally polarized.

This is the basis of the horizontal loop antenna (HLA), Figure 20. When vertically-polarized short wave signals are reflected by the ionosphere, it usually happens that their polarization becomes distorted and acquires a horizontal component to which a HLA can respond. Thus, in theory, a HLA responds to all distant transmissions while ignoring all local ones. In practice, even the signal from a local jammer with a vertical aerial is not quite vertically polarized because the effect of the ground (wave drag) imparts a tilt. This can be dealt with by giving a compensating tilt to the HLA but even without this a useful degree of attenuation (20–30 dB) of local jamming may be obtained, irrespective of the direction of the jammer. So the HLA can give protection against multiple jammers on the same frequency provided that their signals are not too intense.

The HLA is also a convenient table-top aerial for general use. It can be made by laying a band of aluminium foil round the edge of a wooden table top, leaving a gap for a tuning capacitor. The developers of the HLA report good results from compression tuners made by insulating the foil near the gap with waxed paper, plastic film, etc., and laying a strip of metal on this insulation and straddling the gap. The sheet is dished slightly and placed concave side down to form an air gap. Tuning is accomplished by compressing the sheet to alter the gap. This can be done either by moving a heavy object along the sheet or by squeezing it with a G-clamp.

A table-top HLA can be made unobtrusive by omitting the insulating foil and covering the entire table with a tablecloth, preferably thin and made of a good insulator such as nylon. Tuning can be done by placing a metal tray on

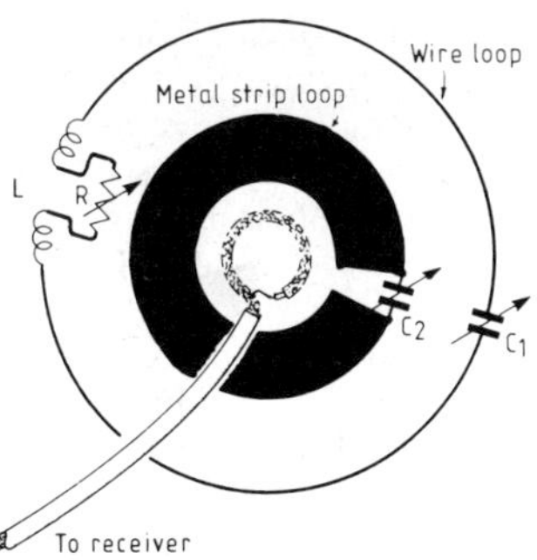

Figure 21 Coplanar twin loop (CTL) aerial. The outer, high-impedance wire loop is tuned by loading coil L and capacitance C1 which has a low value (e.g. 10pF). Damping resistance R (100 ohms variable) adjusts the Q and hence the coupling to the inner, low-impedance metal strip loop, tuned by C2 (a few hundred pF). The CTL can be adjusted to give an unidirectional null to a transmission edge-on to the loops and closest to the side carrying the loading coil.

the cloth, straddling the gap, and moving it about to vary the overlap. A wooden or plastic tray with a sheet of foil stuck to the bottom also works.

Coupling to the receiver may be performed as illustrated or by the coupling-loop method. To permit normal upright use of the receiver the coupling coil may be wound round the base of the cabinet. Alternatively, a remote coupling loop may be used, as illustrated for the CTL antenna described next.

The coplanar twin loop

As anti-jamming devices, the aerials so far described are effective only against vertically polarized interference. Since interference which arrives via the ionosphere usually has a horizontal component, they are of little use in avoiding it. A more elaborate aerial, the coplanar twin loop is capable of dealing with sky-wave interference (as well as ground wave). It is also a very good HF direction finding aerial.

The CTL (Figure 21) makes use of the fact that a high-impedance loop responds to both the electric and magnetic parts of the radio wave. This contrasts with a low-impedance loop like the box loop and the HLA which are responsive mainly to the magnetic field of the wave. In the CTL, this dual responsiveness of a high impedance loop is played off against the single response of a low impedance loop to achieve special directional properties.

To create a high-impedance loop, a single turn of wire is used, with a gap which contains a very small tuning capacitance (e.g. 10 pF). With a loop of modest size this would result in too high a tuned frequency, so the frequency is brought down into the HF band by inserting a loading inductance opposite the gap.

When a high-impedance loop is set edge-on to a transmitter, the signal which is picked up is somewhat different when the transmitter is to the right than when it is to the left. The CTL emphasizes this difference with the aid of an inner low-imedance loop tuned to the same frequency. When the coupling between outer and inner loops is correctly adjusted, a balanced condition is obtained in which the 'left' transmission, for example, is nulled out while the 'right' transmission is maximized. (By turning the CTL through 180 degrees the reverse is obtained.) The maximum is broad but the null is sharp. This enables an interfering station on the same frequency to be nulled so long as its angular separation from the wanted station is more than about 90 degrees. The CTL works with both ground wave and sky wave signals. The CTL can be coupled to a receiver by the methods already described or by a separate remote-coupling loop as illustrated. All loops (outer, inner and coupling) must be in the same plane so that they all see the same kind of signal. This is ensured by fixing all three to a rigid support such as a sheet of plywood. In its normal (long-distance reception) role the plane of the loops is vertical.

The CTL is a brilliant innovation. Its only drawback from the domestic user's point of view is that three adjustments are needed:

tuning the inner loop
tuning the outer loop
adjusting the coupling between them.

(The coupling is in practice adjusted by means of a low-value damping resistance R, which changes the Q of the outer loop.) However, the inner-loop tuning and the coupling adjustment hold good over a typical HF broadcast band and only the outer loop need be retuned when the channel is changed. When directional nulling is not needed the inner loop can be used on its own.

References for further information

Short, G. W., Smith V. (1987). The Box Loop. Electronics and Wireless World. Vol. **93**, no. 1616, 637.

BBC World Service Science Unit, *How to Make a Box Aerial.* PO Box 76, Bush House, London WC2B 4PH.

Short G. W. (1988). HF Developments. *Electronics and Wireless World.* Vol. **94**, no. 1629, 644.

Fourth International Conference on HF Radio Systems and Techniques. IEE Conference Publication no. **284**.

Villard O. G. *Portable unidirectional HF receiving aerial for reducing Co-Channel multihop.* Sky-wave interface.

Hagn C. A., Hagh G. H., Villard O. G. *The Wide-strip horizontal loop antenna: an effective solution for ground-wave interference.* London: Institute of Electrical Engineers.

5 Long, medium and short wave broadcasting stations in order of frequency

Data used in the compilation of the following lists of broadcasting frequencies has been obtained from a variety of sources, including the staff of the stations themselves, who have been extremely helpful.

The list of long and medium wave frequencies, includes only those stations which have recently been active on their allotted frequencies and which are audible in Europe. In the main, the area is bounded by the North African states, the countries of the Eastern Mediterranean and the meridian at 40°E. The column headed 'kHz' gives the frequency in kilohertz (which used to be known as 'kilocycles per second' or kc/s) and the power of each station is given in kilowatts effective radiated power.

Short waves are heard world wide and the list reflects the fact.

Abbreviations used in the lists of broadcast frequencies

A	Arabic
ABC	Australian Broadcasting Corporation
AFN	American Forces Network
AIR	All India Radio
AKR	Azad Kashmir Radio (Pakistan)
RM	Radio-Television Malagasy (Madagascar)
AWR	Adventist World Radio (Guam)
B	Bulgarian
BBCS	Burma Broadcasting Service
BRT	Belgische Radio En Televisie
BSKSA	Broadcasting Service of the Kingdom of Saudi Arabia
Bu	Burmese
C	Czechoslovakian
Ca	Cantonese
CBC	Canadian Broadcasting Corporation / Société Radio-Canada
CBS	Central Broadcasting System (Taiwan)
CPBS	Central Peoples' Broadcasting Station (P. Rep. of China)
DW	Deutsche-Welle (West Germany)
EbyR	English by Radio (BBC WS)
ER	Emissor Regional (stations in Angola)
ERT	Elliniki Radiophonia Tileorassis (Greece)
FEBA	Far East Broadcasting Association
FEBC	Far East Broadcasting Company
Fi	Finnish
FIBC	Falkland Islands Broadcasting Station
FPBS	Fujian Peoples' Broadcasting Station (P. Rep. of China)
Fr	French
GBC	Guyana Broadcasting Corporation
GBCC	Ghana Broadcasting Corporation
Ge	German
GPBS	Gansu Peoples' Broadcasting Station (P. Rep. of China)
Gr	Greek
Ha	Hausa
Hi	Hindi
HPBS	Heilongjiang Peoples' Broadcasting Station (P. Rep. of China)
Hu	Hungarian
I	Indonesian
IBRA	IBRA Radio AB (Sweden)
ILR	Independent Local Radio (UK)
IRIB	Islamic Republic of Iran Broadcasting
J	Japanese
JPBS	Jilin Peoples' Broadcasting Station (P. Rep. of China)
KBS	Korean Broadcasting System (Rep. of Korea)
KCBS	Korean Central Broadcasting System (Democratic Peoples' Republic)
KNR	Kalaallit Nunaata Radioa (Greenland)

LBC	Liberian Broadcasting System
LPBS	Liaoning Peoples' Broadcasting Station (P. Rep. of China)
LR	Local radio
LRCN	Liberian Rural Communications Network
LV	La Voz. La Voix,etc.
Man	Mandarin
MBCC	Malawi Broadcasting Corporation
N	Nepali
NBC	National Broadcasting Commission of Papua New Guinea
NHK	Nippon Hoso Kyokai (Japan)
NSB	Nihon Shortwave Broadcasting Co. Ltd (Japan)
O	Ondas, Ondes, etc. (Waves)
ORF	Österreichischer Rundfunk (Austria)
ORTM	Office de Radiodiffusion-Television de Mauritanie
Pa	Pashto
PBC	Pakistan Broadcasting Corporation
PBS	Peoples' Broadcasting Station (P. Rep. of China)
Pe	Persian
PFCB	Philippine Federation of Catholic Broadcasters
Pol	Polish
Por	Portuguese
QBS	Qatar Broadcasting Service
QPBS	Qinghai Peoples' Broadcasting Station (P. Rep. of China)
R	Radio (as in station names - R.Moscow, etc.)
R.Dif	Radio Difusora (Brazil)
RA	Radio Aquiduana (Brazil)
RAE	Radio Argentina al Exterior
RB	Radio Beijing
RB/RK	R.Budapest/R.Kossuth
RBI	Radio Berlin International (East Germany)
RNC	Radiodiffusion Nationale du Cameroun
RNASG	Radio Nacional Arcangel San Gabriel
RCBS	Red Cross Broadcasting Service
RCI	Radio Canada International
RDP	Radiodifusao Portuguesa
RE	Radio Educadora (Brazil)
REE	Radio Exterior España
RENB	Radio East New Britain (Papua New Guinea)
RER	Radio Educaçao Rural (Brazil)
RFE/RL	Radio Free Europe / Radio Liberty
RFI	Radio France International
RFO	Radiodiffusion Française d'Outre-mer (French Guiana)
RKIP	Radio Khusus Informasi Pemerintah (Indonesia)
RKPD	Radio Khusus Pemerintah Daerah (Indonesia)
RM	Radio Moscow
RMI	Radio Mexico International
RN	Radio Nacional,Nationale,etc.
RNA	Radio Nueva América (Bolivia)
RNASG	Radio Nacional Arcangel San Gabriel
RNI	Radio Norway International
RNS	Radio North Solomons (Papua New Guinea)
RNW	Radio Nederland Wereldomroep
Ro	Romanian

RP	Radio Pakistan
RPP	Radio station "Peace and Progress" (USSR)
RRI	Radio Republik Indonesia
RRR	Radiodiffusion de la République Rwandaise (Rwanda) (Colombia)
RSA	Radio RSA (South Africa)
RSI	Radio Sweden International (will shortly drop the "I")
RSWA	Radio Southwest Africa
RT	Radio Tanzania
RTM	Radio Television Malaysia
RTV	Radio Television (in station names - RTV Italiana, etc.)
Ru	Russian
RW	Radio Western (Papua New Guinea)
RZ	Radio Zaracay (Ecuador)
SABC	South African Broadcasting Corporation
SBC	Singapore Broadcasting Corporation
SC	Serbo-Croat
SDR	Süddeutscher Rundfunk (West Germany)
Se	Slovene
SF	Standard frequency or time transmission
SFB	Sender Freies Berlin (West Germany)
SIBC	Solomon Islands Broadcasting Corporation
Sk	Slovak
SLBC	Sri Lanka Broadcasting Corporation
SLBS	Sierra Leone Broadcasting Service
So	Somali
Sp	Spanish
SPBS	Sichuan Peoples' Broadcasting Station (P. Rep. of China)
SR	Sveriges Riksradio AB (Sweden)
SRI	Swiss Radio International
S.s.b.	Single-sideband
Sw	Swahili
SWF	Südwestfunk (West Germany)
T	Turkish
Ta	Tamil
Th	Thai
TWR	Trans World Radio
U	Urdu
UBR	Ulan Bator Radio (Mongolia)
V	Vietnamese
VFC	Voice of Free China (Taiwan)
VO	Voice of ... (station names - VO Andes, etc.)
VOA	Voice of America
VOK	Voice of Kenya
VOS	Voice of the Straits (P. Rep. of China)
VOV	Voice of Vietnam
VRTC	Vietnam Radio and Television Committee
WHRI	World Harvest Radio (USA)
WS	World Service (UK)
XPBS	Xinjiang Peoples' Broadcasting Station (P. Rep. of China)
YPBS	Yunnan Peoples' Broadcasting Station (P. Rep. of China)
ZBC	Zimbabwe Broadcasting Corporation
ZPBS	Zhejiang Peoples' Broadcasting Station

Long wave

Long wave

kHz	*metres*	*Station*	*Country*	*Power*
153	1921	Béchar Arab Net.	Algeria	1000
		Brasov Prog.1	Romania	1200
		Donebach Home Sce	West Germany	500/250
		Tromsoe Prog.1	Norway	10
162	1850	Agri Net.1	Turkey	1000
		Allouis(SF)Net.A	France	2000
		Tachkent Mos.1	USSR	150
171	1754	Kaliningrad Mos.1	USSR	1000
		Lvov Mos.1,2	USSR	500
		Medi I-- Nador Rad. Med. Intl	Morocco	1200
		Moscow Mos.1,2	USSR	500
180	1667	Alma Ata Mos.1,L	USSR	150
		Oranienburg Stimme der DDR	East Germany	750
		Polatli Net.1	Turkey	1200
		Saarlouis Europe 1	West Germany	2000
189	1587	Caltanissetta Prog.2	Italy	10
		Gorno Altaisk	USSR	50
		Motala	Sweden	300
		Tbilisi Mos.1	USSR	500
198	1515	Burghead R4	UK	50
		Droitwich R4 and WS	UK	400
		El Qusiya	Egypt	500
		Etimesgut Net.1	Turkey	200
		Leningrad	USSR	150
		Moscow	USSR	100
		Warsaw Home Sce	Poland	200
		Westerglen R4	UK	50
		Ouargla Arab Net.	Algeria	1000
		Warsaw Home Sce	Poland	200
207	1449	Azilal Arab Net.	Morocco	800
		Caltanissetta	Italy	60
		Eidar Prog.1	Iceland	20
		Erching	West Germany	500
		Floinn	Iceland	500
		Passau	West Germany	250/500
		Qasr Kheraneh	Jordan	200

Long wave				
kHz	*metres*	*Station*	*Country*	*Power*
207	1449	Kiev	USSR	500
		Reykjavik Prog.1	Iceland	100
216	1388	Baku	USSR	500
		Monte Carlo 1st	Monaco	1400
		Oslo Bastøy	Norway	1200
		Oslo Kløfta	Norway	200
225	1333	Warsaw Home Sce	Poland	2000
		Abis	Egypt	200
234	1282	Archangel	USSR	150
		Jefren	Libya	1000
		Junglinster (French)	Luxembourg	2000
		Kishinev	USSR	1000
		Leningrad	USSR	1000
245	1224	Erzurum Net.1	Turkey	200
		Kalundborg 1st	Denmark	200
254	1181	Barcelona	Spain	800
		Bilbao	Spain	400
		Lahti Finnish 1&2	Finland	200
		Linares	Spain	400
		Lugo	Spain	200
		Tipaza French Net.	Algeria	1500/750
		Van	Turkey	600
		Westerglen	UK	50
		Yerevan	USSR	150
263	1141	Burg	East Germany	200
		Moscow	USSR	2000
272	1103	Topolná Hvezda	Czechoslovakia	1500
281	1068	Sverdlovsk	USSR	500

Medium wave

Medium wave

kHz	*metres*	*Station*	*Country*	*Power*
531	565	Ain Beida	Algeria	600/300
		Beromünster	Switzerland	500
		Cheboksary	USSR	30
		Dublin	Eire	20
		Greifswald	East Germany	5
		IRIB	Iran	20
		Jerusalem	Israel	200
		Leipzig	East Germany	100
		Oviedo	Spain	10
		Porto Santo	Madeira	10
		Titovo Uzice	Jugoslavia	10
		Tórshavn	Faroes	5
		Petrosani	Romania	15
540	556	IRIB	Iran	200
		Oulu	Finland	100
		Sidi Bennour	Morocco	600
		Solt	Hungary	2000
		Sulabiyah	Kuwait	1500
		Wavre	Belgium	150/50
549	546	Bayreuth	West Germany	200
		Belikriz	Jugoslavia	20
		Guriat,BSKSA	Saudi Arabia	2000
		Kaliningrad	USSR	25
		Kishinev	USSR	1000
		Leningrad	USSR	100
		Les Trembles	Algeria	600/300
		Minsk	USSR	1000
		Moscow	USSR	100
		Nordkirchen	West Germany	100
558	546	Abu Zaabal	Egypt	40
		Denizli	Turkey	600
		Faro	Portugal	10
		Guarda	Portugal	10
		Helsinki	Finland	--
		IRIB	Iran	1000
		La Coruña	Spain	20
		Maribor	Jugoslavia	20
		Monte Ceneri-C	Switzerland	300
		Neubrandenburg	East Germany	20
		Paphos	Cyprus	10
		Rostock	East Germany	20

Medium wave

kHz	*metres*	*Station*	*Country*	*Power*
558	546	Rutba	Iraq	300
		Targu Jiu	Romania	200
		Tatry	Czechoslovakia	14/3
		Valencia	Spain	20
567	529	Adra	Syria	1000
		Aosta	Italy	2
		Berlin	West Germany	100
		Bologna	Italy	25
		Brasov	Romania	50
		Caltanissetta	Italy	25
		Salento	Italy	6
		Sassari	Italy	10
		Satu Mare	Romania	50
		Strumica	Jugoslavia	10
		Tullamore	Eire	500
		Valença do Minho	Portugal	10
		Volgograd	USSR	250
		Zilina	Czechoslovakia	14/3
576	521	Béchar	Algeria	400/10
		Braga	Portugal	10
		Prijedor	Jugoslavia	2
		Riga	USSR	500
		Schwerin	East Germany	250
		Stuttgart	West Germany	300
		Tarragona	Spain	5
		Tel Aviv	Israel	200
		Vidin	Bulgaria	100
585	513	Dumfries BBC R.Scot.	UK	2
		Gafsa	Tunisia	350
		Lugo	Spain	10
		Madrid	Spain	200
		Marseilles	France	4
		Paris	France	10
		Riyadh,BSKSA	Saudi Arabia	1200
		Vitoria	Spain	4
		Vienna	Austria	600/240
595	505	Duba,BSKSA	Saudi Arabia	2000
		Frankfurt	West Germany	400
		Malatya	Turkey	600
		Meissner	West Germany	200
		Muge	Portugal	100
		Oujda	Morocco	100
		Pleven	Bulgaria	250
		Zagreb	Jugoslavia	20
603	498	Botosani	Romania	50
		Bucharest	Romania	30
		Littlebourne ILR	UK	0.1
		Lyon	France	300
		Newcastle BBC R4	UK	2
		Nicosia	Cyprus	20

Medium wave				
kHz	*metres*	*Station*	*Country*	*Power*
603	498	Nineva	Iraq	300
		Oradea	Romania	2
		Pico do Arieiro	Madeira	10
		Sousse	Tunisia	10
		Spain	Seville	20
		Turnu-Severin	Romania	14
612	490	Amman	Jordan	200
		Athlone	Eire	100
		Homs	Syria	300
		IRIB	Iran	400
		Sarajevo	Jugoslavia	600
		Sebaa-Aioun	Morocco	300
		Tallinn	USSR	100
		Tullamore	Eire	100
621	483	Alicante	Spain	10
		Batra	Egypt	1000
		IRIB	Iran	20
		Orava	Czechoslovakia	14/3
		Tenerife	Canary Is	100
		Wavre	Belgium	300
630	476	Chaves	Portugal	1
		Çukurova	Turkey	300
		Dannenburg	West Germany	10
		Djedeida	Tunisia	600
		Luton BBC LR	UK	0.3
		Miranda do Douro	Portugal	1
		Monte Morvelho	Portugal	50
		Redruth BBC LR	UK	2
		Timisoara	Romania	400
		Trebinje	Jugoslavia	2
		Vigra	Norway	100
		Zenica	Jugoslavia	2
639	469	Albacete	Spain	10
		Almeria	Spain	20
		Bilbao	Spain	20
		IRIB	Iran	400
		La Coruña	Spain	100
		Prague	Czechoslovakia	1500
		Soko Banja	Jugoslavia	1
		Progozhina	Albania	300
		BBC WS	Cyprus	500
		Zaragoza	Spain	20
648	463	Jeddah,BSKSA	Saudi Arabia	2000
		Lazarevac	Jugoslavia	0.1
		Las Palmas	Canary Is	--
		Murska Sobota	Jugoslavia	10
		Plovdiv	Bulgaria	30
		Rrogozhina	Albania	300
		Simferopol	USSR	150
		Tobruk	Libya	300

Medium wave				
kHz	metres	Station	Country	Power
648	463	Orfordness BBC WS	UK	500
656	457	Laayoune	Morocco	50
657	457	Bodmin BBC LR	UK	0.5
		Bolzano	Italy	25
		Burg	East Germany	250
		Chernovtsy	USSR	25
		Firenze	Italy	100
		Madrid	Spain	20
		Murmansk	USSR	150
		Naples	Italy	120
		Neubrandenburg	East Germany	20
		Reichenbach	East Germany	5
		Sadiyat	Utd Arab Emirates	100
		Tel Aviv	Israel	200
		Turin	Italy	50
		Venice	Italy	20
		Wrexham BBC R.Clwyd	UK	2
666	450	Athens	Greece	15
		Bodensee	West Germany	300/180
		Braganza	Portugal	1
		Sabboura	Syria	100
		Exeter BBC LR/ILR	UK	0.5
		Fulford BBC LR	UK	0.5
		Höfn	Iceland	5
		Lisbon	Portugal	135
		Sombor	Jugoslavia	10
		Tindouf	Algeria	0.5
		Vila Real	Portugal	10
		Vilnius	USSR	500
		York BBC LR	UK	0.5
675	444	QBS, Al Khaisa	Qatar	100
		Benghazi	Libya	100
		Bodø	Norway	10
		Bosilegrad	Jugoslavia	10/5
		Jerusalem	Israel	20
		Lopik	Holland	100
		Marseilles	France	600
		Uzhgorod	USSR	50
		Volochisk	USSR	50
684	439	Belgrade	Jugoslavia	2000
		Burgos	Spain	10
		Hof-Saale	West Germany	40
		IRIB	Iran	100
		Seville	Spain	250
		Tanaf	Iraq	200
693	433	Ain-el-Hamam	Algeria	5
		Barcelona	Spain	20
		Barrow BBC R2	UK	1
		Basra	Iraq	1200
		Berlin	East Germany	250

Medium wave				
kHz	*metres*	*Station*	*Country*	*Power*
693	433	Bexhill BBC R2	UK	1
		Brighton BBC R2	UK	1
		Burghead BBC R2	UK	50
		Droitwich BBC R2	UK	150
		Enniskillen BBC R2	UK	1
		Folkestone BBC R2	UK	1
		Negotin	Jugoslavia	10/5
		Nicosia	Cyprus	20
		Oufa	USSR	150
		Postwick BBC R2	UK	10
		Redmoss BBC R2	UK	1
		Reggane	Algeria	5
		Santa Barbara	Azores	10
		Stagshaw BBC R2	UK	50
		Start Point BBC R2	UK	50
		Viseu	Portugal	10
695	432	--	Libya	--
702	427	Aachen	West Germany	5/1
		BBC WS	Oman	--
		Banská Bystrica	Czechoslovakia	400
		El Khârga	Egypt	10
		Finnmark	Norway	20
		Flensburg	West Germany	5/1
		Herford	West Germany	2
		IRIB	Iran	100
		Kaliningrad	USSR	500
		Kleve	West Germany	3
		Monte Carlo	Monaco	300
		Orava	Czechoslovakia	14
		Presov	Czechoslovakia	400
		Rimavska Sobata	Czechoslovakia	14
		Sabac	Jugoslavia	10
		Sebaa-Aïoun	Morocco	140
		Siegen	West Germany	2
		Tatry	Czechoslovakia	14
		Umraniye	Turkey	150
		Zilina	Czechoslovakia	14
711	422	Abu Zaabal	Egypt	100
		Bopfingen	West Germany	0.2
		Donetsk	USSR	150
		Ghadames	Libya	50
		Heidelberg	West Germany	5
		Heilbronn	West Germany	5
		IRIB	Iran	20
		Jefren	Libya	50
		Jerusalem	Israel	--
		Kohtla-Järva	USSR	5
		Laayoune	Morocco	500
		Nis	Jugoslavia	20
		Pärnu	USSR	5

Medium wave

kHz	*metres*	*Station*	*Country*	*Power*
711	422	Rennes	France	300
		Sebha	Libya	50
		Sighet	Romania	30
		Tallinn	USSR	50
		Tartu	USSR	5
		Ulm	West Germany	5
		Wertheim	West Germany	0.2
720	417	Borsa	Romania	1
		BBC WS	Cyprus	--
		Castelo Branco	Portugal	10
		Faro	Portugal	10
		Holzkirchen RFE/RL	West Germany	150
		IRIB	Iran	400
		Isaccea	Romania	1
		Langenberg	West Germany	200
		Lisnagarvey BBC R4	UK	10
		London BBC R4	UK	0.1
		Londonderry BBC R4	UK	0.25
		Mirandela	Portugal	10
		Norte-Azurara	Portugal	100
		Predeal	Romania	14
		Santa Cruz	Canary Is	20
		Sfax	Tunisia	200
729	412	Alicante	Spain	10
		Athens	Greece	150
		Cork	Eire	10
		Cuenca	Spain	5
		Logrono	Spain	20
		Maglaj	Jugoslavia	1
		Malaga	Spain	20
		Manningtree BBC R2/LR	UK	0.2
		Oviedo	Spain	50
		Puttbus	East Germany	5
		Sadiyat	Utd Arab Emirates	700
		Valladolid	Spain	10
738	407	Barcelona	Spain	250
		Chelyabinsk	USSR	150
		In Amenas	Algeria	5
		Krusevac	Jugoslavia	10
		Poznan	Poland	300
		Sibenik	Jugoslavia	2
		Tel Aviv	Israel	1200
		Zagreb	Jugoslavia	25
747	402	Cadiz	Spain	10
		Flevoland	Holland	400
		IRIB	Iran	800
		Las Palmas	Canary Is	20
		Petric	Bulgaria	500
		Sarakeb	Syria	100
		Titovo	Jugoslavia	1

Medium wave				
kHz	*metres*	*Station*	*Country*	*Power*
756	397	Brunswick	West Germany	800/200
		Carlisle BBCLR	UK	1
		Delimara	Malta	20
		Hurriyah	Iraq	300
		Karaotok	Jugoslavia	10
		Lugoj	Romania	400
		Qena	Egypt	10
		Ravensburg	West Germany	100
		Redruth BBC R4	UK	2
		Shrewsbury BBC R4	UK	1
765	392	Chelmsford BBC LR/R2	UK	0.5
		Gaziantep	Turkey	600
		Ioannina	Greece	10
		IRIB	Iran	1200
		Koprivnica	Jugoslavia	1
		Medvezhyegorsk	USSR	150
		Odessa	USSR	150
		Sottens	Switzerland	500
		Zadar	Jugoslavia	2
774	388	Abis	Egypt	500
		Agadir	Morocco	5
		Bihac	Jugoslavia	2
		Bonn	West Germany	5
		Cáceres	Spain	60
		Cheltenham BBC R4	UK	0.2
		East Kent BBC LR	UK	
		Enniskillen BBC R4	UK	1
		Gloucester ILR	UK	0.6
		Granada	Spain	4
		Hradec Kralove	Czechoslovakia	25
		Langenfeld	Austria	0.05
		Leeds BBCLR	UK	0.5
		Littlebourne BBCLR	UK	0.7
		Orense	Spain	20
		Plymouth BBC R4	UK	1
		Sankt Gallenkirch	Austria	0.05
		San Sebastian	Spain	50
		Soria	Spain	10
		Stolnik	Bulgaria	60
		Valencia	Spain	50
		Varna	Bulgaria	30
		Voronezh	USSR	100
783	383	Burg	East Germany	1000
		Djanet	Algeria	5
		Miramar	Portugal	50
		Kazan	USSR	150
		Kiev	USSR	100
		Simferopol	USSR	50
		Tartus	Syria	600
		Uzhgorod	USSR	50

Medium wave				
kHz	*metres*	*Station*	*Country*	*Power*
783	383	Zagreb	Jugoslavia	10
792	379	Arandjelovac	Jugoslavia	2
		Astrakhan	USSR	50
		Banovici	Jugoslavia	1
		Bedford ILR	UK	0.2
		Bratislava	Czechoslovakia	6
		Capljina	Jugoslavia	1
		Kaválla,VOA	Greece	500
		Limoges	France	300
		Londonderry R.Foyle	UK	1
		Prague	Czechoslovakia	30
		Seville	Spain	20
		Sirte	Libya	20
801	375	Ajlun	Jordan	2000
		Amman	Jordan	200
		Barnstaple BBCLR	UK	2
		Leningrad	USSR	1000/500
		Munich	West Germany	450/420
		Nuremberg	West Germany	50
810	370	Berlin	West Germany	5
		Burghead BBC R.Scot.	UK	100
		Dumfries BBC R.Scot.	UK	2
		Madrid	Spain	20
		Maqta	Utd Arab Emirates	800
		Redmoss BBC R.Scot.	UK	5
		Skopje	Jugoslavia	1000
		Volgograd	USSR	150
		Vyru	USSR	5
		Westerglen BBC R.Scot.	UK	100
819	366	Batra	Egypt	450
		Rabat	Morocco	25
		Radio Monique	At sea	50
		Sud Radio	Andorra	900
		Trieste	Italy	25
		Warsaw	Poland	300
828	362	Barcelona	Spain	20
		Bournemouth ILR	UK	0.5
		Castelo Branco	Portugal	1
		Coimbra	Portugal	1
		Covilha	Portugal	1
		Deir el Zor	Syria	1500
		Freiburg	West Germany	40
		Gorki	USSR	100
		Guarda	Portugal	1
		Hanover	West Germany	100/5
		Leeds ILR	UK	0.2
		Luton ILR	UK	0.2
		Oujda	Morocco	100
		Sebha	Libya	300
		Shumen	Bulgaria	500

Medium wave				
kHz	*metres*	*Station*	*Country*	*Power*
828	362	Sofia	Bulgaria	60
		Wolverhampton BBC LR	UK	0.2
		Viseu	Portugal	1
		Vrbovec	Jugoslavia	1
837	358	Barossa	Azores	10
		Barrow BBC LR	UK	1
		Beni Abbès	Algeria	5
		IRIB	Iran	400
		Kharkov	USSR	150
		Las Palmas	Canary Is	10
		Leicester BBC LR	UK	0.7
		Nancy	France	200
		Seville	Spain	10
		Zagreb Dubrovnik	Jugoslavia	2
		Zagreb Gospic	Jugoslavia	10
846	355	Ceske Budejovice	Czechoslovakia	30
		Elista	USSR	30
		Moscow	USSR	60
		Nasiriya	Iraq	300
		Ostrava	Czechoslovakia	30
		Rome	Italy	540
		Zefat	Israel	5
855	351	Amman	Jordan	10
		Berlin	West Germany	100
		Bucharest	Romania	1500
		Huelva	Spain	5
		Murcia	Spain	125
		Pamplona	Spain	10
		Penza	USSR	30
		Plymouth BBC LR	UK	1
		Pontevedra	Spain	20
		Postwick BBC LR	UK	1
		Ponferrada	Spain	10
		Preston BBC LR	UK	1
		Salamanca	Spain	10
		Santander	Spain	20
		Teruel	Spain	10
864	347	Blagoevgrad	Bulgaria	30
		Ciudad Real	Spain	10
		Er Rachidia	Morocco	15
		Ivanic Grad	Jugoslavia	1
		Kelcyra	Albania	1
		Olomouc	Czechoslovakia	20/2
		Paris	France	300
		Santah	Egypt	500
		Sokolac	Jugoslavia	1
		Ustínad Labem	Czechoslovakia	6/1
		Yerevan	USSR	150
		Zagreb	Jugoslavia	10
873	344	Budapest	Hungary	20

Medium wave				
kHz	*metres*	*Station*	*Country*	*Power*
873	344	Abu Zaabal	Egypt	50
		Kharabo	Syria	10
		Enniskillen R.Ulster	UK	1
		Frankfurt AFN	West Germany	150
		Ghardaia	Algeria	5
		Kaliningrad	USSR	100
		King's Lynn BBC LR	UK	0.25
		Leningrad	USSR	150
		Pecs	Hungary	15
		Stara Zagora	Bulgaria	30
		Zaragoza	Spain	20
882	340	Bet Hillel	Israel	1
		Forden BBC R.Wales	UK	1
		Königswuster-hausen	East Germany	100
		La Laguna	Canary Is	20
		Matruh	Egypt	10
		Penmon BBC R.Wales	UK	10
		Pijevlja	Jugoslavia	10
		Remada	Tunisia	1
		Sabadell	Spain	1
		Titograd	Jugoslavia	300/100
		Tywyn BBC R.Wales	UK	5
		Washford BBC R.Wales	UK	70
891	337	Algiers	Algeria	600/300
		Antalya	Turkey	600
		Berlin	East Germany	5
		Bundoran	Eire	100
		Dniepropetrovsk	USSR	20
		Hulsberg	Holland	20
		Uzhgorod	USSR	150
		Vila Moura	Portugal	10
900	333	Belgrade	Jugoslavia	2
		Brno	Czechoslovakia	30
		BSKSA,Guriat	Saudi Arabia	1000
		Yoshkar-Ola	USSR	50
		Karlovy-Vary	Czechoslovakia	30
		Milan	Italy	600
909	330	Angraheroismo	Azores	10
		Bournemouth BBC R2	UK	0.25
		Brookman's P., BBC R2	UK	150
		Clevedon BBC R2	UK	50
		Cluj	Romania	50
		Exeter BBC R2	UK	1
		Fareham BBC R2	UK	1
		Fernbarrow BBC R2	UK	1
		Giaghboub	Libya	20
		Hurriyah	Iraq	300
		Kufra	Libya	10
		Lisnagarvey BBC R2	UK	10

Medium wave				
kHz	*metres*	*Station*	*Country*	*Power*
909	330	Londonderry BBC R2	UK	1
		Moorside Edge BBC R2	UK	150
		Redruth BBC R2	UK	2
		Resita	Romania	15
		Safi	Morocco	5
		Tamanrasset	Algeria	5
		Westerglen BBC R2	UK	50
		Whitehaven BBC R2	UK	1
918	327	Al-Hassake	Syria	200
		Bawiti	Egypt	10
		Liubliana	Jugoslavia	600/100
		Madrid	Spain	20
		Makhach Kala	USSR	50
		Mezen	USSR	100
		Paphos	Cyprus	2
927	324	Bratislava	Czechoslovakia	14
		Evora	Portugal	1
		Izmir	Turkey	200
		Timimoun	Algeria	5
		Wolvertem	Belgium	200
		Zakynthos	Greece	50
930	323	BBC WS	Montserrat	--
936	321	Agadir	Morocco	600
		Bremen	West Germany	100
		Bremerhaven	West Germany	5
		Cairo	Egypt	20
		Djacovica	Jugoslavia	20
		Dorji Miholjac	Jugoslavia	0.05
		Gevgelija	Jugoslavia	10
		Lérida	Spain	1
		Lvov	USSR	500
		Ruma	Jugoslavia	1
		Trapani	Italy	5
		West Wiltshire ILR	UK	0.2
945	317	Backi Petrovac	Jugoslavia	0.1
		Derby ILR	UK	0.2
		Gnjilane	Jugoslavia	2
		Kumanovo	Jugoslavia	2
		Larissa	Greece	5
		Miercurea Ciuc	Romania	14
		Pleven	Bulgaria	30
		Riga	USSR	50
		Rostov-on-Don	USSR	300
		Sarajevo	Jugoslavia	300
		Smederevo	Jugoslavia	1
		Toulouse	France	300
954	314	Brno	Czechoslovakia	100
		Deir el Zor	Syria	60
		QBS,Al Aris	Qatar	1500
		Hereford ILR	UK	0.2

Medium wave				
kHz	*metres*	*Station*	*Country*	*Power*
954	314	Iráklion	Greece	20
		Madrid	Spain	20
		Torbay ILR	UK	0.4
		Trabzon	Turkey	300
963	321	Beirut	Lebanon	100
963	321	Celje	Jugoslavia	2
		Djedeida	Tunisia	200
		Korce	Albania	15
		Lisbon	Portugal	1
		Paris	France	8
		Pori	Finland	600
		Radio Caroline	At sea	50
		Seixal REE	Portugal	10
		Soba	Sudan	60
		Sofia	Bulgaria	150
		Tir Chonaill	Eire	10
972	309	Fujeira	Utd Arab Emirates	100
		Hamburg	West Germany	300
		Jean	Spain	5
		Knin	Jugoslavia	1
		Marrakesh	Morocco	1
		Nikolaev	USSR	500
		Puke	Albania	20
		Vukovar	Jugoslavia	1
981	306	Algiers	Algeria	600/300
		Assiut	Egypt	1
		Baris	Egypt	5
		Bor	Jugoslavia	10
		Bjelovar	Jugoslavia	1
		Cacak	Jugoslavia	10
		Ceske	Czechoslovakia	7
		Dhekelia	Cyprus	1
		Karlovy Vary	Czechoslovakia	7
		Megara	Greece	200
		Ostrava	Czechoslovakia	1
		Trieste	Italy	10
990	303	Aberdeen BBC R.Scot.	UK	1
		Barcelona	Spain	10
		Berlin	West Germany	300
		Bilbao	Spain	10
		Ceuta	Spain	0.5
		Doncaster ILR	UK	0.3
		Exeter BBC LR	UK	1
		Foca	Jugoslavia	1
		Idfu	Egypt	1
		Kladovo	Jugoslavia	1
		Kukes	Albania	10
		Pozarevac	Jugoslavia	1
		Redmoss BBCLR/R.Scot.	UK	1

Medium wave				
kHz	*metres*	*Station*	*Country*	*Power*
990	303	IRIB	Iran	400
		Tywyn BBC R2	UK	1
		Wolverhampton ILR	UK	0.1
		Zupanja	Jugoslavia	1
999	300	Addakhla	Morocco	10
		QBS, Al Khaisa	Qatar	50
		Delimara	Malta	20
		Fareham BBCLR	UK	1
		Hoyerswerda	East Germany	20
		Kishinev	USSR	500
		Kladovo	Jugoslavia	1
		Madrid	Spain	20
		Nottingham ILR	UK	0.2
		Preston ILR	UK	0.8
		Rimini	Italy	6
		Schwerinn	East Germany	20
		Turin	Italy	50
		Vatican City	Vatican	2
		Weimar	East Germany	20
1008	298	Aleksinac	Jugosavia	400/120
		Belgrade	Jugoslavia	200/120
		Beni Suef	Egypt	1
		Flevoland	Holland	400
		Kerkyra	Greece	50
		Las Palmas	Canary Is	10
		Malaga	Spain	10
		Slonim	USSR	50
		Uchachi	USSR	50
1017	245	Bratislava	Czechoslovakia	6
		Genoa	Italy	1
		Istanbul	Turkey	1200
		Kardjali	Bulgaria	30
		Kosice	Czechoslovakia	2
		Mnich Hradiste	Czechoslovakia	40
		Nitra	Czechoslovakia	50
		Rimavska Sobata	Czechoslovakia	6
		Seelow	East Germany	3
		Stoke-on-Trent ILR	UK	1
		Tangier	Morocco	1
		Venice	Italy	20
		Wolfsheim	West Germany	600
1026	292	Alicante	Spain	3
		Bar	Jugoslavia	5
		Belfast ILR	UK	1
		Brest	USSR	5
		Chesterton Fen BBC LR	UK	0.5
		Dornbirn Lauterach	Austria	50
		Gijon	Spain	1
		Grodno	USSR	5
		Hassi Messaoud	Algeria	5

Medium wave				
kHz	*metres*	*Station*	*Country*	*Power*
1026	292	IRIB	Iran	100
		Jersey BBC LR	UK	1
		Kragujevac	Jugoslavia	10
		Linz Kronstorf	Austria	100
		Niandoma	USSR	5
		Pinsk	USSR	5
		Rabat	Morocco	1
		Reus	Spain	2
		Scharnitz	Austria	0.05
		Skopje	Jugoslavia	2
		Tel Aviv	Israel	5
		Trinity BBCLR	UK	1
		Vigo	Spain	3
1035	290	Aberdeen ILR	UK	0.5
		Ayr ILR	UK	0.5
		Babylon	Iraq	1000
		Caltanissetta	Italy	2
		Chatham BBC LR	UK	0.5
		Damascus	Syria	--
		Firenze	Italy	6
		Genoa	Italy	10
		Hoo BBCLR	UK	0.5
		Lisbon	Portugal	135
		Milan	Italy	50
		Naples	Italy	20
		Oristano	Italy	2
		Pescara	Italy	6
		Potenza	Italy	1
		Salala	Oman	100
		Salento	Italy	6
		Sheffield BBCLR	UK	1
		Tallinn	USSR	500
		T.Mitrovica	Jugoslavia	5
		Venice	Italy	20
1044	287	Dresden	East Germany	250
		Limassol	Cyprus	10
		Podravska Slatina	Jugoslavia	1
		Sebaa-Aioun	Morocco	300
		Tbilisi	USSR	100
		Temerin	Jugoslavia	0.1
		Thessaloniki	Greece	150
1053	285	Barnstaple BBC R1	UK	1
		Barrow BBC R1	UK	1
		Bexhill BBC R1	UK	2
		Brighton BBC R1	UK	2
		Burghead BBC R1	UK	20
		Dundee BBC R1	UK	1
		Droitwich BBC R1	UK	150
		Enniskillen BBC R1	UK	1
		Folkestone BBC R1	UK	1

Medium wave				
kHz	*metres*	*Station*	*Country*	*Power*
1053	285	Hull BBC R1	UK	1
		Iasi	Romania	1000
		Londonderry BBC R1	UK	1
		Postwick BBC R1	UK	10
		Start Point BBC R1	UK	100
		Stagshaw BBC R1	UK	50
		Tangier	Morocco	600
		Tripoli	Libya	50
1062	282	Abu Zaabal	Egypt	50
		Azurara	Portugal	100
		Catania	Italy	2
		Diyabakir	Turkey	300
		Gagliari	Italy	25
		Kalundborg	Denmark	250
		Livorno	Italy	1
		Novi Pazar	Jugoslavia	1
		Saransk	USSR	150
		Squinzano	Italy	25
		Svetozarevo	Jugoslavia	10
		Trento	Italy	1
		Udine	Italy	2
		Verona	Italy	2
		Zagreb	Jugoslavia	10
1071	280	Banja Luka	Jugoslavia	20
		Bastia	France	20
		Brest	France	20
		Ceske Budejovice	Czechoslovakia	7
		Grenoble	France	20
		Kuldiga	USSR	50
		Lille	France	40
		Mnich Hradiste	Czechoslovakia	50
		Riga	USSR	60
		Tartus	Syria	60
		Valmiera	USSR	50
1080	278	Ajedabia	Libya	40
		Casablanca	Morocco	1
		El Minya	Egypt	10
		Granada	Spain	5
		IRIB	Iran	600
		Jalo	Libya	5
		Katowice	Poland	1500
		La Coruña	Spain	5
		Luxor	Egypt	10
		Orestias	Greece	20
		Palma (Mallorca)	Spain	2
		Toledo	Spain	2
1089	275	Adrar	Algeria	5
		Akrotiri	Cyprus	10
		Brookman's P.,BBC R1	UK	150
		Durres	Albania	150

Medium wave				
kHz	*metres*	*Station*	*Country*	*Power*
1089	275	Fareham BBC R1	UK	1
		Krasnodar	USSR	300
		Lisnagarvey BBC R1	UK	2
		Moorside Edge BBC R1	UK	150
		Novi Sad	Jugoslavia	--
		Redmoss BBC R1	UK	2
		Redruth BBC R1	UK	2
		Tywyn BBC R1	UK	1
		Washford BBC R1	UK	50
		Westerglen BBC R1	UK	50
		Whitehaven BBC R1	UK	1
1098	273	Alma Ata	USSR	150
		Bologna	Italy	60
		Bratislava	Czechoslovakia	400
		IRIB	Iran	200
		Quargla	Algeria	5
		Vologda	USSR	5
		Yeni Iskele	Northern Cyprus	100
1107	271	Barcelona	Spain	20
		Batra	Egypt	600
		Berlin AFN	West Germany	600
		Cáceres	Spain	5
		Grafenwohr AFN	West Germany	10
		Inverness ILR	UK	1
		Kaisers-lautern AFN	West Germany	10
		Kaunas	USSR	150
		Munich AFN	West Germany	100
		Murcia	Spain	5
		Northampton BBC LR	UK	0.5
		Novi Sad	Jugoslavia	150
		Nuremberg AFN	West Germany	150
		Palencia	Spain	2
		Ponferrada	Spain	5
		Rome	Italy	6
		Santander	Spain	10
		Socuellamos	Spain	2
		Turuel	Spain	5
		Valladolid	Spain	2
		Vigo	Spain	5
		Wallasey BBC R1	UK	0.5
1116	269	Aosta	Italy	2
		Bari	Italy	150
		Bologna	Italy	60
		Bloemendaal	Holland	0.05
		Derby BBCLR	UK	0.5
		Erimoupolis	Greece	150/350
		Erimoupolis	Greece	300/150
		Guernsey BBC LR	UK	0.5
		IRIB	Iran	125

Medium wave				
kHz	*metres*	*Station*	*Country*	*Power*
1116	269	Kaliningrad	USSR	30
		Karl-Marx-Stadt	East Germany	5
		Miscolc	Hungary	12
		Moscow	USSR	5
		Moson-Magyarovar	Hungary	2
		Palermo	Italy	10
		Pisa	Italy	25
		Quarzazarte	Morocco	15
		Rutba	Iraq	300
		Tangier	Morocco	1
		Trieste	Italy	6
1125	267	Al-Hassake	Syria	200
		El Beida	Libya	500
		La Louviere	Belgium	20
		Leningrad	USSR	150
		Llandrindod Wells BBC R.Wales	UK	1
1134	265	Almeria	Spain	2
		Astorga	Spain	2
		Aviles	Spain	2
		Bilbao	Spain	10
		Cáceres	Spain	2
		Ciudadela	Spain	2
		Ciudad Real	Spain	2
		Ferrol	Spain	2
		Figueras	Spain	2
		Jaen	Spain	2
		Lorca	Spain	2
		Orense	Spain	2
		Pamplona	Spain	2
		Salamanca	Spain	2
		Sulabiya	Kuwait	1500
		Zadar	Jugoslavia	1200
		Zaragoza	Spain	10
1143	262	Bremerhaven AFN	West Germany	5
		Dublin	Eire	20
		Heidelberg AFN	West Germany	1
		Hof(AFN)	West Germany	1
		Karlsruhe AFN	West Germany	1
		Kuibyshev	USSR	100
		Sohag	Egypt	5
		Stuttgart AFN	West Germany	10
		Zagreb	Jugoslavia	85
		11 low-power	West Germany	0.3
1152	260	Birmingham ILR	UK	0.8
		Cluj	Romania	950
		Glasgow ILR	UK	2
		IRIB	Iran	100
		Manchester ILR	UK	0.35
		Marrakesh	Morocco	1

Medium wave				
kHz	*metres*	*Station*	*Country*	*Power*
1152	260	Norwich ILR	UK	1
		London ILR	UK	5.5
		Plymouth ILR	UK	0.5
		Tyne and Wear ILR	UK	1
1161	258	Tanta	Egypt	60
		Bedford BBC LR	UK	0.08
		Bexhill BBC LR	UK	1
		Dundee ILR	UK	0.5
		Hull ILR	UK	0.5
		In Salah	Algeria	5
		Stara Zagora	Bulgaria	500
		Sofia	Bulgaria	60
		Strasbourg	France	200
		Swindon ILR	UK	0.4
		Toulouse	France	50
1170	256	Backa Topola	Jugoslavia	1
		Beli Kriz	Jugoslavia	300/100
		Bernburg	East Germany	20
		Ipswich ILR	UK	0.3
		Keula	East Germany	5
		Maikop	USSR	500
		Moghilev	USSR	1000
		Plauen	East Germany	3
		Portsmouth ILR	UK	0.2
		Stoke-on-Trent ILR	UK	0.25
		Stockton-on-Tees ILR	UK	0.5
		Swansea ILR	UK	0.5
		Vila Real	Portugal	10
		Vrnjacka Banja	Jugoslavia	1
1179	254	Bacau	Romania	200
		Barcelona	Spain	10
		Murcia	Spain	5
		Qena	Egypt	10
		Samobor	Jugoslavia	1
		Smederevska Palanka	Jugoslavia	1
		Solvesborg	Sweden	600
		Thessaloniki	Greece	50
		Van Iskelesi	Turkey	2
		Vascau	Romania	5
1188	253	Casablanca	Morocco	1
		Dublin	Eire	--
		IRIB	Iran	100
		Kuurne	Belgium	5
		Ras Gharib	Egyot	10
		San Remo	Italy	6
		Szolnok	Hungary	135
		Szombathely	Hungary	25
		Wachenbrunn	East Germany	--
1197	251	Agadir	Morocco	20

Medium wave				
kHz	*metres*	*Station*	*Country*	*Power*
1197	251	Alexandria	Egypt	25
		Bjeljina	Jugoslavia	2
		Bosanski Novi	Jugoslavia	1
		Bournemouth BBC R3	UK	1
		Cambridge BBC R3	UK	0.2
		Enniskillen BBC R3	UK	1
		Kriva Palanka	Jugoslavia	1
		Minsk	USSR	50
		Munich VOA	West Germany	300
		Nineva	Iraq	300
		Portalegre	Portugal	1
		Tallinn	USSR	--
		Torquay BBC R3	UK	0.5
		Visoko	Jugoslavia	1
1206	249	Bordeaux	France	100
		Bosanski Brod Majdanpek	Jugoslavia	1
		Haifa	Israel	50
		Kielce	Poland	10
		Korce	Albania	10
		Koszalin	Poland	10
		Lublin	Poland	60
		Sombor	Jugoslavia	10
		Wroclaw	Poland	200
		--	USSR	--
1215	247	Brighton BBC R3	UK	1
		Brookman's P.,BBC R3	UK	50
		Burghead BBC R3	UK	20
		Djurdjevac	Jugoslavia	1
		Droitwich BBC R3	UK	30
		Fareham BBC R3	UK	1
		Hull BBC R3	UK	0.3
		Kursk	USSR	20
		Lisnagarvey BBC R3	UK	10
		Londonderry BBC R3	UK	1
		Lushnje	Albania	500
		Tartu	USSR	50
		Mladenovac	Jugoslavia	1
		Moorside Edge BBC R3	UK	50
		Orrisare	USSR	30
		Plymouth BBC R3	UK	1
		Postwick BBC R3	UK	1
		Redmoss BBC R3	UK	2
		Redruth BBC R3	UK	2
		Tyne and Wear BBC R3	UK	2
		Tywyn BBC R3	UK	1
		Washford BBC R3	UK	60
		Westerglen BBC R3	UK	40
1224	245	Albacete	Spain	2
		Avelva	Spain	2

Medium wave				
kHz	*metres*	*Station*	*Country*	*Power*
1224	245	Beer-Sheva	Israel	20
		Bijelina	Jugoslavia	2
		Cordoba	Spain	2
		Granada	Spain	5
		Jerez	Spain	2
		Krapina	Jugoslavia	1
		Lerida	Spain	2
		Lugo	Spain	2
		Nasiriya	Iraq	300
		Palma Mallorca	Spain	2
		Puertolland	Spain	2
		San Sebastian	Spain	2
		Santander	Spain	2
		Vidin	Bulgaria	500
1233	243	QBS, Al Khaisa	Qatar	100
		Cape Greco	Cyprus	600
		Ceske Budejovice	Czechoslovakia	60
		Hradec Kralove	Czechoslovakia	6
		Ilijas	Jugoslavia	1
		Karlovy Vary	Czechoslovakia	50
		Liége	Belgium	1
		Pilsen	Czechoslovakia	7
		Prague	Czechoslovakia	400
		Strakonice	Czechoslovakia	7
		Tangier	Morocco	200
1242	242	Donetsk	USSR	30
		Kiev	USSR	150
		Maidstone ILR	UK	--
		Marseille	France	150
		Modrica	Jugoslavia	0.1
		Muscat	Oman	200
		Odessa	USSR	30
		Ohrid	Jugoslavia	5
		Simferopol	USSR	50
		Vaasa	Finland	25
		Volotchisk	USSR	50
1251	240	Bury St Edmunds ILR	UK	0.5
		Castelo Brancu	Portugal	0.1
		Chaves	Portugal	1
		Gorazde	Jugoslavia	1
		Hulsberg	Holland	20
		Nyiregyhasa	Hungary	25
		Porto	Portugal	10
		Siofok	Hungary	500
		Tripoli	Libya	500
		Viseu	Portugal	10
		Westport	Eire	50
1260	238	Algeciras	Spain	5
		Badajoz	Spain	5
		Bristol ILR	UK	0.8

Medium wave				
kHz	*metres*	*Station*	*Country*	*Power*
1260	238	Fier	Albania	1
		Horta	Azores	1
		Leicester ILR	UK	0.2
		Rhodes	Greece	500
		San Sebastian	Spain	10
		Scarborough BBC LR	UK	0.1
		Starachovice	Poland	5
		Szczecin	Poland	160
		Wrexham ILR	UK	0.6
		Valencia	Spain	10
		Vatican City	Vatican	5
1269	236	La Orotava	Canary Is	--
		Las Palmas	Canary Is	20
		Neumunster	West Germany	600
		Novi Sad	Jugoslavia	600/150
1278	235	Aswan	Egypt	10
		Bradford ILR	UK	0.3
		Cork	Eire	10
		Dublin	Eire	10
		Florina	Greece	20
		IRIB	Iran	200
		Odessa	USSR	150
		Strasbourg	France	300
		Turku	Finland	4
1287	233	Bratislava	Czechoslovakia	200
		Ceskoslovensko	Czechoslovakia	300
		El Golea	Algeria	5
		Kocani	Czechoslovakia	1
		Liblice	Czechoslovakia	200
		Petrinja	Jugoslavia	1
		Presov	Czechoslovakia	30
		Tatry	Czechoslovakia	14
		Tel Aviv	Israel	100
1296	231	Baku	USSR	150
		Kardjali	Bulgaria	150
		Loznica	Jugoslavia	10
		Orfordness BBC WS	UK	500
		Rabat	Morocco	1
		Vranje	Jugoslavia	10
1301	231	Milan	Italy	5
1305	230	Assiut	Egypt	1
		Barnsley ILR	UK	0.3
		Bialystok	Poland	60
		Bosanska Krupa	Jugoslavia	1
		Cakovec	Jugoslavia	1
		Constantine	Algeria	20
		Cork City	Eire	--
		Eilat	Israel	5
		Gdansk	Poland	60
		Gjirokaster	Albania	15

Medium wave				
kHz	*metres*	*Station*	*Country*	*Power*
1305	230	Haifa	Israel	20
		Herceg Novi	Jugoslavia	1
		Lodz	Poland	60
		Marche	Belgium	10
		Newport ILR	UK	0.23
		Pisa	Italy	2
		Rzeszow	Poland	100
		Vincovci	Jugoslavia	1
1314	228	BBC WS	Cyprus	--
		Ancona	Italy	6
		Aleppo	Syria	10
		Cadiz	Spain	2
		Campobasso	Italy	1
		Catanzaro	Italy	1
		Constantza	Romania	14
		Craiova	Romania	7
		Dabiya	Utd Arab Emirates	1000
		Hurghada	Egypt	10
		Kvitsoy	Norway	1200
		Matera	Italy	2
		Nag Hamadi	Egypt	1
		Ohrid	Jugoslavia	10
		Sama Langreo	Spain	2
		San Sebastian	Spain	10
		Skopje	Jugoslavia	100
		Soria	Spain	5
		Tarrega	Spain	2
		Timisoara	Romania	30
		Tripolis	Greece	10
		Valladolid	Spain	10
1323	227	Bitola	Jugoslavia	10
		Brighton ILR	UK	0.5
		Delcevo	Jugoslavia	10
		Gostivar	Jugoslavia	2
		Leipzig	East Germany	150
		Limassol WS	Cyprus	200
		Safi	Morocco	5
		Shkoder	Albania	10
		Sid	Jugoslavia	1
		Targu Mures	Romania	10
		Taunton BBC LR	UK	1
1332	225	Bari	Italy	50
		Elvas	Portugal	1
		Galatzi	Romania	15
		Gnjilane	Jugoslavia	2
		IRIB	Iran	100
		Jihlava	Czechoslovakia	14
		Khohtla	USSR	15
		Palermo	Italy	10
		Parnu	USSR	20

Medium wave				
kHz	*metres*	*Station*	*Country*	*Power*
1332	225	Pescara	Italy	25
		Peterborough ILR	UK	0.5
		Rome	Italy	300
		Vyru	USSR	30
1341	224	Budapest	Hungary	150
		Cairo	Egypt	100
		Idfu	Egypt	10
		Lisnagarvey BBC Ulst.	UK	100
		Magwa	Kuwait	200
		Markneukirchen	East Germany	1
		Santa Cruz (Tenerife)	Canary Is	20
		Zajecar	Jugoslavia	10/1
1350	222	Erevan	USSR	150
		Gyor	Hungary	5
		Kuldiga	USSR	20
		Madona	USSR	50
		Nancy	France	100
		Nice	France	100
		Pecs	Hungary	10
		Purgos	Greece	4
		Quseir	Egypt	2
		Szolnok	Hungary	5
		Zabok	Jugoslavia	1
1359	221	Berlin	East Germany	250/100
		Bournemouth BBC LR	UK	0.25
		Cardiff ILR	UK	0.25
		Chelmsford ILR	UK	0.3
		Coventry ILR	UK	0.1
		Kirkuk	Iraq	120
		Moscow	USSR	150
		Tirana	Albania	150
		Vrbas-Kula	Jugoslavia	2
1368	219	Bari	Italy	1
		Catania	Italy	2
		Cracow	Poland	60
		Firenze	Italy	2
		Foxdale Manx Radio	UK	2
		Genoa	Italy	10
		Lincoln BBC LR	UK	2
		Messina	Italy	2
		Milan	Italy	10
		Naples	Italy	10
		Reigate BBC LR	UK	0.5
		Rosh Pina	Israel	5
		Sanski Most	Jugoslavia	1
		Sassari	Italy	2
		Shivta	Israel	20
		Trento	Italy	0.15
		Turin	Italy	6

Medium wave				
kHz	*metres*	*Station*	*Country*	*Power*
1368	219	Valjevo	Jugoslavia	10
		Venice	Italy	20
		Zielona Gora	Poland	30
1377	218	Canidelo	Portugal	10
		Lille	France	300
		Lutsk	USSR	50
		Prizren	Jugoslavia	10/2
		Shumen	Bulgaria	30
		Tanaf	Iraq	1000
		Chernovtsy	USSR	50
		Vinnitsa	USSR	30
		Zagreb	Jugoslavia	4
1386	216	Athens	Greece	50
		IRIB	Iran	400
		Kaunas	USSR	500
		Kratovo	Jugoslavia	1
1395	215	Alicante	Spain	10
		Angra Heroismo	Azores	1
		Bugojno	Jugoslavia	1
		Ciudad Real	Spain	2
		Doboj	Jugoslavia	1
		Granada	Spain	5
		Huelva	Spain	2
		La Coruña	Spain	5
		Leon	Spain	5
		Lushnje	Albania	1000
		Tortosa	Spain	2
1404	214	Ajaccio	France	20
		Baia Mare	Romania	15
		Brest	France	20
		Dijon	France	1
		Dniepropetrovsk	USSR	30
		Donegal	Eire	--
		Grenoble	France	1
		Helsinki	Finland	2
		Izmail	USSR	25
		Komotini	Greece	100
		Lvov	USSR	30
		Komotini	Greece	100
		Pau	France	20
1413	212	Bad Mergentheim	West Germany	3
		BBC WS	Oman	--
		Heideheim	West Germany	0.2
		Oviedo	Spain	2
		Pristina	Jugoslavia	1000
		Salamanca	Spain	5
		Seville	Spain	20
		Vitoria	Spain	5
		Zaragoza	Spain	20
1422	211	Algiers	Algeria	50

Medium wave				
kHz	*metres*	*Station*	*Country*	*Power*
1422	211	IRIB	Iran	100
		Liepaia	USSR	5
		Ras Ghareb	Egypt	10
		Rezekne	USSR	5
		Saarbrucken	West Germany	1200/600
		Valmiera	USSR	50
		7 low-powers	Romania	--
1431	210	Bernburg	East Germany	20
		Caramulo	Portugal	10
		Dresden	East Germany	20
		Foggia	Italy	2
		Krivoi Rog	USSR	500
		Krizevci	Jugoslavia	0.05
		Missan	Iraq	1000
		Pesaro	Italy	2
		Probistip	Jugoslavia	1
		Reading ILR	UK	0.2
		Seelow	East Germany	5
		Southend ILR	UK	0.4
		Taranto	Italy	1
		Wachenbrunn	East Germany	20
		Weida	East Germany	5
1440	208	Dammam,BSKSA	Saudi Arabia	1600
		Marnach	Luxembourg	1200
		Mizurata	Libya	20
		Svetozarevo	Jugoslavia	10
1449	207	Berlin	West Germany	5
		IRIB	Iran	800
		Kalinin	USSR	30
		Karlovac	Jugoslavia	2
		Misurata	Libya	20
		Peterborough BBC LR	UK	0,1
		Redmoss BBC R4	UK	2
		Squinzano (plus 24 low-powers)	Italy	50
1458	206	Birmingham BBC LR	UK	7
		Brookman's P. BBC LR	UK	50
		Constantza	Romania	50
		Eilat	Israel	1
		Gibraltar	Gibraltar	2
		Jerusalem	Israel	10
		Kraljevo	Jugoslavia	10
		Kudymkar	USSR	50
		Langley Mill BBCLR	UK	7
		Lushnje	Albania	500
		Manchester BBCLR	UK	5
		Newcastle BBCLR	UK	2
		Torquay BBCLR	UK	1
		Weida	East Germany	--
		Whitehaven BBCLR	UK	0.5

Medium wave				
kHz	*metres*	*Station*	*Country*	*Power*
1458	206	Valpovo	Jugoslavia	1
1467	204	Frunze	USSR	30
		IRIB	Iran	200
		Kiev	USSR	300
		Monte Carlo	Monaco	1000/400
		Yalta	USSR	30
		Zrenjanin	Jugoslavia	2
		Zvornik	Jugoslavia	1
1476	203	Albacete	Spain	5
		Almeria	Spain	5
		Bilbao	Spain	10
		Cordoba	Spain	5
		Guildford ILR	UK	0.5
		Lvov	USSR	120
		Orense	Spain	5
		Palma Mallorca	Spain	2
		Sohag	Egypt	10
		Vienna	Austria	600
1485	202	Arezzo	Italy	0.15
		Antequerra (plus 10 low-powers)	Spain	2
		Arezzo	Italy	0.15
		Baden-Baden (plus 7 low-powers)	West Germany	1
		5 low-powers	Poland	--
		Berovo	Jugoslavia	1
		Bournemouth BBC R1	UK	1
		Brighton BBC LR	UK	1
		Bugibba	Malta	1
		Carlisle BBC R4	UK	1
		Casablanca	Morocco	1
		Crna Trava	Jugoslavia	1
		El Tur	Egypt	1
		Fernbarrow BBCLR	UK	1
		Homs	Syria	10
		Hull BBC LR	UK	1.5
		Kladovo	Jugoslavia	1
		Novi Sad	Jugoslavia	2/1
		Orestias	Greece	1
		Oxford BBC LR	UK	0.5
		Pilsen	Czechoslovakia	1
		Saviese	Switzerland	1
		Tours	France	0.05
		Volos	Greece	1
		Wallasey BBC LR	UK	2
		10 low-powers	East Germany	1
		25 low-powers	Jugoslavia	1
1494	201	Bastia	France	20
		Bayonne	France	4
		Besancon	France	1

Medium wave				
kHz	*metres*	*Station*	*Country*	*Power*
1494	201	Clermont Ferrand	France	20
		Edintsy	USSR	25
		Leningrad	USSR	1000
		Prenjas	Albania	1
		Rhodes	Greece	100
1503	201	Avila	Spain	5
		Badajoz	Spain	5
		Belgrade	Jugoslavia	10
		Burgos	Spain	5
		El Arish	Egypt	1
		IRIB	Iran	100
		Jaen	Spain	2
		Kutina	Jugoslavia	1
		Lugo	Spain	5
		Marbella	Spain	2
		Nicosia	Cyprus	1
		Pamplona	Spain	10
		Stargard	Poland	300
		Stoke-on-Trent BBCLR	UK	1
		Tarragon	Spain	5
		Ulcinj	Jugoslavia	5
		Zavidovici	Jugoslavia	1
1512	198	Chania	Greece	5
		Jeddah,BSKSA	Saudi Arabia	1000
		Palermo	Italy	2
		Pristina	Jugoslavia	10
		Sochi	USSR	30
		Tallinn	USSR	30
		Wolvertem	Belgium	100
1521	197	Banska Bystrica	Czechoslovakia	14
		Bratislava	Czechoslovakia	6
		Duba,BSKSA	Saudi Arabia	2000
		Kosice	Czechoslovakia	600
		Manresa	Spain	1
		Monastir	Tunisia	10
		Nitra	Czechoslovakia	40
		Nottingham BBCLR	UK	1
		Ostrava	Czechoslovakia	60
		Oviedo	Spain	5
		Pontevedra	Spain	3
		Quseir	Egypt	10
		Reigate ILR	UK	0.7
1530	196	Donja Vakuf	Jugoslavia	1
		Jitomir	USSR	5
		Halifax ILR	UK	1
		Mahmudia	Romania	15
		Mihaeleni	Romania	15
		Southend BBC LR	UK	0.1
		Worcester ILR	UK	0.5
		Vatican City	Vatican	450

Medium wave				
kHz	*metres*	*Station*	*Country*	*Power*
1539	195	Arbat	Iran	1000
		Castellon	Spain	2
		Mainflingen	West Germany	700
		Mut	Egypt	1
		Patrai	Greece	2.5
		Pec	Jugoslavia	2
		Sadiyat	Utd Arab Emirates	100
		Sisak	Jugoslavia	1
		Yalta	USSR	25
		Valladolid	Spain	5
		Voice of Peace	At sea	75
1548	194	Bristol BBC LR	UK	8
		Edinburgh ILR	UK	2
		Laghouat	Algeria	20
		Liverpool ILR	UK	1
		London ILR	UK	27
		Mangotsfield BBCLR	UK	5
		Sheffield ILR	UK	0.3
		Stockton BBCLR	UK	1
1557	193	Cyclops DW	Malta	600
		Kaunas	USSR	75
		Klaipeda	USSR	5
		Lancaster BBC LR	UK	0.25
		Nice	France	300
		Northampton ILR	UK	0.76
		Osijek	Jugoslavia	20
		Oxcliffe BBCLR	UK	1
		Southampton ILR	UK	0.5
		Vechintos	USSR	50
1566	192	Covilha	Portugal	1
		IRIB	Iran	100
		Leningrad	USSR	60
		Monte Ceneri-Cima	Switzerland	300
		Odessa	USSR	5
		Sarnen	Switzerland	300
		Sfax	Tunisia	1200
		Smarje	Jugoslavia	2
		Vila do Porto	Azores	10
		Vrgin Most	Jugoslavia1	
1575	190	Burg	East Germany	250
		Canidelo	Portugal	10
		Cordoba	Spain	5
		Genoa	Italy	50
		Queseir	Egypt	10
		Nuoro	Italy	2
		Sharja	Utd Arab Emirates	50
		17 low-powers	Italy	0.1-2
1584	189	Amalias	Greece	1
		Idfu	Egypt	1
		Jerez	Spain	1

Medium wave				
kHz	*metres*	*Station*	*Country*	*Power*
1584	189	Mansfield BBC LR	UK	1
		Orense	Spain	1
		Ostroda	Poland	1
		Pamplona	Spain	1
		Perth ILR	UK	0.2
		Toulon	France	1
		Woofferton BBC LR	UK	0.3
		11 low-powers	East Germany	1
		18 low-powers	Jugoslavia	2-0.005
1593	188	Aibiu	Romania	7.5
		Dniepropetrovsk	USSR	5
		El Minya	Egypt	10
		IRIB	Iran	100
		Kishinev	USSR	5
		Langenburg	West Germany	800
		Liberec	Czechoslovakia	6
		Lisbon	Portugal	10
		Marrakesh	Morocco	1
		Miercurea	Romania	14
		Oradea	Romania	7
1602	187	Dakla	Egypt	1
		Linares	Spain	--
		Leskovac	Jugoslavia	1
		Lugo	Spain	2
		Mesolongiou	Greece	1
		Negotin	Jugoslavia	1
		Onteniente	Spain	2
		Rusthall BBC LR	UK	0.25
		Resen	Jugoslavia	1
		Segovia	Spain	2
		Vitoria	Spain	1
		2 low-powers	Austria	0.05
		4 low-powers	Poland	1
		9 low-powers	Italy	1-0.1
		9 low-powers	Jugoslavia	2-0.1
		13 low-powers	East Germany	1
1611	186	Vatican City	Vatican	5

Short wave

Short wave				
kHz	*metres*	*Station*	*Country*	*Power*
2300	130.43	KCBS Hyesan	Korea(DPR)	--
2307	130.04	RRI Jakarta	Indonesia	5
2310	129.87	ABC Alice Springs	Australia	50
		PBS Yunnan	P. Rep. of China	15
		RP Souza	Brazil	0.25
2325	129.03	ABC Tennant Creek	Australia	50
2340	128.21	RD Itacoatiara	Brazil	1
		Fuzhou	P. Rep. of China	10
2350	127.66	RRI Yogyakarta	Java	1
		KCBS Sariwôn	Korea(DPR)	--
2360	127.12	R.Maya de Barillas	Guatemala	0.5
		RRI Tanjung	Indonesia	0.5
2377	126.21	RRI Surabaya	Java	1
2380	126.05	RE, Limeira	Brazil	0.25
		FIBC, Stanley	Falklands	3.5
2390	125.52	La Voz de Atitlán	Guatemala	1
		RRI, Cirenon	Java	1
		R.Huayacocotlá	Mexico	0.5
2400	125.00	KCBS Hamhung	Korea(DPR)	--
2410	124.48	R.Enga	Papua New Guinea	2
2419	124.02	RRI Bandung	Indonesia	10
2420	123.97	R.Sâo Carlos	Brazil	0.5
2430	123.46	VOS Fuzhou	P. Rep. of China	--
2435	123.20	RRI Banda Aceh	Indonesia	50
2445	122.70	Nanchang	P. Rep. of China	10
2460	121.95	YPBS	P. Rep. of China	--
2475	121.21	ZPBS	P. Rep. of China	10
2485	120.72	ABC Catherine	Australia	50
2490	120.48	VOS Fuzhou	P. Rep. of China	10
2500	120.00	WWV(S)Fort Collins	USA	2.5
		WWVH(S)Kekaha	Hawaii	5
		MSF(S)Rugby	UK	0.5
		RCH(S)Tashkent	USSR	1
2560	117.19	PBS Urumqi	P. Rep. of China	15
2850	105.26	KCBS Pyongyang	Korea(DPR)	100
2901	103.41	RRI Lombok	Indonesia	--
3000	100.00	RKPD Surabaya	Indonesia	1
3200	93.75	VOS Fuzhou	P. Rep. of China	--
		TWR Manzini	Swaziland	25
3205	93.60	TWR,Manzini	Swaziland	25
3215	93.31	SABC Meyerton	South Africa	100

Short wave				
kHz	*metres*	*Station*	*Country*	*Power*
3215	93.31	RRI Manado	Indonesia	10
3220	93.17	V.of Andes Quito	Ecuador	10
		R.Elwa Monrovia	Liberia	10
		SABC,Meyerton	South Africa	100
3230	92.88	R.Nepal	Nepal	100
		R.RSA Meyerton	South Africa	250/500
3235	92.74	AIR Gauhati	India	10
		RWNB Kimbe	Papua New Guinea	2
3240	92.59	TWR Manzini	Swaziland	25
3245	92.45	R.Gulf Kerema	Papua New Guinea	10
		R.Clube Varginha	Brazil	1
3250	92.31	PBS Pyongyang	Korea(DPR)	100
		RRI Banjarmasin	Indonesia	20
3255	92.17	LBC Monrovia	Liberia	50
		BBC WS	Lesotho	100
		BBC WS;Por.	UK	--
3260	92.02	Guiyang	P. Rep. of China	--
		V.du Sahel,Niamey	Niger	100
3265	91.88	RRI Bengkulu	Indonesia	10
3268	91.80	AIR Kohima	India	2
3270	91.74	RSWA Windhoek	Namibia	100
3275	91.60	TWR Manzini	Swaziland	25
		RK Srinagar	India	7.5
3280	91.46	Beira, Sofala	Mozambique	100
3285	91.32	R. Bandeirantes	Brazil	2.5
3288	91.24	Antananarivo	Madagascar	100
3290	91.19	RSWA Windhoek	Namibia	100
		Tristan Radio	Tristan da Cunha	0.4
		RC Port Moresby	Papua New Guinea	2
3295	91.05	AIR Delhi	India	10
3300	90.91	VOS Fuzhou	P. Rep. of China	10
		R.Cultural G.City	Guatemala	10
		Bujumbura	Burundi	25
3305	90.77	AIR Ranchi	India	2
		ZBC Gweru	Zimbabwe	100
		RRI Dili	Indonesia	10
		RW Daru	Papua New Guinea	10
3310	90.63	PBS Changchun	P. Rep. of China	10
3315	90.50	AIR Bhopal	India	10
3320	90.36	SABC Meyerton	South Africa	100
3325	90.23	RRI Palangkaraya	Indonesia	10
		R.Nigeria Lagos	Nigeria	50
		RNS Kieta	Papua New Guinea	10
3330	90.09	RRR Kigali	Rwanda	50
		R.Comoro, Moroni	Comoros	4
3335	89.96	CBS Taipei	Taiwan	10
		R.East Sepik	Papua New Guinea	10
3345	89.82	RK Jammu	India	2
		RRI Ternate	Indonesia	10
		R.Zambia,Lusaka	Zambia	120

Short wave				
kHz	*metres*	*Station*	*Country*	*Power*
3345	89.82	R.Northern	Papua New Guinea	2
3350	89.55	GBC Accra	Ghana	10
3355	89.42	RN Luanda	Angola	10
		AIR Kurseong	India	20
		RB Gaborone	Botswana	50
		RFO Noumea	New Caledonia	20
3365	89.15	TWR Manzini	Swaziland	25
		AIR Delhi	India	10
		GBC Accra	Ghana	50
3370	89.02	Beira, Sofala	Mozambique	10
3375	88.88	RN Luanda	Angola	10
		AIR Gauhati	India	50
3380	88.76	MBCC Blantyre	Malawi	100
		R.Iris,Esmeraldas	Ecuador	10
3385	88.63	RRI, Kupang	Indonesia	10
		RTM, Miri	Sarawak	10
		RENB,Rabaul	Papua New Guinea	10
3395	88.37	RRI,Tanjungkarang	Indonesia	10
		RZ Santo Domingo	Ecuador	10
		ZBC, Gweru	Zimbabwe	100
3400	88.24	Ríkisútvarpid	Iceland	10
3535	84.87	VOS Fuzhou	P. Rep. of China	10
3905	76.82	AIR Delhi	India	100
		RRI Banda Aceh	Indonesia	50
3910	76.73	US military,Yamata	Japan	10
3915	76.63	BBC WS	Hong Kong	100
		BBC WS;Ru, Bu,I,M, Th,V,EbyR	UK	--
3925	76.43	AIR Delhi	India	10
		NSB Tokyo	Japan	50
		NSB Sapporo	Japan	10
3927	76.40	Cap. Rad. Umtata	South Africa	203
3930	76.34	KBS Suwon	Korea(Rep)	5
3931	76.32	Mindelo	Cape Verde	10
3935	76.24	RRI Semarang	Indonesia	10
3945	76.05	NSB Tokyo	Japan	10
		RRI	Indonesia	5
		R.Vanuatu	Vanuatu	10
		RRI Tanjungkarang	Indonesia	5
3955	75.85	SABC Meyerton	South Africa	100
		BBC WS Daventry	UK	100/250
3958	75.80	FIBC Stanley	Falklands	3.5
3960	75.76	Beijing	P. Rep. of China	10
		Urümqui	P. Rep. of China	50
		RFE/RL	West Germany	100
		Kanggye	Korea(DPR)	--
		UBR, Dalandzadgad	Mongolia	12
3965	75.66	RFI Allouis	France	4
		R.Kabul	USSR	--
3970	75.57	RFE/RL	West Germany	100

Short wave

kHz	*metres*	*Station*	*Country*	*Power*
3345	89.82	R.Northern	Papua New Guinea	2
3350	89.55	GBC Accra	Ghana	10
3355	89.42	RN Luanda	Angola	10
		AIR Kurseong	India	20
		RB Gaborone	Botswana	50
		RFO Noumea	New Caledonia	20
3365	89.15	TWR Manzini	Swaziland	25
		AIR Delhi	India	10
		GBC Accra	Ghana	50
3370	89.02	Beira, Sofala	Mozambique	10
3375	88.88	RN Luanda	Angola	10
		AIR Gauhati	India	50
3380	88.76	MBCC Blantyre	Malawi	100
		R.Iris,Esmeraldas	Ecuador	10
3385	88.63	RRI, Kupang	Indonesia	10
		RTM, Miri	Sarawak	10
		RENB,Rabaul	Papua New Guinea	10
3395	88.37	RRI,Tanjungkarang	Indonesia	10
		RZ Santo Domingo	Ecuador	10
		ZBC, Gweru	Zimbabwe	100
3400	88.24	Ríkisútvarpid	Iceland	10
3535	84.87	VOS Fuzhou	P. Rep. of China	10
3905	76.82	AIR Delhi	India	100
		RRI Banda Aceh	Indonesia	50
3910	76.73	US military,Yamata	Japan	10
3915	76.63	BBC WS	Hong Kong	100
		BBC WS;Ru, Bu,I,M, Th,V,EbyR	UK	--
3925	76.43	AIR Delhi	India	10
		NSB Tokyo	Japan	50
		NSB Sapporo	Japan	10
3927	76.40	Cap. Rad. Umtata	South Africa	203
3930	76.34	KBS Suwon	Korea(Rep)	5
3931	76.32	Mindelo	Cape Verde	10
3935	76.24	RRI Semarang	Indonesia	10
3945	76.05	NSB Tokyo	Japan	10
		RRI	Indonesia	5
		R.Vanuatu	Vanuatu	10
		RRI Tanjungkarang	Indonesia	5
3955	75.85	SABC Meyerton	South Africa	100
		BBC WS Daventry	UK	100/250
3958	75.80	FIBC Stanley	Falklands	3.5
3960	75.76	Beijing	P. Rep. of China	10
		Urümqi	P. Rep. of China	50
		RFE/RL	West Germany	100
		Kanggye	Korea(DPR)	--
		UBR, Dalandzadgad	Mongolia	12
3965	75.66	RFI Allouis	France	4
		R.Kabul	USSR	--
3970	75.57	RFE/RL	West Germany	10C

Short wave				
kHz	*metres*	*Station*	*Country*	*Power*
3970	75.57	NHK,Sapporo	Japan	1
		NHK,Nagoya	Japan	1
		Buea	Cameroon	4
3975	75.47	BBC WS;Fr,Ge,EbyR	UK	250
		LRCN Monrovia	Liberia	10
3980	75.38	VOA Ismaning	West Germany	8
3985	75.28	RB Beromünster	Switzerland	250
		RFE/RL	West Germany	100
3990	75.19	Urümqi	P. Rep. of China	50
		RFE/RL	West Germany	100
		VOA Monrovia	Liberia	250
3995	75.09	DW Jülich	West Germany	100
		RTV Italiana, Rome	Italy (Rad,1)	50
		Khabarovsk	USSR	50
		Kyzyl	USSR	15
		RRI Pontianak	Indonesia	10
3999	75.02	KNR Nuuk	Greenland	1
		VOV Hanoi	N.Vietnam	30
4000	75.00	RNC Bafoussam	Cameroon	20
		RRI Kendari	Indonesia	5
4003	74.94	RRI Padang	Indonesia	10
4010	74.81	R.Kirghiz Frunze	USSR	25
4020	74.63	Beijing	P. Rep. of China	50
4025	74.53	Khabarovsk	USSR	50
4030	74.44	R.Moscow Anadyr	USSR	15
4035	74.35	Lhasa	Tibet	50
4040	74.26	Yerevan	USSR	15
		Vladivostok	USSR	50
4045	74.17	VOS Fuzhou	P. Rep. of China	10
4050	74.07	R.Kirghiz Frunze	USSR	50
		R.Sakhalin	USSR	15
4055	74.12	Kalinin	USSR	50
4060	73.89	Kharkov	USSR	100
4080	73.53	Ulan Bator	Mongolia	100
4130	72.64	R.Beijing	P. Rep. of China	50
4200	71.43	R.Beijing	P. Rep. of China	50
4250	70.59	R.Beijing	P. Rep. of China	50
4330	69.28	CPBS Urumqi	P. Rep. of China	50
		VOS Fuzhou	P. Rep. of China	10
4340	69.12	RPDT2 Kutai	Indonesia	--
4395	68.26	Yakutsk	USSR	100
4450	67.42	R.Kabul Dushanbé	USSR	15
4460	67.27	CPBS Beijing	P. Rep. of China	15
4465	67.19	RFE/RL	West Germany	10
4485	66.89	Petropavlovsk	USSR	50
4500	66.67	XPBS Urumqi	P. Rep. of China	50
4510	66.52	Uzbek Radio	USSR	15
4520	66.37	Khanty-Mansiysk	USSR	50
		Palana	USSR	15
4545	66.01	Alma-Ata	USSR	50

Short wave				
kHz	*metres*	*Station*	*Country*	*Power*
4585	65.43	R.RSA Meyerton	South Africa	250/500
4610	65.08	Khabarovsk	USSR	50
4620	64.94	Beijing	P. Rep. of China	10
4635	64.72	Dushanbé	USSR	50
4682	64.08	R.Paititi	Bolivia	1
4700	63.83	RKIP Surabaya	Indonesia	2
4719	63.57	RRI Ujung Padang	Indonesia	50
4725	63.49	BBCS Rangoon	Burma	50
4735	63.36	CPBS Urumqi	P. Rep. of China	50
4740	63.29	R.Mamore	Bolivia	1
		R.Kabul Ashkhabad	USSR	100
4750	63.16	RNC Bertoua	Cameroon	20
		XPBS Lhasa	Tibet	50
		UBR Ulgii	Mongolia	15
4753	63.12	RRI Ujung Padang	Indonesia	20
4755	63.09	RER Campo Grande	Brazil	10
		R.Maranhao	Brazil	2
		R.Huanta	Peru	1
4760	63.03	YPBS Kunming	P. Rep. of China	50
		R.Elwa Monrovia	Liberia	10
		TWR Manzini	Swaziland	100
4762	63.00	R.Inca Lima	Peru	2
		Guayaquil	Ecuador	5
4764	62.97	RRI Medan	Indonesia	50
4765	62.96	Huanay	Bolivia	1
		RN Cruzeiro do Sul	Brazil	10
		Santarem	Brazil	10
		R.Moscow Havana	Cuba	10
4770	62.89	ER da Lunda Norte	Angola	1
		CPBS Beijing	P. Rep. of China	15
		RN Kaduna	Nigeria	1
		R.Mundial	Venezuela	1
4775	62.83	R.Kabul, Kabul	Afghanistan	100
		AIR Gauhati	India	10
		R.Los Andes	Bolivia	3
		Jakarta	Indonesia	50
4777	62.80	Libreville	Gabon	100
4780	62.76	Djibouti	Djibouti	20
		Voz de Carabobo	Venezuela	1
4783	62.72	Bamako	Mali	18
4785	62.70	R.Ballivián	Bolivia	0.5
		R.Brazil,Campinas	Brazil	1
		ZPBS	P. Rep. of China	50
		Ecos del Combeima	Colombia	5
		RT Dar-es-Salaam	Tanzania	50
		Baku	USSR	50
		R.Cooperativa	Peru	1
4790	62.63	RRI Fak Fak	Indonesia	1
		R.Atlántida	Peru	5
4795	62.57	RNA La Paz	Bolivia	10

Short wave				
kHz	*metres*	*Station*	*Country*	*Power*
4795	62.57	RA Aquidauna	Brazil	2
		RNC Douala	Cameroon	100
		LV Los Caras	Ecuador	5
		Ulan-Ude	USSR	50
4800	62.50	AIR Hyderabad	India	10
		R.Lesotho,Maseru	Lesotho	100
		Yakutsk	USSR	50
		R.Popular	Ecuador	5
		XPBS Urumqi	P. Rep. of China	50
4805	62.43	R.Itatiaia	Brazil	1
		D.do Amaz.,Manaus	Brazil	5
		RRI Kupang	Indonesia	0.5
4807	62.41	RN Sao Tomé	Sao Tomé e Principe	10
4810	62.37	R.RSA Meyerton	South Africa	250/500
		Yerevan	USSR	50
		R.San Martin	Peru	3
		LV Galápagos	Ecuador	5
4815	62.31	R.Dif. Londrina	Brazil	0.5
		Ouagadougou	Burkina Faso	50
		Togtoh	P. Rep. of China	10
		R. Guatapuri	Colombia	1
4820	62.24	Gaborone	Botswana	50
		LV Evangelica	Honduras	5
		AIR, Calcutta	India	10
		Khanty-Mansiysk	USSR	50
		ER da Huila	Angola	25
4825	62.18	R.Educ. Bragança	Brazil	5
		Radio Mam	Guatemala	1
		LV de la Selva	Peru	10
		RM Vladivostok	USSR	100
		Ashkhabad	USSR	50
4830	62.11	R.Grigota,S.Cruz	Bolivia	1
		LPBS Shenyang	P. Rep. of China	10
		Africa 1	Gabon	250
		R.Tachira	Venezuela	10
		R.Thailand, B'kok	Thailand	10
4832	62.09	R.Reloj,San José	Costa Rica	3
4835	62.05	Bamako	Mali	18
		RRI Ambon	Indonesia	10
		ABC Alice Springs	Australia	50
		R.Tezulutlan	Guatemala	3
		RTM Kuching	Malysia	10
		R.Atalaia	Brazil	5
4839	62.00	R.Bukavu	Zaire	5
4840	61.98	HPBS Harbin	P. Rep. of China	50
		VOS Fuzhou	P. Rep. of China	10
		AIR Bombay	India	10
		R.Andahuaylas	Peru	10
		R.Interoceánica	Ecuador	1
		R.Valera	Venezuela	1

Short wave				
kHz	*metres*	*Station*	*Country*	*Power*
4845	61.92	R.Fides, La Paz	Bolivia	10
		R.Nacional,Manaus	Brazil	250
		RM Kajang	Malaysia	50
		ORTM Nouakchott	Mauretania	100
		R.Bucaramanga	Colombia	1
4850	61.86	RNC Yaoundé	Cameroon	100
		Tashkent	USSR	50
		R.Moscow, U.Bator	Mongolia	100
		AIR Kohima	India	2
		Loja	Ecuador	5
4855	61.79	R.por Mundo Melhor	Brazil	1
		R.Aruana	Brazil	1
		Mauritius BC	Mauritius	10
		RRI Palembang	Indonesia	10
4860	61.73	ER do Lunda Sul	Angola	5
		AIR Delhi	India	10
		Chita	USSR	15/100
4865	61.66	R.Verdes Florestas	Brazil	5
		GPBS Lanzhou	P. Rep. of China	50
		LV del Cinaruco	Colombia	1
		Maputo	Mozambique	20
		Ulan Bator	Mongolia	12
4870	61.60	Cotonou	Benin	30
		R.Rio Amazonas	Ecuador	5
		SLBC Colombo	Sri Lanka	10
4875	61.54	RRI Sorong	Indonesia	10
		R.Jornal, Rio	Brazil	10
		RC Boa Vista	Brazil	10
		RS Medellin	Colombia	2
		Uralsk	USSR	15
4876	61.53	La Paz	Bolivia	10
4880	61.48	PBC Quetta	Pakistan	10
		R.Dif. Acreana	Brazil	5
		SABC Meyerton	South Africa	100
		Dhaka	Bangladesh	100
4883	61.44	RB Hohhot	P. Rep. of China	50
4885	61.41	ER do Zaire	Angola	5
		R.Clube do Pará	Brazil	5
		Ondas del Meta	Colombia	5
		VOK Nairobi	Kenya	10
		R.Huancavelica	Peru	1
4890	61.35	R.Centinela do Sur	Ecuador	2
		NBC Port Moresby	Papua New Guinea	10
		R. France Intl	Gabon	250
		Dakar	Senegal	100
4895	61.29	R.Ulan Bator,Murun	Mongolia	12
		R.Baré, Manaus	Brazil	1
		AIR Kurseong	India	20
		Ashkhabad	USSR	50
		Tyumen	USSR	15

Short wave				
kHz	*metres*	*Station*	*Country*	*Power*
4895	61.29	Kuching	Malaysia	10
		ER do Bié	Angola	1
4900	61.22	Conakry	Guinea	18
		RRI Surakarta	Indonesia	--
		R.Libertador	Ecuador	1
4902	61.20	SLBC,Colombo	Sri Lanka	10
4904	61.17	N'Djamena	Chad	100
4905	61.16	R.Relógio Federal	Brazil	5
		CPBS, Beijing	P. Rep. of China	10
4910	61.10	R.Tawantinsuyo	Peru	5
		Tennant Creek	Australia	50
		Lusaka	Zambia	50
		RRI Bukittingi	Indonesia	1
		Quito	Ecuador	10
4915	61.04	R.Anhanguera	Brazil	10
		R.Nacional,Macapá	Brazil	10
		GPBS,Nanning	P. Rep. of China	10
		GBCC Accra	Ghana	50
		VOK Nairobi	Kenya	100
		Armonias Caquetá	Colombia	3
4920	60.98	ABC Brisbane	Australia	10
		AIR Madras	India	10
		Yakutsk	USSR	50
		RRI Tangjungpinang	Indonesia	10
		R. Quito	Ecuador	5
		R.Kabul, via USSR	USSR	--
		R.Central	Peru	1
4922	60.95	O. del Titicaca	Peru	1
4925	60.91	R.Difusora	Brazil	1
		HPBS,Harbin	P. Rep. of China	50
4926	60.90	Batá	Equatorial Guinea	100
4927	60.89	RRI,Jambi	Indonesia	7.5
4930	60.85	RM, Ashkhabad	USSR	50
		RM, Tbilisi	USSR	50
		R.4VEH	Haiti	2
		RSA,Windhoek	Namibia	100
4936	60.78	R.Tropical	Peru	1
		R.Capixaba,Vitória	Brazil	1
		R.Difusora, Jatai	Brazil	2.5
		R.Critica, Manaus	Brazil	5
		R.Monteagudo	Bolivia	--
4940	60.73	QPBS,Xining	P. Rep. of China	10
		Ukraine Radio, Kiev	USSR	10
		Abidjan	Ivory Coast	--
		Majuro	Marshall Is	10
		SLBC,Colombo	Sri Lanka	10
4945	60.67	R.Illimani, La Paz	Bolivia	10
		R.Dif,Poços de Caldas	Brazil	1
		R. Nac.,Porto Velho	Brazil	50
		V.do Sao Francisco	Brazil	2

Short wave				
kHz	*metres*	*Station*	*Country*	*Power*
4945	60.67	Neiva	Colombia	2.5
4950	60.60	Nairobi	Kenya	5
		Kuching, Sarawak	Malaysia	10
		PBC,Peshawar	Pakistan	10
		R. Madre de Dios	Peru	5
4955	60.54	RRI Banda Aceh	Indonesia	--
		R. Marajoara	Brazil	10
		R.Clube,Rondonópolis	Brazil	10
		R.Cultura, Campos	Brazil	2.5
4957	60.52	Baku	USSR	50
4960	60.48	R.Beijing, Kunming	P. Rep. of China	50
		R. Federación	Ecuador	5
		R. La Merced	Peru	1
		AIR Delhi	India	10
4965	60.42	R. Juan XXIII	Bolivia	3
		R. Poti	Brazil	1
		SWABC, Windhoek	Namibia	100
4968	60.39	SLBC, Colombo	Sri Lanka	10
4970	60.36	R. Rumbos. Caracas	Venezuela	10
		ER da Cabinda	Angola	1
		CPBS, Urumqi	P. Rep. of China	10
		Kota Kinabalu	Malaysia	10
		R.Imagen	Peru	1
4971	60.35	RNC Yaoundé	Cameroon	30
4975	60.30	VOS Fuzhou	P. Rep. of China	10
		R.del Pacifico,Lima	Peru	4
		Dushanbé	USSR	50
		Ondas Orteguaza	Colombia	1
		R.Maria Auxiliadora	Bolivia	1
		R. Iguatemi	Brazil	1
		R. Timbira	Brazil	2.5
4976	60.29	R.Uganda, Kampala	Uganda	20
4980	60.24	R.Batallón Topater	Bolivia	5
		Swazi Comm. Radio	Swaziland	50
		Ecos del Torbes	Venezuela	10
		AKR	Islamabad	10
4985	60.18	R.Brazil Central	Brazil	10
4990	60.12	R.RSA Meyerton	South Africa	250
		R.Yerevan	USSR	50
		R.Beni	Bolivia	1
		HPBS, Changsha	P. Rep. of China	10
		R.Baha'i	Ecuador	1
		R.Nigeria,Lagos	Nigeria	50
		R. Ancash	Peru	10
4991	60.11	R.Animas	Bolivia	1
4995	60.06	Choibalasan	Mongolia	12
		R.Andina	Peru	1
5000	60.00	WWV Fort Collins(SF)	USA	10
		WWVH Kekaha (SF)	Hawaii	5
		IBF Turin(SF)	Italy	5

Short wave				
kHz	*metres*	*Station*	*Country*	*Power*
5000	60.00	MSF Rugby(SF)	UK	0.5
		RCH Tashkent(SF)	USSR	1
		LOL Buenos Aires(SF)	Argentina	2
5004	59.95	RID Irkutsk(SF)	USSR	1
5005	59.94	R.Cristal, La Paz	Bolivia	1
		R.Nepal	Nepal	100
5010	59.88	PBC,Rawalpindi	Pakistan	10
		R. Eco	Peru	1
		RNC,Garoua	Cameroon	100
		GPBS,Nanning	P. Rep. of China	10
		RM Antananarivo	Madagascar	100
5015	59.82	R.Copacabana	Brazil	1
		R.Cultura,Cuiabá	Brazil	5
		R.Pioneira,Teresina	Brazil	1
		Arkhangelsk	USSR	50
		Vladivostok	USSR	50
		Riobamba	Ecuador	10
		Moyobamba	Peru	1
5020	59.76	Cuarto Centenario	Bolivia	1
		JPBS,Nanchang	P. Rep. of China	10
		SIBC,Honiara	Solomon Islands	10
		R.Nacional,Caracas	Venezuela	1
		LV du Sahel,Niamey	Niger	20
		SLBC,Colombo	Sri Lanka	10
5025	59.70	R.Transamazonica	Brazil	5
		R.Borborema	Brazil	1
		Rad. Splendit	Ecuador	3
		Parakou	Benin	20
		ABC,Katherine	Australia	50
5027	59.68	R.Uganda, Kampala	Uganda	20
5030	59.64	CPBS	P. Rep. of China	10
		Kuching	Malaysia	10
		R. Los Andes	Peru	1
5035	59.58	Schulungssender,Wien	Austria	10
		R.Educaçao Rural	Brazil	1
		R.Aparacida	Brazil	2.5
		Kazakh Rad.,Alma-Ata	USSR	50
		RTV Centrafricaine	Cent.African Rep.	100
5039	59.54	R.Sudan,Omdurman	Sudan	20
5040	59.52	FPBS,Fuzhou	P. Rep. of China	10
		Tbilisi	USSR	50
		R.Maturin	Venezuela	10
		R.Libertad	Peru	1
5045	59.46	R.Cultura do Pará	Brazil	10
		R.Rioja	Peru	1
5046	59.45	RRI Yojyakarta	Indonesia	20
5047	59.44	R.Lomé	Togo	100
5050	59.41	AIR Aizawal	India	10
		Dar es Salaam	Tanzania	10
		R.Cangallo	Peru	1

Short wave				
kHz	*metres*	*Station*	*Country*	*Power*
5050	59.41	R.Beijing	P. Rep. of China	50
		Yopal	Colombia	1
		R.Jesus Gran Poder	Ecuador	5
5052	59.38	SBC	Singapore	50
5055	59.35	R.Maua,Rio de Janeiro	Brazil	5
		Faro del Caribe	Costa Rica	5
		TWR,Manzini	Swaziland	25
		R.Católica,Quito	Ecuador	10
		RFO-Guyane	French Guiana	10
5057	59.32	Gjirokastër	Albania	50
5060	59.29	R.Amazonas	Peru	1
		ER do Huambo	Angola	1
		--	P. Rep. of China	10
		R.Nacional Progreso	Ecuador	5
5065	59.23	Bunia	Zaire	1
5075	59.11	CPBS,Urumqi	P. Rep. of China	50
5090	58.94	PBC Islamabad	Pakistan	10/100
		CPBS	P. Rep. of China	50
5095	58.88	R.Sutatenza,Bogotá	Colombia	50
5125	58.54	CPBS Beijing	P. Rep. of China	10
5145	58.37	R.Beijing	P. Rep. of China	120
5163	58.11	CPBS	P. Rep. of China	50
5192	57.78	ER do Moxico	Angola	5
5198	57.71	R.Origenes	Peru	--
5220	57.47	R.Beijing	P. Rep. of China	10
5240	57.25	VOS Fuzhou	P. Rep. of China	10
5250	57.14	R.Beijing	P. Rep. of China	50
5257	57.07	RRI,Sibolga	Indonesia	1
5260	57.03	Kazakh Rad.,Alma-Ata	USSR	50
5275	56.87	WYFR	Taiwan	250
5290	56.71	Krasnoyarsk	USSR	100
5295	56.66	R.Beijing	P. Rep. of China	15
5320	56.39	R.Beijing	P. Rep. of China	15
5325	56.34	R.Acobamba	Peru	1
5405	55.50	ER do Namibe	Angola	5
5420	55.35	CPBS,Beijing	P. Rep. of China	10
5660	53.00	Xieng Kouang	Laos	1
5770	51.99	VOS Fuzhou	P. Rep. of China	10
5800	51.72	CPBS, Urumqi	P. Rep. of China	50
5850	51.28	R.Beijing	P. Rep. of China	100
5860	51.20	CPBS	P. Rep. of China	50
5875	51.06	BSKSA,Riyadh	Saudi Arabia	50
5880	51.02	CPBS,Beijing	P. Rep. of China	10
5886	50.97	RRI, Pekanbaru	Indonesia	1
5894	50.90	RRI, Pekanbaru	Indonesia	5
5900	50.85	VOS,Fuzhou	P. Rep. of China	50
		SPBS, Chengdu	P. Rep. of China	15
		R.Moscow	USSR	100
5905	50.80	R.Moscow/RPP	USSR	100
		PBC/R.Pak.,Islamabad	Pakistan	10

Short wave				
kHz	*metres*	*Station*	*Country*	*Power*
5910	50.76	R.Moscow/RPP	USSR	50/100
		BRT,Wavre	Belgium	100
5915	50.72	CPBS,Beijing	P. Rep. of China	50
		R.Alma-Ata	USSR	100
5920	50.68	R.Moscow/RPP	USSR	100
		Hanoi	Vietnam	5
		TWR,Monte Carlo	Monaco	50
5925	50.63	R.Tallinn	USSR	50
		Tashkent	USSR	50
5930	50.59	R.Prague	Czechoslovakia	120
		Murmansk	USSR	50
		Tbilisi	USSR	50
5935	50.55	R.Beijing, Lhasa	Tibet	50
		Latvian R.,Riga	USSR	50
		R.Moscow,Riga	USSR	50
5940	50.50	R.Moscow ,Serpukhov	USSR	100
		R.Magadan	USSR	50
5945	50.46	ORF,Moosbrunn	Austria	100
		TWR,Monte Carlo	Monaco	100
		R.Moscow	USSR	15
		R.Tashkent	USSR	100
5950	50.42	RFI, Allouis	France	100
		R.Arequipa	Peru	1
		HPBS,Harbin	P. Rep. of China	50
		GBC,Georgetown	Guyana	10
		R.Moscow/RPP,L'grad	USSR	100
		Petropavlovsk	USSR	100
		WYFR,Okeechobee	USA	100
5954	50.39	R.Pio Doce	Bolivia	1
5955	50.38	R.Gazeta	Brazil	7.5
		RFE/RL	West Germany	250
		RFE/RL	Portugal	250
		RFE/RL	Spain	250
		VOA,Kaválla	Greece	250
		R.Cultural,G.City	Guatemala	10
		RNW,Flevoland	Holland	500
		R.Huancayo	Peru	0.5
		R.Botswana,Gaborone	Botswana	50
		RNC, Bafoussam	Cameroon	20
		TWR,Manzini	Swaziland	25
		Ankara	Turkey	250
5960	50.34	RCI/NHK,Sackville	Canada	250
		YPBS,Kunming	P. Rep. of China	50
		DW	West Germany	100
		R.Kashmir,Jammu	India	1
		Ulan Bator	Mongolia	50
		Ankara	Turkey	250
		Alma-Ata	USSR	50
		Abu Dhabi	UAE	500
		WYFR,Okeechobee	USA	100

Short wave				
kHz	*metres*	*Station*	*Country*	*Power*
5965	50.29	RBI,Nauen	East Germany	50/500
		SRI/RCBS	Switzerland	250
		VOA,Rhodes	Greece	50
		VOA,Woofferton	UK	250
		R.Nacional,Huanuni	Bolivia	2.5
		BBC WS	Oman,Canada	--
		BBC WS;Ru,J,EbyR		
		RCI	UK	300
		R.Habana, Havana	Cuba	500
		NHK,Yamata	Japan	50
		R.Malaysia,Kajang	Malaysia	50
		Jos	Nigeria	10
5970	50.25	AIR, Gauhati	India	10
		RFE/RL	West Germany	100
		RFE/RL	Portugal	250
		R. el Sol	Peru	2
		Kazakh Rad.,Alma-Ata	USSR	100
			Yemen(PDR)	100
		GPBS,Lanzhou	P. Rep. of China	50
		RRI,Banjarmasin	Indonesia	1
		R.Itatiaia	Brazil	10
5975	50.21	R.Korea	Korea(Rep.)	10/250
		BBC WS	UK,O,Sing,Ant	100-500
		BBC WS;Por,A,Fr.		
		R.Beijing	P. Rep. of China	120
		R.Korea,Suwon	Korea(Rep)	50
		ZBC,Gweru	Zimbabwe	100
		R.Moscow/RPP	USSR	100
		R.Nacional,Cochabamba	Bolivia	1
		R.Macarena	Colombia	5
5980	50.17	R.RSA Meyerton	South Africa	250/500
		R.Garujá	Brazil	10
		VoFC/VoASIA,T'ai-pei	Taiwan	50
		R.Moscow/RPP(multiple)	USSR	50-240
		Kiev	USSR	--
		R.J.	Jugoslavia	500
		PBC,Quetta	Pakistan	10
		SLBS	Sierra Leone	10
		Kota-Kinabalu	Maysia	10
		R.XEUJ,Linares	Mexico	1
		WCSN,Maine	USA	500
5983	50.14	RRI,Biak	Indonesia	1
5985	50.13	Burma BCS,Rangoon	Burma	50
		RFE/RL	West Germany	100
		RFE/RL	Portugal	50/250
		Rabaul	Papua New Guinea	10
		VOA,Kaválla	Greece	250
		WYFR,Okeechobee	USA	100
		VFC,Okeechobee	USA	100
5990	50.08	RNW Flevo	Netherlands	500

Short wave				
kHz	*metres*	*Station*	*Country*	*Power*
5990	50.08	RFI,Allouis	France	500
		RTV Italiana,Rome	Italy	100
		R.Bucharest	Romania	250
		AIR,Bhopal	India	10
		R.Mec,Rio de Janeiro	Brazil	7.5
		DW	West Germany	100
		DW	Sri Lanka	250
		NHK,Yamata	Japan	100
5995	50.04	DW	West Germany	100/500
		DW	Sri Lanka	250
		RA Shepparton	Australia	100
		RFI. Allouis	France	100
		R. Loyola	Bolivia	1
		R.Polonia,Warsaw	Poland	8
		CPBS,Lhasa	Tibet	50
		RCI	UK	300
		Bamako	Mali	50
		VOA,Greenville	USA	50/500
		VOA,Tangier	Morocco	100
		BBC WS;Ge,J,Man,EbyR	Singapore	100
		BBC WS	Singapore	100
		Blantyre	Malawi	100
		R.Melodia,Arequipa	Peru	5
6000	50.00	R.Aust. Intl, Vienna	Austria	10-100
		DW	West Germany	100/500
		DW,Cyclops	Malta	250
		VOS,Fuzhou	P. Rep. of China	50
		SBC	Singapore	50
		WHR,Noblesville	USA	100
		R.Guaiba,Pôrto Alegre	Brazil	7.5
6005	49.96	BBC WS	UK,Asc.	--
		BBC WS;Ru,Ha.		
		Zanzibar	Tanzania	10
		San José	Costa Rica	10
		GPBS,Lanzhou	P. Rep. of China	15
		SLBC,Colombo	Sri Lanka	10
		KUSW. S.Lake City	USA	100
		RNC, Buea	Cameroon	4
		R. Moscow/RPP	USSR	120
6010	49.92	R.RSA Meyerton	South Africa	250/500
		RBI	East Germany	100
		R.Inconfidéncia	Brazil	25
		BBC WS;Fr,Ge,EbyR		
		AIR,Calcutta	India	10
		Lima	Peru	2.5
		RNI,Fredrikstad	Norway	350
		R.los Andes, Merida	Venezuela	1
		DW	West Germany	100
		DW	Portugal	250
		RCI	UK	300

Short wave				
kHz	*metres*	*Station*	*Country*	*Power*
6010	49.92	Kiev	USSR	--
6012	49.90	US military, McMurdo	Antarctica	1
6015	49.88	VOA,Kaválla	Greece	250
		VOA	Philippines	250
		VOA	UK	250
		KBC,Suwon	Korea (Rep)	50
		RCI, Sines	Portugal	250
		RCI	UK	300
		BBC WS;Ge,Ru.	UK	500
		Vat.Radio	Vatican	100
		CPBS,Beijing	P. Rep. of China	50
		Abidjan	Ivory Coast	500
		WYFR,Okeechobee	USA	100
		Managua	Nicaragua	50
		Santa Cruz	Bolivia	10
6020	49.83	RNW Flevo	Netherlands	500
		RNW Talata	Madagascar	300
		RNW Bonaire	Neth. Antilles	300
		DW	West Germany	500
		R.Moscow/RPP	USSR	50/100
		BBC WS;Sw.	Ascension Island	250
		ZBC,Gweru	Zimbabwe	100
		AIR,Simla	India	2.5
		R.North Solomons	Papua New Guinea	10
		VOA,Greenville	USA	250
		R.Victoria,Lima	Peru	10
		REE	Spain	350
		R.Gaucha,Pôrto Alegre	Brazil	7.5
		R.Educadora,Salvador	Brazil	10
6025	49.79	DW	West Germany	100
		DW,Cyclops	Malta	250
		RB/RK,Jaszberény	Hungary	250
		VOA	UK	300
		VOA	West Germany	100/500
		Beira	Mozambique	10
		Fed.Rad.Corp.,Enugu	Nigeria	10
		RM,Kajang	Malaysia	100
		R.Nacional,Asunción	Paraguay	2
6030	49.75	SDR,Mühlacker	West Germany	20
		Military,Cincinnatti	USA	250
		BBC WS;Por,T,A.	UK	250
		BBC WS	Cyprus	100
		BBC WS	Oman	100
		FEBC,Bocaue	Philippines	50
		VOA,Poro/Tinang	Philippines	250
		R.Globo,Rio	Brazil	10
6035	44.19	R.Aust., Carnarvon	Australia	250
		RNI,Kvitsøy	Norway	500
		R.Sofia	Bulgaria	250
		DW	West Germany	500

Short wave				
kHz	*metres*	*Station*	*Country*	*Power*
6035	44.19	R.Moscow,Vladivostok	USSR	100
		SRI,Schwarzenburg	Switzerland	150
		AIR,Delhi	India	100
		VOA,Monrovia	Liberia	250
		La Voz de Guaviare	Colombia	5
		BRTV,Wavre	Belgium	100
		Vatican Radio	Vatican	100
		BBCS,Thimbu	Bhutan	5
6040	49.67	RFI,Allouis	France	100
		DW	West Germany	500
		DW	Antigua	250
		VOA,Woofferton	UK	250
		VOA,Dixon	USA	250
		VOA,Tangier	Morocco	100
		RBI	East Germany	50/500
		RNW Bonaire	Neth. Antilles	300
		R.Milne Bay	Papua New Guinea	10
6045	49.63	RFI,Allouis	France	100
		DW	West Germany	500
		DW,Sackville	Canada	250
		DW	Antigua	250
		AIR,Delhi	India	100
		VOA,Monrovia	Liberia	250
		Tambacounda	Senegal	4
		R.Sport,Montevideo	Uruguay	1
		ZBC,Gweru	Zimbabwe	10
		RRI,Jakarta	Indonesia	100
		R.Moscow/RPP	USSR	240
		R.Universidad	Mexico	0.5
		RSI,Hörby	Sweden	4
		V.of Kenya,Nairobi	Kenya	250
		Mongol PBS,Hohhot	P. Rep. of China	15
		Lima	Peru	10
		BBC WS	UK	250
6050	49.59	RTB Française,Wavre	Belgium	100
		BBC WS	Cyprus	100-500
		BBC Ext;Bul,Gr,Ro,Sc, Se,T,Hi,EbyR	multiple	--
		RFE/RL	West Germany	250
		RFE/RL	Portugal	250
		VO Los Andes, Quito	Ecuador	100
		RTV Italiana,Rome	Italy	100
		AIR,Delhi	India	50
		RTM Sarawak, Sibu	Malaysia	10
		Fed.Rad.Corp.,Ibadan	Nigeria	50
		R.Moscow/RPP	USSR	100
		RCI,Daventry	UK	300
		R.Guarani	Brazil	10
6055	49.55	R.Prague	Czechoslovakia	250/500
		RFI,Allouis	France	500

Short wave				
kHz	*metres*	*Station*	*Country*	*Power*
6055	49.55	RFI	Fr. Guiana	250
		Kigali	Rwanda	50
		R.Kuwait	Kuwait	250
		NSB,Tokyo	Japan	50
		BBC,Delano	USA	50
		RCI,Tokyo	Japan	50
6060	49.50	R.Korea	Korea(Rep)	10/250
		VOA,Woofferton	UK	300
		VOA	West Germany	100
		VOA,Kaválla	Greece	100
		R.Nacional/RAE	Argentina	50
		RDP,Lisbon	Portugal	100
		RTVI,Caltanissetta	Italy	50
		R.Habana,Havana	Cuba	100
		RZ,Lusaka	Zambia	20
		RTM Sarawak, Miri	Malaysia	10
		RA, Shepparton	Australia	100
		LV du Sahel, Niamey	Niger	4-100
		R.Moscow/RPP,Chita	USSR	250
		R.JSV,Huánaco	Peru	5
6065	49.46	RSI/SR,Hörby/ Karlsborg	Sweden	500
		R.Moscow/RPP	USSR	100
		VOA	Philippines	250
		WYFR,Okeechobee	USA	50/100
		R.Super,Bogotá	Colombia	5
		CBC,Sackville	Canada	100
		DW	West Germany	500
		DW	Sri Lanka	250
		AIR,Kohima	India	2
		PBC,Islamabad	Pakistan	100
		R.RSA Meyerton	South Africa	250/500
		BBC WS;BU,Hi,Ind,M, N,Ta,Th,U,V,EbyR	multiple	--
6070	49.42	BBC WS;Ru	Cyprus	100
		Patum Thani	Thailand	10
		R.Sofia	Bulgaria	150
		RRI,Jayapura	Indonesia	20
		CFRX Toronto	Canada	1
		R.Moscow/RPP	USSR	100
		RBI,Leipzig/Nauen	East Germany	100
		TWR,Manzini	Swaziland	100
		R.Capital,Rio de J.	Brazil	7.5
		JPBS,Changchun	P. Rep. of China	20
		R.Elwa,Monrovia	Liberia	50
		Majuro	Marshall Is	10
		RFE/RL	West Germany	100
		RFE/RL	Portugal	250
6075	49.38	R.Beijing	P. Rep. of China	50
		DW	West Germany	100/500

Short wave				
kHz	*metres*	*Station*	*Country*	*Power*
6075	49.38	SLBC,Colombo	Sri Lanka	10
		R.Tashkent	USSR	100
		Santa Barbara	Honduras	2
		VO Los Andeś,Quito	Ecuador	100
		VO Kenya,Nairobi	Kenya	250
6080	49.34	FEBA	Seychelles	100
		BBC WS;Cant,Ind,Th, V,EbyR	Singapore	--
		R.Tirana	Albania	50
		R.Aust.,Shepparton	Australia	100
		RBI,Nauen	East Germany	50/100
		R.Moscow	USSR	50/100
		R.West,Daru	Papua New Guinea	10
		VOA	USA	500
		VOA,Rhodes	Greece	50
		VOA,Woofferton	UK	250
		Hailar	P. Rep. of China	10
		NHK,Tokyo	Japan	100
		R.San Gabriel,La Paz	Bolivia	5
		VO Los Andes,Quito	Ecuador	100
6085	49.30	DW	West Germany	100/500
		DW	Antigua	250
		DW	Malta	250
		Bayerische Rundfunk	West Germany	100
		R.Sofia,Stolnik	Bulgaria	500
		R.Afghanistan,Kabul	Afghanistan	10
		BBC WS;Gr,T,EbyR	UK	500
		R.Oman,Sib	Oman	100
		Ondas del Darien	Colombia	1
		VOA,Kaválla	Greece	250
		WYFR,Okeechobee	USA	50/100
		CBS,T'ai-pei	Taiwan	50
6090	49.26	Islamabad	Pakistan	10/100
		R.Habana,Havana	Cuba	100
		R.Moscow/RPP	USSR	100/240
		Irkutsk	USSR	50
		Kiev	USSR	--
		R.Lux.,Junglinster	Luxembourg	500
		Phnom Penh	Kampuchea	50
		VOA	West Germany	100
		VOA,Tangier	Morocco	100
		R.Belgrano,B.Aires	Argentina	20
		LBS,Monrovia	Liberia	50
		Union Rad.- AWR	Guatemala	10
6095	49.22	VOA,Munich	West Germany	100
		VOA,Tangier	Morocco	100
		R.Polonia,Warsaw	Poland	100
		R.Mogadishu	Somalia	50
		Espinal	Colombia	5
		R.Moscow	USSR	100

Short wave				
kHz	*metres*	*Station*	*Country*	*Power*
6095	49.22	RFE/RL	West Germany	100
		RDP,Lisbon	Portugal	100
		CPBS,Nanchang	P. Rep. of China	50
		KGEI	USA	250
6100	49.18	R.Vilnius	Lithuania	50
		Belgrade	Jugoslavia	100
		DW	West Germany	500
		Kajang	Malaysia	100
		R.Moscow/RPP	USSR	50/100
		VOA	Philippines	50
		World Harvest	USA	100
		XPBS,Urümqi	P. Rep. of China	50
		Nairobi	Kenya	250
		RNZ,Wellington	New Zealand	7.5
		Managua	Nicaragua	50
		Caracas	Venezuela	1
6105	49.14	RFE/RL	West Germany	250
		Mérida	Mexico	0.25
		R.Moscow/RPP	USSR	120/500
		AIR,Delhi	India	100
		VOA,Rhodes	Greece	50
		WYFR	USA	100
		R.Universidad	Costa Rica	2
		La Paz	Bolivia	10
		RBI,Nauen	East Germany	100
		R.Cultura	Brazil	5
6110	49.09	R.Budapest	Hungary	3/250
		BBC WS;Por,Sp,EBYR	UK	250
		Flevoland	Holland	500
		Baku	USSR	50
		R,Kashmir,Srinagar	India	7.5
		VOA	Plhilippines	250
		R.Med.,Cyclops	Malta	250
6115	49.06	RBI	East Germany	50/500
		R.Universidad	Mexico	1
		R.Moscow/RPP	USSR	50/500
		Maputo	Mozambique	50
		RFE/RL	West Germany	100
		RFE/RL	Portugal	250
		Brazzaville	Congo	50
		NSB,Tokyo	Japan	50
		R.Unión,Lima	Peru	10
		R.Sofia,Plovdiv	Bulgaria	500
		RCI,Sines	Portugal	250
		RFI,Allouis	France	500
6120	49.02	BBC WS;Arabian	Cyprus	100
		AIR,Hyderabad	India	10
		R.Nacional,B.Aires	Argentina	10
		DW	West Germany	500
		DW	Antigua	250

Short wave				
kHz	*metres*	*Station*	*Country*	*Power*
6120	49.02	DW	Sri Lanka	250
		FEBC	Philippines	100
		Pori	Finland	100/500
		R.Moscow/RPP,Armavir	USSR	240
		Bluefields	Nicaragua	2
		XPBS,Urümqi	P. Rep. of China	50
		R.Habana,Havana	Cuba	50
		R.Globo,Sao Paulo	Brazil	7.5
		NHK,Sackville	Canada	250
6125	48.98	BBC WS;Cz,Hung,Sk, EbyR	UK	500
		R.Beijing	P. Rep. of China	50
		VOA	USA	250
		VOA,Woofferton	UK	300
		US military,Delano	USA	250
		CBC	Cyprus	250
		R.Moscow	USSR	100
		Arganda	Spain	100
		R.Tirana	Albania	100
6130	48.94	PBC,Islamabad	Pakistan	10/100
		R.Pakistan,Karachi	Pakistan	50
		DW	West Germany	500
		DW	Malta	250
		VOA	USA	500
		VOA,Woofferton	UK	250
		VOA	Philippines	250
		SLBC,Colombo	Sri Lanka	10
		R.Moscow	USSR	100
		NHK,Kumamoto	Japan	1
		Vientiane	Laos	10
		VO Los Andes,Quito	Ecuador	100
		RDP,Lisbon	Portugal	100
		Accra	Ghana	100
		CHNX,Halifax	Canada	50
6135	48.90	R.Korea,Suwon	Korea(Rep)	10/250
		SRI,Schwarzenburg	Switzerland	250
		Baku	USSR	100
		R.Polonia,Warsaw	Poland	100
		Papeete	Tahiyi	4
		R.Aparecida	Brazil	7.5
		RRI,Samarinda	Indonesia	1
		Antananarivo	Madagascar	100
		Concepción	Chile	10
		R.Sofia,Plovdiv	Bulgaria	500
		RFE/RL	West Germany	100
		RFE/RL,Lisbon	Portugal	250
		RFE/RL,Pals	Spain	250
		VO Palestine,San'a	Yemen	50
		KUSW,Utah	USA	100

Short wave				
kHz	*metres*	*Station*	*Country*	*Power*
6140	48.86	BBC WS;Bu,Ru,SC,T, EbyR	UK	500
		Santa Cruz	Bolivia	1
		DW	West Germany	100/500
		ABC,Perth	Australia	10
		Bujumbura	Burundi	25
		VOA	USA	500
		VOA,Kaválla	Greece	50
		VOA,Woofferton	UK	300
		R.Moscow/RPP	USSR	100
		R.E.Sepik,Wewak	Papua New Guinea	10
		AIR,Ranchi	India	10
		RCI,Sackville	Canada	250
		Huayllay	Peru	1
		R.Habana,Havana	Cuba	100/250
		R.Beijing,Kunmimg	P. Rep. of China	50
		Montevideo	Uruguay	1.5
6143	48.84	Phnom Penh	Kampuchea	--
6145	48.82	AIR,Delhi	India	100
		BBC WS;Spanish,EbyR	UK	500
		DW	West Germany	100/500
		R.Moscow/RPP,Moscow	USSR	100
		Calabar	Nigeria	10
		VO Palestine	Algeria	50
		RTV Algerienne	Algeria	50
		FEBC,Bocaue	Philippines	50
		TWR,Bonaire	Neth. Antilles	50
		VOA,Kaválla	Greece	250
		Vatican Rad.	Vatican	100
6150	48.78	BBC WS;CZ,H,Pol.	UK	500
		VOA	West Germany	100
		VOA,Kaválla	Greece	250
		VOA,Tangier	Morocco	100
		VOA,Woofferton	UK	300
		R.Impacto,San José	Costa Rica	20
		Neiva	Colombia	1
		HPBS,Harbin	P. Rep. of China	50
		ER de Benguela	Angola	1
		R.Record,Sao Paulo	Brazil	7.5
		RFI,Allouis	France	100
		Vatican Rad.	Vatican	500
		VO Kenya,Nairobi	Kenya	250
		R.Denmark,Copenhagen	Denmark	50
		KGEI	USA	250
6155	48.74	ORF,Vienna	Austria	100/500
		R.Fides,La Paz	Bolivia	1
		R.Moscow,Nikolayevsk	USSR	50
		SBC,Seletar	Singapore	50
		R.Bucharest	Romania	250
		Conakry	Guinea	18

Short wave				
kHz	*metres*	*Station*	*Country*	*Power*
6155	48.74	Tripoli	Libya	500
		Comm. Rad.,Sandlane	Swaziland	10
		R.Kara	Togo	10
		GPBS,Lanzhou	P. Rep. of China	100
		AIR,Delhi	India	100
		BBC WS;French	UK	--
		BBC WS	Ascension Is.	250
		Turk.RTV Corp.,Ankara	Turkey	250
		VOA,Dixon	USA	250
		US military,Tokyo	Japan	10
		World Harvest Rad.	USA	100
		KUSW,Utah	USA	100
6160	48.70	R.RSA Meyerton	South Africa	250/500
		VOA,Woofferton	UK	300
		VOA,Kaválla	Greece	250
		WYFR,Okeechobee	USA	100
		AIR,Delhi	India	100
		R.Sofia	Bulgaria	250
		R.Moscow,Kazan	USSR	100
		VO Palestine	Algeria	50
		DW	Antigua	250
		Bogotá	Colombia	10
		R.Malargüe	Argentina	0.5
		Radio Veritas Asia	Philippines	100
		R.Pampa,Porto Alegre	Brazil	5
6165	48.66	R.Korea,Suwon	Korean(Rep)	10/250
		RNW Bonaire	Neth. Antilles	300
		SRI/R.Beijing	Switzerland	150
		Kiev/Vladivostok	USSR	100
		R.Habana	USSR	100
		Lusaka	Zambia	50
		Mexico City	Mexico	10
		RBI	East Germany	100
		RTV Italiana	Rome	100
		R.Beijing,Kunming	P. Rep. of China	50
		R.Korea	Korea(Rep)	100
6170	48.62	DW	West Germany	500
		DW	Sri Lanka	250
		PFCB	Philippines	10
		R.Moscow,Armavir	USSR	100
		LV de la Selva	Colombia	1
		R.Tirana	Albania	100
		Cayenne	French Guiana	4
		RFE/RL	West Germany	100
		R.Cultura,Sao Paulo	Brazil	7.5
6175	48.58	R.Pakistan	Pakistan	50/250
		BBC WS	Antigua	250
		VO Malaysia,Kajang	Malaysia	50
		RFI,Allouis	France	100/500
		RFI,Montsinery	French Guiana	500

Short wave				
kHz	*metres*	*Station*	*Country*	*Power*
6175	48.58	NHK,Tokyo/Hiroshima	Japan	1
		XPBS,Xi'an	P. Rep. of China	15
		Luanda	Angola	100
		Faro del Caribe	Costa Rica	2.5
		WYFR,Okeechobee	USA	100
6180	48.54	BBC WS	UK	250
		R.Nacional,Mendoza	Argentina	1
		VOA,Woofferton	UK	250
		VOA,Tangier	Morocco	100
		VOA,Monrovia	Liberia	250
		VOA,Kaválla	Greece	50
		Kazakh Radio,Alma-Ata	USSR	100
		R.Moscow/RPP,Tula	USSR	100
		R.Turismo	Venezuela	1
		ORT du S.,Ziguinchor	Senegal	4
		Guatemala City	Guatemala	1
		Pyongyang	Korea(DPR)	--
		TWR,Bonaire	Neth. Antilles	250
		R.Nacional,Brasilia	Brazil	250
6185	48.50	R.Tirana	Albania	500
		SLBC,Colombo	Sri Lanka	10
		DW	Sri Lanka	250
		DW	West Germany	100
		DW	Malta	250
		R.Jamahiriya,Tripoli	Libya	100
		R.Educación,M.City	Mexico	1
		Ryazan	USSR	240
		VOA	Philippines	250
		Vatican Radio	Vatican	100
		WRNO,New Orleans	USA	100
		R.Beijing,Kunming	P. Rep. of China	50
6190	48.47	BBC WS;Portuguese	UK	100
		BBC WS	Lesotho	100
		BBC WS	Singapore	--
		Vatican Radio	Vatican	100
		DW	West Germany	500
		DW	Portugal	250
		R.Bremen/SFB,Bremen	West Germany	10
		VOA	USA	250
		AIR,Delhi	India	10
		R.Moscow/RPP,Omsk, Nikolayevsk	USSR	50/100
		NHK,Osaka	Japan	0.5
		RRI,Padang	Indonesia	10
		SRI,Schwarzenburg	Switzerland	150
		R.Baghdad	Iraq	500
		R.Beijing	P. Rep. of China	50
6195	48.43	BBC WS;Gr,Por,EbyR	UK	100/500
		BBC WS	Ant,UK,Sing	250
		R.Moscow,Baku	USSR	50

Short wave				
kHz	*metres*	*Station*	*Country*	*Power*
6195	48.43	Sokoto	Nigeria	10
		CBC,Sackville	Canada	100
6200	48.39	R.Tirana	Albania	100
		R.Moscow/RPP	USSR	50/100
		R.Vilnius,Leningrad	USSR	100
		R.Veritas Asia	Philippines	250
		LV de Huamanga	Peru	2
6205	48.35	VO Los Andes,Quito	Ecuador	500
6210	48.31	WYFR	Taiwan	250
6215	48.27	Voice of Hope	Lebanon	12
6225	48.19	R.Beijing	P. Rep. of China	--
6230	48.15	VO Los Andes,Quito	Ecuador	100/500
		TWR,Monte Carlo	Monaco	100
6240	48.08	Dhaka	Bangladesh	250
6243	48.05	R.Municipal,Calca	Peru	--
6245	48.04	Vatican Radio	Vatican	80
6250	48.00	R.Nacional,Malabo	Equatorial Guinea	10
		Pyongyang	Korea(DPR)	500
6260	47.92	QPBS,Xining	P. Rep. of China	10
6280	47.78	Voice of Hope	Lebanon	12
		R.Huancabamba	Peru	1.5
6300	47.62	WYFR	Taiwan	250
6350	47.24	R.Polonia,Warsaw	Poland	100
6383	47.00	R.Ulan Bator	Mongolia	50
6400	46.88	VO the Strait,Fuzhou	P. Rep. of China	10
		Pyongyang	Korea(DPR)	50
6480	46.30	R.Korea	Korea(Rep)	10/250
6500	46.13	QPBS,Xining	P. Rep. of China	10
6540	45.87	Pyongyang	Korea(DPR)	100
6565	45.70	WYFR	Taiwan	250
6576	45.62	Pyongyang	Korea(DPR)	400
6600	45.45	Pyongyang	Korea(DPR)	50
6660	45.04	Pakse	Laos	1
6725	44.61	R.Satélite	Peru	1
6765	44.35	VO the Strait,Fuzhou	P. Rep. of China	10
6790	44.18	CPBS,Beijing	P. Rep. of China	10
6825	43.96	R.Beijing,Xi'an	P. Rep. of China	120
6860	43.73	R.Beijing	P. Rep. of China	--
6890	43.54	R.Beijing	P. Rep. of China	--
6900	43.48	Meteorological Sce	Turkey	2.5
6920	43.35	R.Beijing	P. Rep. of China	--
6930	43.29	R.Dublin	Eire	1
6937	43.25	YPBS,Kunming	P. Rep. of China	50
6955	43.13	R.Beijing	P. Rep. of China	--
6974	43.02	CPBS/R.Beijing,Hohhot	P. Rep. of China	10
6995	42.89	R.Beijing	P. Rep. of China	--
7010	42.80	R.Beijing	P. Rep. of China	--
7035	42.64	R.Beijing	P. Rep. of China	--
7050	42.55	R.Beijing,Urümqi	P. Rep. of China	120
7055	42.52	R.Beijing,Xi'an	P. Rep. of China	120

Short wave				
kHz	*metres*	*Station*	*Country*	*Power*
7065	42.46	R.Tirana	Albania	100
		R.Beijing	P. Rep. of China	100
7080	42.37	R.Tirana	Albania	50
		R.Beijing	P. Rep. of China	--
7090	42.31	R.Tirana	Albania	50
		Islamabad	Pakistan	10
7098	42.27	RRI,Yogyakarta	Indonesia	10
7100	42.25	R.Moscow/RPP	USSR	50/500
7105	42.25	BBC WS;Bu,Ro,Fr,Ha	Ascension Is	250
		BBC WS	Asc,Sing	250
		VOA	W.Germany,Greece,	250
		VOA	Sri Lanka,	
		VOA	Philippines	
		Radio Time-IBC	Italy	1
		RBI	East Germany	100
		Dhaka	Bangladesh	100
		R.Tirana	Albania	50
		TWR,Monte Carlo	Monaco	100
		R.Moscow	USSR	100
		CBS,T'ai-pei	Taiwan	50
7110	42.19	RNW Flevo	Netherlands	500
		R.Moscow,Omsk	USSR	100
		DW	West Germany	100
		Maputo	Mozambique	10
		Gedja	Ethiopia	100
		AIR,Delhi	India	50
		Lhasa	Tibet	50
7112	42.18	Vientiane	Laos	25
7115	42.16	Bangkok	Thailand	10
		RFE/RL	West Germany	100
		RFE/RL	Portugal	100
		VOA	Sri Lanka	10
		R.Sofia,Plovdiv	Bulgaria	500
		RBI,Leipzig	East Germany	100
7120	42.14	BBC WS	UK	500
		VOA,Woofferton	UK	300
		VOA	Philippines	250
		R.Nationale,N'djamena	Chad	100
		R.Tirana	Albania	100
		R.Hargeisa	Somalia	10
		R.Moscow	USSR	50/100
		R.Kuwait	Kuwait	250
		AIR,Delhi	India	100
		RFI,Allouis	France	500
		R.Baghdad	Iraq	500
		R.Beijing,Hohhot	P. Rep. of China	50
		DW	West Germany	100
		R.Australia,multiple	Australia	250/300
7125	42.11	Conakry	Guinea	100
		Nairobi	Kenya	10

Short wave				
kHz	*metres*	*Station*	*Country*	*Power*
7125	42.11	R.Polonia,Warsaw	Poland	10
		VOA,Kaválla	Greece	250
		VOA,Woofferton	UK	300
		VOA	Sri Lanka	25
		Vatican Radio	Vatican	500
7130	42.08	BBC WS;Pol,Ru	UK	250
		VOA,Woofferton	UK	300
		VOA,Kaválla	Greece	250
		VOA	Philippines	250
		RCI	UK	300
		Kuching	Malaysia	10
		DW	West Germany	100/500
		DW,Cyclops	Malta	250
		R.Moscow/RPP	USSR	100
		VFC,T'ai-pei	Taiwan	250
		FEBC,Mahé Is	Seychelles	100
7135	42.05	VOA,Monrovia	Liberia	50
		R.Moscow/RPP	USSR	100/500
		RFI,Allouis	France	250
		VOA,Kaválla	Greece	250
		R.Sofia,Plovdiv	Bulgaria	500
		BBC WS;Pa,Pe	Cyprus	250
		R.Aust.,Shepparton	Australia	100
		RFI,Moyabi	Gabon	250
		DW	West Germany	500
		Ankara	Turkey	250
7140	42.02	BBC WS;Por,Sw,U,A,	UK,Oman	100/500
		AIR,Hyderabad	India	50
		VO Kenya,Nairobi	Kenya	100/250
		R.Moscow/RPP	USSR	100
		NHK,Yamata	Japan	100
		R.Spoleto	Iraly	0.5
		Wavre	Belgium	100
7145	41.99	Kuching-Sarawak	Malaysia	10
		R.Polonia,Warsaw	Poland	100
		R.Moscow,Tula	USSR	100
		R.Tashkent	USSR	100
		VO Palestine	Algeria	100
		BBC WS	Singapore	250
		VOA,Kaválla	Greece	250
		RFE/RL,Lisbon	Portugal	50/250
		RFE/RL,Pals	Spain	250
		DW	West Germany	100/500
		RFI,Allouis	France	500
		R.Bucharest	Romania	250
		Ilorin	Nigeria	10
		BSKSA,Riyadh EbyR	Saudi Arabia	350
7150	41.96	R.Moscow/RPP	USSR	500
		BBC WS	Multiple	250

Short wave				
kHz	*metres*	*Station*	*Country*	*Power*
7150	41.96	Nairobi	Kenya	10
		DW	West Germany	500
		RNC,Douala	Cameroon	100
		R.Cairo,Abu Zaabal	Egypt	100
		Bunia	Zaire	5
		CBS,T'ai-pei	Taiwan	100
		AIR,Delhi	India	50
		AIR,Gauhati	India	10
		Pyongyang	Korea(DPR)	100
		BSKSA,Riyadh	Saudi Arabia	350
		R.Sofia,Plovdiv	Bulgaria	500
7155	41.93	DW	West Germany	500
		RFE/RL	West Germany	100/250
		RFE/RL,Lisbon	Portugal	50/250
		RFE/RL,Pals	Spain	250
		VOA,Woofferton	UK	300
		RCI	UK	300
		Amman	Jordan	100
		R.Budapest	Hungary	250
		LV du Sahel,Niamey	Niger	100
		BSKSA,Riyadh	Saudi Arabia	350
		R.Tirana	Albania	50
		R.Sofia	Bulgaria	250
		R.Nacional,Mindelo	Cape Verde	10
		NHK/Yamata	Japan	100
7160	41.90	Kuching	Malaysia	10
		BBC WS;I,Man,Pe,	HK,Oman	250
		BBC WS	Asc.Is.,Oman	100/250
		AIR,Madras	India	10
		AIR,Aligarh	India	250
		R.Moscow/RPP	USSR	240
		RFI	Multiple	100/500
		DW	West Germany	500
		R.Aghanistan	USSR	--
		RFI	Gabon	250
7165	41.87	RFE/RL	West Germany	250
		RFE/RL,Lisbon	Portugal	250
		R.Moscow/RPP	USSR	500
		Kiev	USSR	--
		Gedja	Ethiopia	100
		Katmandu	Nepal	100
		R.Beijing	P. Rep. of China	50
		R.Tirana	Albania	50
		R.Vilnius	Lithuania	--
		R.Habana	USSR	250
		Dar es Salaam	Tanzania	10
		SBC	Singapore	10
		RBI	East Germany	50/500
7170	41.84	BBC WS;Russian	UK	250/500
		VOA,Kavälla	Greece	250

Short wave				
kHz	*metres*	*Station*	*Country*	*Power*
7170	41.84	VOA,Woofferton	UK	300
		Dakar	Senegal	100
		R.Moscow	USSR	100/500
		AIR,Kohima	India	2
		XPBS,Lhasa	Tibet	50
		SBC,Seletar	Singapore	10
		R.Tirana	Albania	50
		RBI	East Germany	50
		Noumea	New Caledonia	50
		ER do Lobito	Angola	1
7175	41.81	DW	West Germany	500
		RTVI,Caltanissetta	Italy	50
		R.Moscow/RPP	USSR	100/500
		VOA,Monrovia	Liberia	250
		R.Pakistan,Quetta	Pakistan	50/250
7180	41.78	BBC WS;Gr,Ca,I,J, Man,Th,V,EbyR	multiple	100/250
		BBC WS	Hong Kong	250
		VOA,Woofferton	UK	300
		RFE/RL	West Germany	100
7185	41.75	RBI	East Germany	50/500
		BBC WS	UK	300
		RCI	UK	300
		R.Moscow/RPP	USSR	500
		BBS,Rangoon	Burma	50
		R.Beijing,Xi'an	P. Rep. of China	150
7190	41.73	SLBC,Colombo	Sri Lanka	10
		VOA,Tangier	Morocco	100
		RFE/RL	West Germany	100
		RFE/RL	Portugal	50/250
		Parakou	Benin	20
		R.Beijing,Kunming	P. Rep. of China	50
		VO Palestine	Yemen	500
7195	41.69	R.Bucharest	Romania	250
		VOA,Monrovia	Liberia	50
		R.Moscow/RPP	USSR	100/240
		PBC,Rawalpindi	Pakistan	10
		R.Uganda,Kampala	Uganda	10
		BSKSA	Saudi Arabia	350
7200	41.67	VOA,Woofferton	UK	300
		VOA	Philippines	100
		RFE/RL	West Germany	100
		RFE/RL	Portugal	250
		Afrique 1, Moanda	Gabon	250
		R.Moscow	USSR	50/100
		R.Beograd	Jugoslavia	100
		Pyongyang	Korea(DPR)	200
		DW	Sri Lanka	250
		R.Mogadishu	Somalia	50
7205	41.64	R.Moscow/RPP	USSR	100/500

Short wave				
kHz	*metres*	*Station*	*Country*	*Power*
7205	41.64	R.Kiev	USSR	500
		VOA,Kaválla	Greece	250
		VOA,Rhodes	Greece	50
		RNC,Yaoundé	Cameroon	30
		LV Zaire,Lubumbashi	Zaire	10
		Shepparton/Carnarvon	Australia	100/300
		TWR,Monte Carlo	Monaco	500
		R.Tirana	Albania	100
7210	41.61	BBC WS;CZ.Fr,H,SC, Sk,T,EbyR	multiple	250/500
		VOA,Woofferton	UK	300
		VOA,Kaválla	Greece	250
		VOA	Philippines	250
		RCBS,Schwarzenburg	Switzerland	150
		AIR,Calcutta	India	10
		Khabarovsk/Minsk	USSR	15/50
		R.Moscow/RPP	USSR	100
		RRI,Biak	Indonesia	--
		Kunming	P. Rep. of China	--
		BSKSA,Riyadh	Saudi Arabia	350
		NHK,Yamata	Japan	100
		Dakar	Senegal	4
7215	41.58	Abidjan	Ivory Coast	20
		AIR,Delhi	India	100
		IRIB	Iran	500
		Sofia	Bulgaria	500
		R.Nacional,Luanda	Angola	10
		Ankara	Turkey	250
		Abu Dhabi	UAE	500
		Shepparton	Australia	100
		RFE/RL,Lisbon	Portugal	250
		RNI,Kvitsøy	Norway	500
7220	41.55	R.Budapest	Hungary	20/250
		RFE/RL	West Germany	100/250
		VOA,Woofferton	UK	300
		R.Moscow/RPP	USSR	500
		R.Zambia,Lusaka	Zambia	50
		Bangui	Cent.African Rep.	100
7225	41.52	R.Bucharest	Romania	250
		AIR,Aligarh	India	250
		VOA	Philippines	250
		Sfax	Tunisia	100
		SPBS,Chengdu	P. Rep. of China	15
		DW	West Germany	100
		DW,Kigali	Rwanda	250
		R.Budapest	Hungary	100
		BSKSA,Riyadh	Saudi Arabia	350
7230	41.49	BBC WS;H,Ru,EbyR	multiple	250/500
		RCI	UK	300
		R.Moscow/RPP	USSR	100/240

Short wave				
kHz	*metres*	*Station*	*Country*	*Power*
7230	41.49	VOA	Philippines	250
		Ouagadougou	Burkina Faso	50
		R.Pyongyang	Korea(DPR)	100/400
		IRIB,Tehran	Iran	100/500
7235	41.47	RCI	UK	300
		DW	West Germany	500
		DW,Cyclops	Malta	250
		AIR,Madras	India	100
		RTV Italiana,Rome	Italy	100
		R.Zambia,Lusaka	Zambia	50
		R.Tirana	Albania	500
		RFI,Allouis	France	500
		CPBS	P. Rep. of China	50
7240	41.44	R.Moscow/RPP	USSR	240
		RNC,Garoua	Cameroon	50
		Maputo	Mozambique	100
		Belgrade	Jugoslavia	100
		AIR,Bombay/Delhi	India	10/50
		VO Kenya,Nairobi	Kenya	10
		VOA	West Germany	100
		VOA	Philippines	50
		BBC WS;Be,Ca,Hi,Pa, U,EbyR	multiple	250
		Kiev	USSR	--
7245	41.41	RFE/RL	West Germany	100/250
		RFE/RL,Lisbon	Portugal	250
		RFE/RL,Pals	Spain	250
		VOA	West Germany	100
		Nouakchott	Mauretania	100
		R.Nacional,Luanda	Angola	100
		Khabarovsk	USSR	240
		R.Algiers	Algeria	50
		R.Jamahiriya	Libya	500
7250	41.38	R.Moscow/RPP	USSR	100
		SBC,Seletar	Singapore	50
		Vatican Radio	Vatican	100
		AIR,Lucknow	India	10
		CBC,T'ai-pei	Taiwan	100
7255	41.35	BBC WS;H,Pol	UK	500
		VO Nigeria,Ikorodu	Nigeria	50
		R.Sofia	Bulgaria	150
		RFE/RL	West Germany	100
		RFE/RL,Lisbon	Portugal	250
		VOA	Philippines	250
		Minsk/Alma-Ata	USSR	100
		AIR,Aligarh	India	250
		Gaborone	Botswana	50
7260	41.32	RBI	East Germany	50/500
		BBC WS;EbyR	UK	500
		Vila	Vanuatu	2

Short wave

kHz	*metres*	*Station*	*Country*	*Power*
7260	41.32	AIR,Bombay	India	100
		R.Moscow/RPP	USSR	100
		Moroni	Comoros	4
		Ulan Bator	Mongolia	25
		VOA Philippines	50	
		RCI,Sines	Portugal	50
		RCI	UK	500
		NHK,Yamata	Japan	100
7265	41.18	R.Lome,Togblekope	Togo	100
		R.Moscow/RPP	USSR	100/240
		DW	Malta	250
		DW	Sri Lanka	250
		VOA,Kaválla	Greece	250
		VOA,Monrovia	Liberia	250
		AIR,Delhi	India	100
		SWF,Rohrdorf	West Germany	20
		RSI,Hörby	Sweden	350
		Azad Kashmir,I'mabad	Pakistan	10
		R.Australia,Darwin	Australia	250
		BBC WS; EbyR		--
7270	41.27	R.RSA Meyerton	South Africa	250/500
		Kuching	Malaysia	10
		RRI,Jakarta	Indonesia	50
		VOA	West Germany	100
		VOA,Kaválla	Greece	250
		R.Polonia,Warsaw	Poland	100
		Franceville	Gabon	250
		DW	West Germany	100
		DW,Sines	Portugal	250
		VOK,Nairobi	Kenya	250
		R.Oman,Sib	Oman	10
7275	41.24	R.Korea	Korea(Rep)	10/250
		FEBA	Seychelle	100
		VOA	Philippines	50
		RTV Italiana,Rome	Italy	100
		R.Moscow/RPP	USSR	50
		R.Tashkent	USSR	100
		DW	West Germany	500
		GPBS,Guiyang	P. Rep. of China	10
		REE,Arganda	Spain	100
		BSKSA,Riyadh	Saudi Arabia	350
		BBC WS; Se,Bu,I,N, Ta,V	multiple	100
7280	41.21	R.Moscow/RPP	USSR	200/240
		RFI,Allouis	France	100
		VOA,Monrovia	Liberia	250
		VOA	West Germany	250
		VOA,Kaválla	Greece	250
		AIR,Delhi	India	10
		R.Sofia	Bulgaria	250

Short wave				
kHz	*metres*	*Station*	*Country*	*Power*
7280	41.21	BSKSA,Jeddah	Saudi Arabia	50
		NHK,Yamata	Japan	100
7285	41.18	RNW Talata	Madagascar	300
		R.Polonia,Warsaw	Poland	50
		R.Nigeria,Lagos	Nigeria	50
		DW	West Germany	100/500
		DW,Sines	Portugal	250
		RCI,Sines	Portugal	250
		Bamako	Mali	50
		VOA	Philippines	100
		SABC,Meyerton	South Africa	100
		VoFC/VoA,T'ai-pei	Taiwan	250
		GPBS,Lanzhou	P. Rep. of China	15
		TWR,Manzini	Swaziland	25
7290	41.15	R.Moscow/RPP	USSR	240
		RTV Italian,Rome	Italy	100
		PBC,Islamabad	Pakistan	100
		Pyongyang	Korea(DPR)	200
7295	41.12	GBC,Accra	Ghana	50
		RBI	East Germany	50/100
		RRE/RL	West Germany	250
		VOA,Kaválla	Greece	250
		Kajang	Malaysia	100
		R.Moscow/RPP	USSR	250/500
		RRI,Manado	Indonesia	1
		Mbuji Mayi	Zaire	10
		R.Milan	Italy	5
		AIR,Aizawal	India	10
		RCI,Daventry	UK	250
		R.Beijing	P. Rep. of China	120
		R.RSA,Meyerton	South Africa	250
		RNW, Flevo	Netherlands	500
7300	41.10	R.Tirana	Albania	100
7305	41.07	R.Moscow/RPP	USSR	100
7310	41.04	R.Moscow/RPP	USSR	100
		R.Tirana	Albania	50
		RTV Tunisienne,Sfax	Tunisia	100
7315	41.01	R.Beijing,Xi'an	P. Rep. of China	120
		R.Moscow/RPP	USSR	500
7320	40.98	BBC WS;Arabian	multiple	250/300
		R.Moscow/RPP	USSR	100/500
7325	40.96	BBC WS;Bulgarian	multiple	--
		BBC WS	UK	--
		VOA,Woofferton	UK	300
		R.Moscow/RPP	USSR	500
7330	40.93	R.Moscow	USSR	100/240
7335	40.90	CPBS,Xi'an	P. Rep. of China	50
		CHU(SF),Ottawa	Canada	10
7340	40.87	R.Moscow/RPP	USSR	100/500
7345	40.84	Prague	Czechoslovakia	120

Short wave				
kHz	*metres*	*Station*	*Country*	*Power*
7345	40.84	R.Moscow	USSR	100
		Yakut Radio,Yakutsk	USSR	100
7355	40.79	R.Moscow/RPP	USSR	100
		KNLS,Alaska	USA	100
		WYFR,Okeechobee	USA	100
		WRNO,New Orleans	USA	100
		WHR,Indiana	USA	100
7360	40.76	R.Beijing,Xi'an	P. Rep. of China	120
		R.Moscow/RPP	USSR	500
7365	40.73	AWR,Agat	Guam	100
		KGEI,Redwood City,CA	USA	250
		WCSN,Maine	USA	500
7370	40.71	R.Moscow/RPP	USSR	100
7375	40.68	R.Beijing,Xi'an	P. Rep. of China	120
		RP,Islamabad	Pakistan	100
7380	40.65	R.Moscow/RPP	USSR	100/500
7385	40.62	R.Beijing,Xi'an	P. Rep. of China	120
		XPBS,Urumqi	P. Rep. of China	50
		Savannakhet	Laos	3
7390	40.60	R.Moscow/RPP	USSR	--
7400	40.54	WHRI/R.Earth,Indiana	USA	100
		R.Moscow/RPP	USSR	50/120
7410	40.49	R.Moscow	USSR	50
		AIR,Delhi	India	50
7420	40.43	R.Moscow/RPP	USSR	50/100
		VRTC,Hanoi	Vietnam	--
7430	40.38	VO Vietnam,Hanoi	Vietnam	--
		ERT,Athens/Kaválla	Greece	100/250
7440	40.32	R.Beijing	P. Rep. of China	--
		R.Moscow/RPP	USSR	50/250
7445	40.30	VoFC/VO Asia	Taiwan	50/100
7450	40.27	REE,Noblejas	Spain	350
7470	40.16	R.Beijing,Xi'an	P. Rep. of China	500
7480	40.11	R.Beijing.Beijing	P. Rep. of China	100
7505	39.97	CPBS,Xi'an	P. Rep. of China	120
		Dhaka	Bangladesh	250
7516	39.91	CPBS,Beijing	P. Rep. of China	50
7525	39.87	CPBS	P. Rep. of China	--
7550	39.74	R.Korea	Korea(Rep)	10/250
7590	39.53	R.Beijing,Kunming	P. Rep. of China	120
7620	39.37	CPBS	P. Rep. of China	--
7651	39.21	VOA,Greenville	USA	50
7660	39.16	CPBS	P. Rep. of China	--
7670	39.11	Stolnik	Bulgaria	15
7700	38.96	CPBS,Kunming	P. Rep. of China	50
7775	38.59	R.Beijing	P. Rep. of China	240
7800	38.46	R.Beijing	P. Rep. of China	50
7820	38.36	R.Beijing	P. Rep. of China	120
7925	37.85	R.Moscow,Moscow	USSR	20
7935	37.81	CPBS,Beijing	P. Rep. of China	15

Short wave				
kHz	*metres*	*Station*	*Country*	*Power*
8007	37.47	CPBS,Xi'an	P. Rep. of China	50
8065	37.20	Moyobamba	Peru	--
8167.5	36.73	LQB9(SF),Buenos Aires	Argentina	5
8260	34.80	R.Beijing	P. Rep. of China	--
8300	36.14	R.Beijing	P. Rep. of China	--
8345	35.95	R.Beijing	P. Rep. of China	--
8425	35.61	R.Beijing	P. Rep. of China	--
8450	35.50	R.Beijing	P. Rep. of China	--
8490	35.34	R.Beijing	P. Rep. of China	--
8566	35.02	CPBS	P. Rep. of China	--
8660	34.64	R.Beijing	P. Rep. of China	--
8930	33.60	R.Continente	Peru	0.15
9010	33.30	Kol Israel,Tel Aviv	Israel	100/300
9020	33.26	CPBS	P. Rep. of China	--
9022	33.25	IRIB,Tehran	Iran	350
9030	33.22	CPBS	P. Rep. of China	--
9064	33.10	CPBS	P. Rep. of China	--
9080	33.04	CPBS	P. Rep. of China	--
9170	32.72	CPBS	P. Rep. of China	--
9185	32.66	KUSW,Utah	USA	100
9200	32.61	R.Moscow	USSR	15
9210	32.58	R.Moscow	USSR	--
9220	32.54	Pyongyang	Korea(DPR)	400
9290	32.30	R.Beijing	P. Rep. of China	50
9325	32.17	Pyongyang	Korea(DPR)	200
9335	32.14	R.Beijing	P. Rep. of China	120
9345	32.12	Pyongyang	Korea(DPR)	--
9360	32.05	REE	Spain	350
9365	32.03	R.Beijing,Xi'an	P. Rep. of China	120
9375	32.00	R.Tirana	Albania	50
9380	31.98	CPBS,Beijing	P. Rep. of China	15
9385	31.97	Kol Israel,Tel Aviv	Israel	100
9395	31.93	Athens	Greece	100
9410	31.88	BBC WS	UK	250/300
9420	31.85	Athens	Greece	100/250
9425	31.83	Athens	Greece	100
9430	31.92	R.Tirana	Albania	50
9435	31.80	Kol Israel,Tel Aviv	Israel	300
9440	31.78	R.Beijing	P. Rep. of China	50
9450	31.75	R.Moscow/RPP	USSR	50/240
9455	31.73	R.Pakistan,Islamabad	Pakistan	250
		R.Cairo	Egypt	250
		CPBS	P. Rep. of China	50
		VOA,Greenville	USA	500
		WHRI,Noblesville	USA	100
		WMLK,Bethel,PA	USA	50
9457	31.75	R.Beijing	P. Rep. of China	50
9465	31.70	RP,Islamabad	Pakistan	350
		VOA,Dixon/Greenville	USA	500
		WCSN,Maine	USA	500

Short wave				
kHz	*metres*	*Station*	*Country*	*Power*
9465	31.70	WYFR	Taiwan	250
		AWR,Agat	Guam	100
		Marpi	Northern Marianas	100
9470	31.68	R.Moscow/RPP	USSR	100
9475	31.66	R.Pakistan	Pakistan	50/250
		R.Cairo	Egypt	250
9480	31.65	R.Beijing	P. Rep. of China	250
		R.Moscow/RPP	USSR	120/250
		R.Tirana	Albania	100
9485	31.63	R.Tacna	Peru	0.5
9490	31.61	R.Beijing/XPBS,Lhasa	Tibet	50
		R.Moscow/RPP	USSR	240/500
9495	31.60	R.Pakistan	Pakistan	50/250
		TWR,Monte Carlo	Monaco	500
		KVOH,CA	USA	50
		WCSN,Maine	USA	500
		KYOI,Saipan Island	Northern Marianas	100
9500	31.58	R.Tirana	Albania	100
		R.Moscow/RPP	USSR	100
		Magadan	USSR	50
		R.Nacional	Venezuela	50
9505	31.56	R.Prague	Czechoslovakia	120
		RFE/RL	West Germany	100/250
		RFE/RL,Pals	Spain	250
		RFE/RL,Lisbon	Portugal	250
		Kazakh R.,Alma-Ata	USSR	50
		R.Beograd	Jugoslavia	100
		VOS,Fuzhou	P. Rep. of China	15
		RA,Carnarvon/Darwin	Australia	300
		R.Record,Sao Paulo	Brazil	7.5
		DW	West Germany	500
		DW,Cyclops	Malta	250
		RNW	Madagascar	300
		RZ,Lusaka	Zambia	50
		NHK,Yamata	Japan	300
		R.Pyongyang	Korea(DPR)	100
		R.Veritas,Malolos	Philippines	100
		WYFR,Okeechobee	USA	100
9510	31.55	FEBA,Mahé	Seychelles	100
		BBC WS	Antigua	250
		BBC WS;,Sackville	Canada	250
		R.Bucharest	Romania	250
		R.Nacional,Santiago	Chile	10
		VFC,T'ai-pei	Taiwan	100
		FEBC,Bocaue	Philippines	50
9515	31.53	BBC WS;Por,Sw,	multiple	250
		BBC WS	Ascension, Lesotho	250
		RTVI,Caltanissetta	Italy	50
		AIR,Delhi	India	300
		RNW	Madagascar	300

Short wave				
kHz	*metres*	*Station*	*Country*	*Power*
9515	32.53	RM,Kajang	Malaysia	100
		Mexico City	Mexico	0.5
		R.Moscow/RPP	USSR	240
		R.Korea	Korea(Rep)	100
		DW	Sri Lanka	250
		TWR,Merizo	Guam	100
9520	31.51	R.Moscow/RPP	USSR	240/500
		RFE/RL	West Germany	100/250
		Port Moresby	Papua New Guinea	10
		FEBC	Northern Marianas	10
		R.Budapest	Hungary	250
		BSKSA	Saudi Arabia	350
		R.La Crónica	Peru	5
		WYFR,Okeechobee	USA	100
9525	31.50	R.Polonia,Warsaw	Poland	100
		R.Habana,Havana	Cuba	250
		AIR,Madras	India	100
		NHK,Yamata	Japan	100
		VOA,Cincinnatti	USA	250
		Maputo	Mozambique	100
9530	31.48	BBC WS; Finnish	UK	100
		VOA,Woofferton	UK	300
		VOA,Greenville	USA	500
		VOA,Kaválla/Rhodes	Greece	250/50
		VOA,Tangier	Morocco	100
		R.Jordan,Amman	Jordan	100
		R.Moscow/RPP	USSR	50/500
		R.Beijing,Xi'an	P. Rep. of China	150
		R.Pyongyang	Korea(DPR)	200
		TWR,Merizo	Guam	100
		US military,Bethany	USA	175
		R.Finland,Pori	Finland	500
9535	31.46	SRI	Switzerland	250
		RFI,Allouis	France	100
		RFI,Montsinery	French Guiana	300
		RCI,Sackville	Canada	250
		WYFR,Okeechobee	USA	100
		TWR,Bonaire	Neth. Antilles	50
		NHK,multiple	Japan	0.3/300
		R.Nacional,Luanda	Angola	100
		BBC WS	Oman	100
		R.Beijing	P. Rep. of China	500
9540	31.45	RNW Talata	Madagascar	300
		BBC WS;Russian	UK	100
		VOA,Dixon,CA	USA	250
		VOA,Monrovia	Liberia	250
		VOA,Kaválla	Greece	250
		VOA,Tangier	Morocco	100
		RFE/RL	West Germany	250
		R.Polonia,Warsaw	Poland	100

Short wave				
kHz	*metres*	*Station*	*Country*	*Power*
9540	31.45	R.Nacional,Caracas	Venezuela	50
		R.Moscow/RPP	USSR	100/500
		TWR,Manzini	Swaziland	100
		R.Veritas,Malolos	Philippines	100
		RNZ,Wellington	New Zealand	7.5
9545	31.43	DW	West Germany	100/500
		DW,Cyclops	Malta	250
		DW	Sri Lanka	250
		VOA	Philippines	100
		R.Moscow.Khabarovsk	USSR	50
		Byelorussian R.	USSR	15
		AIR,Aligarh/Delhi	India	250/20
		PBC,Islamabad	Pakistan	100
		SIBC,Honiara	Solomon Is	10
9550	31.41	VOA,Cincinnatti	USA	250
		VOA,Monrovia	Liberia	100
		WYFR,Okeechobee	USA	100
		R.Beijing	P. Rep. of China	500
		R.Habana,Havana	Cuba	50
		R.Nacional,Santiago	Chile	10
		ORF,Moosbrunn	Austria	500
		RFI,Allouis	France	100
		R.Moscow/RPP	USSR	240
		R. ELWA,Monrovia	Liberia	50
		TWR,Manzini	Swaziland	100
		AIR,Aligarh/Delhi	India	250/100
		R.Veritas,Malolos	Philippines	100
		R.Pampa,Porto Alegre	Brazil	10
9553	31.40	R.Nacional,Batá	Equatorial Guinea	50
9555	31.40	RFE/RL,Lisbon	Portugal	250
		RFE/RL	West Germany	250
		RFE/RL,Pals	Spain	250
		VOA	Philippines	250
		WYFR,Okeechobee	USA	100
		La Hora Exacta,M.City	Mexico	0.5
		RCI,Daventry	UK	300
		R.Pyongyang	Korea(DPR)	200
9560	31.38	R.Beijing,Kunming	P. Rep. of China	50
		RBI	East Germany	500
		R.Jordan,Amman	Jordan	100
		SRI/RCBS	Switzerland	150
		Turkish RTVC,Ankara	Turkey	500
		R.Sofia	Bulgaria	250
		R.Finland,Pori	Finland	500
		RNI,Kvitsøy/Sveio	Norway	500
		Gedja	Ethiopia	100
		R.Veritas	Philippines	250
		BBC WS	Ascension	--
9565	31.36	RFE/RL,Pals	Spain	250
		RFE/RL	West Germany	250

Short wave				
kHz	*metres*	*Station*	*Country*	*Power*
9565	31.36	DW,Kigali	Rwanda	250
		DW,Cyclops	Malta	250
		VOA,Woofferton	UK	250
		VOA,Kaválla/Rhodes	Greece	250/50
		R.Moscow/RPP	USSR	240
		WYFR.Okeechobee	USA	100
		RSI,Hörby	Sweden	350
9570	31.35	R.Korea	Korea(Rep)	10/250
		DW	West Germany	500
		NHK,Yamata	Japan	100
		R.Bucharest	Romania	250
		BBC WS;Ge,EbyR	UK	100
		BBC WS	Oman,Singapore	250
		REE,Noblejas	Spain	350
		NHK,Moyabe-Moanda	Gabon	500
		BSKSA,Jeddah	Saudi Arabia	50
		R. Beijing,Xi'an	P. Rep. of China	50
9575	31.33	RFI,Allouis	France	100
		RTV Italiana,Rome	Italy	100
		R.Renascença,Muge	Portugal	100
		RDP,Lisbon	Portugal	100
		VOA	USA	250/500
		VOA	Philippines	250
		VOA	West Germany	100
		R.Moscow/RPP	USSR	240
		Port Moresby	Papua New Guinea	10
		VFC,T'ai-pei	Taiwan	50
		R.Medi-1,Nador	Morocco	250
		Ulan Bator	Mongolia	50
9580	31.32	R.RSA, Meyerton	South Africa	250/500
		RAI,Vienna	Austria	500
		BBC WS;Por,Ru,Fr,Ha, Ca,I,Man,V,EbyR	multiple	--
		BBC WS	Cyprus,Singapore	100
		R.Beijing,Xi'an	P. Rep. of China	150
		RA,Shepparton	Australia	100
		VOA,Rhodes	Greece	300
		VOA,Woofferton	UK	100
		WHRI,Noblesville	USA	100
		ORF,Moosbrunn	Austria	500
		NHK,Yamata	Japan	100
9585	31.30	DW	West Germany	100/500
		DW,Cyclops	Malta	250
		DW	Sri Lanka	250
		R.Budapest	Hungary	100
		R.Excelsior,Sao Paulo	Brazil	10
		VOA,Woofferton	UK	300
		VOA	West Germany	100
		RTV Italiana,Rome	Italy	100
		R.RSA,Meyerton	South Africa	250

Short wave				
kHz	*metres*	*Station*	*Country*	*Power*
9585	31.30	QBS,Doha	Qatar	250
		R.Beijing,Kunming	P. Rep. of China	50
		TWR,Merizo	Guam	100
9590	31.28	RNW, Bonaire	Neth. Antilles	300
		R.RSA Meyerton	South Africa	250/500
		RNW Talata	Madagascar	300
		FEBA,Mahé	Seychelles	80
		RNI,Sveio/Kvitsøy/ Fredrikstad	Norway	500/350
		R.Bucharest	Romania	250
		RCI	UK	300
		VOA,Woofferton	UK	250
		BBC WS;A,Pe	Cyprus	100
		BBC WS	Antigua/Canada	100
		R.Beijing,Xi'an	P. Rep. of China	300
		TWR,Merizo	Guam	100
		IBRA,Sines	Portugal	250
9595	31.27	RFE/RL	West Germany	100
		RFE/RL,Lisbon	Portugal	250
		NSB,Tokyo	Japan	50
		R.Monte Carlo,M'video	Uruguay	1.5
		R.Sofia	Bulgaria	250
		Reykjavik	Iceland	10
		Gedja	Ethiopia	100
		XPBS,Urumqi	P. Rep. of China	50
		R.Veritas	Philippines	250
9600	31.25	BBC WS;Fr,Ru,Be,Hi, Pa,U,EbyR	multiple	--
		BBC WS	Ascension/Cyprus	250
		FEBA,Mahé	Seychelles	80
		R.Prague	Czechoslovakia	120
		DW	Sri Lanka	250
		VFC,T'ai-pei	Taiwan	--
		R.Moscow/RPP	Cuba	100
		R.Moscow/RPP,Moscow	USSR	240
		R.Tashkent	USSR	100
		R.Tirana	Albania	100
		R.Renascença,Muge	Portugal	100
		RDP	Portugal	100
		Omdurman	Sudan	120
		TWR,Manzini	Swaziland	25
		R.Pyongyang	Korea(DPR)	100
		R.UNAM,Mexico City	Mexico	0.25
9605	31.23	R.Prague	Czechoslovakia	120
		RFI,Allouis	France	100
		DW	West Germany	100/500
		DW	Antigua	250
		DW,Cyclops	Malta	250
		DW,Sackville	Canada	250
		RSI,Hörby/Karlsborg	Sweden	350

Short wave

kHz	*metres*	*Station*	*Country*	*Power*
9605	31.23	VOA,Monrovia	Liberia	100
		VOA,Tangier	Morocco	100
		WYFR,Okeechobee	USA	100
		BBC WS;Be,Bu,Hi,Pa, Th,U	multiple	100
		R.Veritas,Malolos	Philippines	100
		R.Finland,Pori	Finland	500
		AWR,Sines	Portugal	250
		Vatican Radio	Vatican	100
		R.Beijing,Kunming	P. Rep. of China	50
		RNI,Sveio	Norway	500
9610	31.22	RNW Flevo	Netherlands	500
		FEBA,Mahé	Seychelles	25
		DW	West Germany	500
		BBC WS;Ru,Se,Fr, So,Por	multiple	--
		BBC WS	Cyprus	-
		TWR,Monte Carlo	Monaco	100
		Nouakchott	Mauretania	100
		AIR,Delhi	India	50
		ABC,Perth	Australia	50
		VFC,T'ai-pei	Raiwan	250
		VOA	Philippines	250
9615	31.20	RSI	Sweden	500
		IBRA Radio,Cyclops	Malta	350
		R.RSA Meyerton	South Africa	250/500
		DW	West Germany	500
		DW,Sines	Portugal	250
		DW	Sri Lanka	250
		AIR,Delhi/Bombay	India	100
		RCI,Sines	Portugal	250
		KGEI	USA	50
		VOA,Kavàlla	Greece	250
		VOA	Philippines	50
		VOA,Tangier	Morocco	100
		Vatican Radio	Vatican	500
		R.Cultura,Sao Paulo	Brazil	7.5
		RNI,Sveio/Kvitsøy/ Fredrikstad	Norway	350/500
9618	31.19	Maputo	Mozambique	120
9620	31.19	R.Cairo,Abu Zaabal	Egypt	100
		RBI	East Germany	50/500
		VOA,Monrovia	Liberia	15
		VOA	Philippines	250
		R.Moscow	USSR	100/240
		Belgrade	Jugoslavia	100
		R.Aust.,Shepparton	Australia	100
		RNI,Kvitsøy	Norway	500
9625	31.17	CBC/RCI,Sackville	Canada	100
		R.Bucharest	Romania	250

Short wave				
kHz	*metres*	*Station*	*Country*	*Power*
9625	31.17	VOA	West Germany	100
		DW,Cyclops	Malta	250
		DW	West Germany	500
		BBC WS;A,Sw,EbyR	Cyprus	100
		RFE/RL	West Germany	100/250
		RFE/RL,Pals	Spain	250
		RFE/RL,Lisbon	Portugal	250
		SRI/RCBS	Switzerland	150
		Vatican Radio	Vatican	500
9630	31.15	R.Prague	Czechoslovakia	250
		REE,Noblejas	Spain	350
		RSI,Karlsborg	Sweden	350
		AWR,Moanda-Moyabi	Gabon	250
		CBS,T'ai-pei	Taiwan	300
		RNW,Bonaire	Neth. Antilles	300
		AIR,Aligarh	India	250
		VOA,Greenville	USA	500
		VOA	Philippines	50
		R.Aparecida	Brazil	10
		R.Agricultura	Chile	10
9635	31.14	BBC WS;Gr,H,Pol,Ru, T,EbyR	multiple	--
		VOA,Woofferton	UK	300
		VOA,Tangier	Morocco	100
		VOA,Kaválla	Greece	250
		RDP,Lisbon	Portugal	100
		Bamako	Mali	50
		R.Baghdad	Iraq	500
		Singapore BC	Singapore	50
		R.Nacional,Bogotá	Colombia	25
		R.Moscow/RPP	USSR	50
		Kabul	Afghanistan	100
		Beira	Mozambique	100
		R.Finland,Pori	Finland	500
9640	31.12	R.Korea	Korea(Rep)	250
		Dhaka	Bangladesh	100
		DW	West Germany	500
		DW	Sri Lanka	250
		DW,Kigali	Rwanda	250
		DW	Antigua	250
		TWR,Manzini	Swaziland	100
		VOA,Greenville	USA	250
		RFE/RL,Lisbon	Portugal	250
		BBC WS	Antigua	--
		R.Moscow/RPP	USSR	500
		Algiers	Algeria	50
9645	31.10	RSI,Hörby	Sweden	500
		Vatican Radio	Vatican	100
		R.Bandeirantes, Sao Paulo	Brazil	7.5

Short wave				
kHz	*metres*	*Station*	*Country*	*Power*
9645	31.10	San José	Costa Rica	1
		NHK,Moyabi	Gabon	250
		VOA,Colombo	Sri Lanka	35
		VOA,Tangier	Morocco	100
		FEBC	Philippines	50
		RA,Carnarvon/Darwin	Australia	100/250
		R.Beijing	P. Rep. of China	300
		DW	West Germany	100
		R.Moscow/RPP	USSR	500
		Byelorussia R., Minsk	USSR	50
		RBI	East Germany	100/500
9650	31.09	DW	West Germany	100/500
		DW,Cyclops	Malta	250
		DW,Sines	Portugal	250
		DW,Colombo	Sri Lanka	250
		REE,Noblejas	Spain	350
		RCI,Sackville	Canada	250
		RCI,Sines	Portugal	250
		RNW,Bonaire	Neth. Antilles	300
		Vatican Radio	Vatican	100
		Conakry	Guinea	100
		VOA,Tangier	Morocco	100
		VOA,Delano	USA	250
		RFE/RL	West Germany	250
		R.Moscow/RPP	USSR	100/500
		R.Pyongyang	Korea(DPR)	100
		R.Veritas,Malolos	Philippines	100
		BBC WS; Russian	UK	--
9655	31.07	RSI,Hörby/Karlsborg	Sweden	500
		R.Finland,Pori	Finland	250/500
		R.Habana,Havana	Cuba	100
		BSKSA,Riyadh	Saudi Arabia	350
		Pathumthani	Thailand	50
		R.Nor Peruana	Peru	1
		R.Moscow/RPP	USSR	100/240
		ORF,Moosbrunn	Austria	500
		RNI,Kvitsøy/ Fredrikstad	Norway	500/350
		RA,Shepparton	Australia	100
		R Nacional,Brasilia	Brazil	250
		R.RSA,Meyerton	South Africa	250
9660	31.06	ABC,Brisbane	Australia	10
		BBC WS;Greek,EbyR	UK	250
		BBC WS	Cyprus/Canada	250
		RFE/RL	West Germany	250
		RFE/RL,Lisbon	Portugal	250
		RFE/RL,Pals	Spain	250
		VOA	West Germany	100
		VOA	Philippines	100
		Ankara	Turkey	350

Short wave				
kHz	*metres*	*Station*	*Country*	*Power*
9660	31.06	WYFR,Okeechobee	USA	100
		R.Rumbos,Caracas	Venezuela	10
9665	31.04	RBI	East Germany	100/500
		Pyongyang	Korea(DPR)	50
		R.Marumbi	Brazil	10
		AIR,Delhi	India	100
		FEBC,Bocaue	Philippines	50
		R.Moscow/RPP	USSR	240/500
		R.Afghanistan	USSR	--
		SABC,Meyerton	South Africa	100
		R.Baghdad	Iraq	500
		R.Malaysia,Kajang	Malaysia	100
		TWR,Bonaire	Neth. Antilles	50
9670	31.02	DW	West Germany	100/500
		DW,Cyclops	Malta	250
		AWR,Sines	Portugal	250
		R.Beijing,Xi'an	P. Rep. of China	--
		FEBC,Bocaue	Philippines	50
		FEBA,Mahé	Seychelles	100
		Saipan Island	Northern Marianas	100
		VOA,Kaválla/Rhodes	Greece	50/250
		VOA,Greenville	USA	500
		R.Moscow/RPP	USSR	50/240
		R.Cairo	Egypt	250
		Ankara	Turkey	250
9675	31.01	R.Polonia,Warsaw	Poland	100
		REE	Spain	350
		R.Cairo	Egypt	250
		AIR,Delhi	India	50
		R.del Pacifico,Lima	Peru	5
		VOA	Philippines	250
		BRT,Wavre	Belgium	100
		R.Moscow/RPP	USSR	500
		FEBC,Bocaue	Philippines	50
		TWR,Merizo	Guam	100
9680	30.99	DW	West Germany	100/500
		RFE/RL	West Germany	100/250
		VOA,Kaválla	Greece	250
		RDP,Lisbon	Portugal	100
		R.Renascença,Muge	Portugal	100
		RRI,Jakarta	Indonesia	100
		WYFR,Okeechobee	USA	100
		SRI,Schwarzenburg	Switzerland	150
		R.Veritas,Malolos	Philippines	150
		BBC WS;I,Th	Singapore	--
9684	30.98	RT,Dar es Salaam	Tanzania	50
9685	30.98	R.Bucharest	Romania	250
		VFC,T'ai-pei	Taiwan	50
		Saipan Island	Northern Marianas	100
		R.Gazeta,Sao Paulo	Brazil	7.5

Short wave				
kHz	*metres*	*Station*	*Country*	*Power*
9685	30.98	ORF,Moosbrunn	Austria	100
		R.Moscow/RPP	USSR	500
		RNW,Bonaire	Neth. Antilles	300
9690	30.96	R.Baghdad	Iraq	250
		DW	West Germany	100/500
		DW,Kigali	Rwanda	250
		DW	Antigua	250
		VOA,Kaválla	Greece	250
		VOA,Woofferton	UK	250
		R.Bucharest	Romania	250
		RTM,Antananarivo	Madagascar	10
		CBS,T'ai-pei	Taiwan	10
		RAE/RN,Buenos Aires	Argentina	100
9695	30.94	RSI,Hörby	Sweden	500
		RFE/RL,Lisbon	Portugal	50/250
		Abu Dhabi	UAE	120
		R.Habana	USSR	200
		VO People, Phnom Penh	Kampuchea	300
		R.Rio Mar,Manaus	Brazil	7.5
		VOA,Rhodes	Greece	50
		NHK,Tokyo	Japan	300
9700	30.93	R.Sofia	Bulgaria	250
		DW	West Germany	100
		DW,Cyclops	Malta	250
		VOA,Greenville	USA	500
		VOA,Kaválla	Greece	250
		R.Beijing	P. Rep. of China	150
		R.Veritas,Malolos	Philippines	50
		RSI,Hörby	Sweden	350
		R.Cairo,Abu Zaabal	Egypt	100
		US military,Delano	USA	100
9705	30.91	RN,Rio de Janeiro	Brazil	10
		RFE/RL	West Germany	100
		RFE/RL,Lisbon	Portugal	250
		VOA,Kaválla	Greece	250
		WYFR,Okeechobee	USA	50/100
		RMI,Mexico City	Mexico	10
		RDP,Lisbon	Portugal	100
		Vatican Radio	Vatican	100
		LV du Sahel,Niamey	Niger	10
		BSKSA,Jeddah	Saudi Arabia	50
		Abu Dhabi	UAE	250
9710	30.90	RTV Italiana/UN,Rome	Italy	100
		R.Moscow/Kiev	USSR	100/500
		Kaunas,Lithuania	USSR	100
		RA,Shepparton	Australia	100
		RN,Buenos Aires	Argentina	7.5
		GPBS,Lanzhou	P. Rep. of China	15
		FEBC,Bocaue	Philippines	100
9715	30.88	RNW,Flevo	Netherlands	500

Short wave				
kHz	*metres*	*Station*	*Country*	*Power*
9715	30.88	RNW,Bonaire	Neth. Antilles	300
		RNW,Talata	Madagascar	300
		BBC WS;H,Pol	UK	250
		RFI,Allouis	France	500
		DW	West Germany	100/500
		VOA,Kaválla	Greece	250
		VOA	Philippines	250
		VOA,Rhodes	Greece	50
		VOA,Tangier	Morocco	100
		WYFR,Okeechobee	USA	50/100
		VO Andes,Quito	Ecuador	100
		RSI,Hörby	Sweden	350
		R.Moscow/RPP	USSR	50/500
		R.Tashkent	USSR	50
		WRNO,New Orleans	USA	100
		R.la Plata	Bolivia	2
		RBI	East Germany	50/500
9720	30.86	SLBC,Colombo	Sri Lanka	100
		RA,Darwin/Carnarvon	Australia	300
		R.Moscow/RPP	USSR	240
		Radio Habana	USSR	120
		R.Nacional,Luanda	Angola	100
		BSKSA	Saudi Arabia	50
9725	30.85	SRI/RBBS,Sottens	Switzerland	500
		BBC WS;Ca.Man,EbyR	Singapore	100
		ORF,Moosbrunn	Austria	300
		RFE/RL	West Germany	250
		RFE/RL,Lisbon	Portugal	250
		TWR,Manzini	Swaziland	25
		R.Beijing	P. Rep. of China	50
		VOA	Philippines	50
		R.Clube Paranaense	Brazil	7.5
9730	30.83	RBI	East Germany	50/100
		BBC WS;Be,Hi,U,EbyR	Singapore	--
		R.Denmark, Copenhagen	Denmark	50
		BSKSA,Riyadh	Saudi Arabia	350
		Ankara	Turkey	500
		BBS,Rangoon	Burma	50
		AIR,Delhi	India	100
		R.Veritas	Philippines	250
		R.Habana,Havana	Cuba	100
		R.Moscow/RPP	USSR	500
		RSI,Karlsborg	Sweden	500
9735	30.82	BBC WS;Slovak	UK	--
		R.Nacional,Asunción	Paraguay	100
		DW	West Germany	100/500
		DW,Cyclops	Malta	250
		DW,Kigali	Rwanda	250
		VOA,Woofferton	UK	250
		VOA	West Germany	100

Short wave				
kHz	*metres*	*Station*	*Country*	*Power*
9735	30.82	R.Oman,Sib	Oman	100
		R.Moscow/RPP	USSR	100/500
9740	30.80	R.Sofia	Bulgaria	250
		R.Prague	Czechoslovakia	100/250
		VOA,Kaválla	Greece	250
		VOA	Philippines	250
		RDP,Lisbon	Portugal	100
		R.Cairo	Egypt	250
		R.Veritas,Malolos	Philippines	100
		R.Moscow/RPP	USSR	240
		R.Denmark,Copenhagen	Denmark	50
		RCI,Daventry	UK	300
		BBC WS;Turkish	Oman	--
		BBC WS	Singapore	--
9745	30.79	RFI,Allouis	France	100
		R.Baghdad	Iraq	500
		Saipan Island	Northern Marianas	100
		VO Andes,Quito	Ecuador	100
		R.Moscow/RPP	USSR	240
		R.Sofia	Bulgaria	500
		R.Denmark,Copenhagen	Denmark	50
		DW	West Germany	100
		RNC,Yaoundé	Cameroon	100
9750	30.77	R.Korea	Korea(Rep)	100/250
		RT,Dar es Salaam	Tanzania	50
		Papeete	Tahiti	4
		R.Tirana	Albania	500
		DW	West Germany	500
		RFE/RL	West Germany	100
		RFE/RL,Pals	Spain	250
		BBC WS;SC;BU;H;Pol, Ru,T	multiple	100/250
		BBC WS	UK	100
		VOA,Monrovia	Liberia	50
		R.Beijing	P. Rep. of China	500
		VFC,T'ai-pei	Taiwan	--
		AIR,Madras	India	100
		R.Korea	Korea(Rep)	250
		KNLS,Alaska	USA	100
		Kajang	Malaysia	100
		R.Bucharest	Romania	250
		R.Moscow/RPP	USSR	100/500
		R.Kuwait	Kuwait	250
		TWR,Merizo	Guam	100
		RCI,Sackville	Canada	250
9755	30.75	R.Sofia	Bulgaria	250
		Vatican Radio	Vatican	100/500
		R.Cairo	Egypt	100
		AIR,Delhi	India	100
		RCI,Sackville	Canada	250

Short wave				
kHz	*metres*	*Station*	*Country*	*Power*
9755	30.75	CPBS	P. Rep. of China	50
		KUSW,Salt Lake City	USA	250
9760	30.74	R.Tirana	Albania	100
		VOA,Tangier	Morocco	100
		VOA	Philippines	250
		BBC WS;C,H,Pol,Ru,	UK	250
		BBC WS	UK	250
		R.Moscow/RPP	USSR	100
		NSB,Tokyo	Japan	50
		RA,Shepparton	Australia	50
		RCI,Sackville	Canada	250
		R.Nacional,Brasilia	Brazil	250
9765	30.72	DW	West Germany	100/500
		R.Beijing	P. Rep. of China	500
		VFC,T'ai-pei	Taiwan	--
		VO Andes,Quito	Ecuador	100
		REE,Arganda	Spain	100
9770	30.71	DW	West Germany	100
		RBI	East Germany	100
		FEBA	Seychelles	100
		VOA,Tangier	Morocco	100
		VOA	Philippines	250
		R.Cairo	Egypt	250
		BBC WS;Bu,Ru,SC,Se	UK	250
		RA,Carnarvon/Darwin/ Shepparton	Australia	100/250
		R.Habana,Havana	Cuba	500
		RNW,Bonaire	Neth. Antilles	300
		R.Baghdad	Iraq	500
		WHRI,Noblesville	USA	100
9775	30.69	R.Moscow/RPP	USSR	100
		RNW Flevo	Netherlands	500
		RNW Bonaire	Neth. Antilles	300
		Dhaka	Bangladesh	250
		CPBS	P. Rep. of China	50
		VOA,Greenville	USA	250
		VOA,Monrovia	Liberia	250
9780	30.68	R.Moscow/RPP	USSR	100/200
		Kazakh R.,Alma-Ata	USSR	50
		San'a	Yemen Arab Rep.	50
		QPBS,Xining	P. Rep. of China	10
9785	30.66	R.Moscow/RPP	USSR	100
		R.Beijing,Xi'an	P. Rep. of China	120
9790	30.64	R.Moscow	USSR	100
		RFI,Allouis	France	500
		RFI,Montsinery	French Guiana	500
9795	30.63	R.Moscow/RPP	USSR	100/500
		Minsk	USSR	50
9800	30.61	RFI	multiple	500
		R.Moscow/RPP	USSR	50/100

Short wave				
kHz	*metres*	*Station*	*Country*	*Power*
9800	30.61	CPBS,Kunming	P. Rep. of China	50
		FEBC	Philippines	100
9805	30.60	R.Cairo,Abu Zaabal	Egypt	100
		RFI,Allouis	France	500
9810	30.58	R.Moscow/RPP	USSR	100
		RFI,Allouis	France	500
9815	30.57	VOA,Delano	USA	250
		WYFR,Okeechobee	USA	50/100
9820	30.55	R.Beijing	P. Rep. of China	--
		R.Moscow/RPP	USSR	100
		TWR,Merizo	Guam	100
9825	30.53	BBC WS;C,Pol,Por,Sk, A,Fr,Ha,Sw,Sp,EbyR	UK	--
		R.Moscow/RPP	USSR	--
9830	30.52	R.Moscow/RPP	USSR	100
		FEBC	Philippines	300
		AWR,Agat	Guam	100
9835	30.50	R.Budapest	Hungary	100/250
9840	30.49	RNW Flevo	Netherlands	500
		Hanoi	Vietnam	30
		VOA,Greenville	USA	500
		TWR,Merizo	Guam	100
		R.Kuwait	Kuwait	500
9845	30.47	VFC,T'ai-pei	Taiwan	100
		VO Andes,Quito	Ecuador	100/500
9850	30.46	R.Cairo	Egypt	250
		R.Moscow/RPP	USSR	--
		WYFR,Okeechobee	USA	50/100
		RNW,Flevo	Netherlands	500
		KUSW,Utah	USA	100
		WCSN,Maine	USA	500
9855	30.44	Athens	Greece	100
9860	30.43	RNW Flevo	Netherlands	500
		R.Pakistan	Pakistan	50/250
		Wavre	Belgium	250
		RFI,Allouis	France	500
		R.Beijing	P. Rep. of China	--
		VO Andes,Quito	Ecuador	500
9865	30.41	R.Moscow/RPP	USSR	--
9870	30.40	R.Korea	Korean(Rep)	100/250
		BSKSA,Riyadh	Saudi Arabia	350
		TWR,Merizo	Guam	100
		VO Andes	Ecuador	100
		WCSN,Maine	USA	500
9875	30.38	REE,Noblejas	Spain	350
		R.Baghdad	Iraq	--
9880	30.36	BRT,Wavre	Belgium	350
		R.Beijing	P. Rep. of China	120
		R.Moscow/RPP	USSR	--
		R.Kuwait	Kuwait	500

Short wave				
kHz	*metres*	*Station*	*Country*	*Power*
9885	30.35	SRI/RCBS,Sottens	Switzerland	500
		RP,Islamabad	Pakistan	100
		BSKSA,Riyadh	Saudi Arabia	350
9890	30.33	Sabrata	Libya	--
		R.Moscow	USSR	--
9895	30.32	RNW Flevo	Netherlands	500
		R.Moscow/RPP	USSR	100/500
9899	30.31	RNW,Flevo	Netherlands	500
9900	30.30	R.Cairo,Abu Zaabal	Egypt	100
		R.Beijing,Xi'an	P. Rep. of China	120
		RTBF,Wavre	Begium	250
9905	30.29	BRT,Wavre	Belgium	100/250
9910	30.27	AIR,Delhi/Aligarh	India	100/250
9915	30.26	BBC WS;Fr,Ru	UK	250/300
		BBC WS	UK	250/300
		R.Beijing	P. Rep. of China	50
9925	30.23	BRT/RTBF,Wavre	Belgium	100/250
9930	30.21	Kol Israel,Tel Aviv	Israel	20
		WYFR	Taiwan	250
9935	30.20	Thessaloniki	Greece	35
9940	30.18	R.Pyongyang	Korea(DPR)	200
9945	30.17	Dhaka	Bangladesh	250
		R.Beijing	P. Rep. of China	120
9950	30.15	AIR,Delhi	India	20
		Adra	Syria	%))
9955	30.14	VFC/WYFR,T'ai-pei	Taiwan	250
9965	30.11	R.Beijing	P. Rep. of China	120
9977	30.07	R.Pyongyang	Korea(DPR)	200
9985	30.05	Reykjavik	Iceland	10
9966	30.10	RWM(SF),Moscow	USSR	5
10000	30.00	WWV(SF),Fort Collins	USA	10
		WWVH(SF)Kekaha	Hawaii	10
		LOL(SF),Buenos Aires	Argentina	2
		MSF(SF),Rugby	UK	0.5
		RTA(SF),Novosibirsk	USSR	5
		RCH(SF),Tashkent	USSR	1
		BPM(SF),Lintong	P. Rep. of China	10/20
		ATA(SF),New Delhi	India	8
		JJY(SF),Tokyo	Japan	2
10004	29.99	RID(SF),Irkutsk	USSR	1
10010	29.97	Hanoi	Vietnam	30
10060	29.82	Hanoi	Vietnam	30
10235	29.31	VOA,Greenville	USA	40
10245	29.28	CPBS,Beijing	P. Rep. of China	50
10260	29.24	CPBS,Beijing	P. Rep. of China	15
10335	29.03	AIR,Delhi	India	50
10380	28.90	VOA,Greenville	USA	40
10420	28.79	RFE/RL	West Germany	10
10454	28.70	VOA,Greenville	USA	40
10510	28.54	R.Tirana	Albania	100

Short wave				
kHz	*metres*	*Station*	*Country*	*Power*
10690	28.06	R.Moscow	USSR	
11000	27.27	CPBS	P. Rep. of China	--
11040	27.17	CPBS	P. Rep. of China	--
11100	27.03	CPBS,Beijing	P. Rep. of China	120
11290	26.57	CPBS	P. Rep. of China	--
11330	26.47	CPBS	P. Rep. of China	--
11375	26.37	CPBS	P. Rep. of China	--
11445	26.21	R.Beijing	P. Rep. of China	240
11455	26.19	CPBS	P. Rep. of China	--
11500	26.09	R.Beijing	P. Rep. of China	120
11505	26.08	CPBS	P. Rep. of China	--
11515	26.05	R.Beijing	P. Rep. of China	--
11550	25.97	Sfax	Tunisia	100
		WYFR	Taiwan	250
11575	25.92	R.Beijing	P. Rep. of China	120
11580	25.91	VOA,Greenville	USA	250
		WYFR,Okeechobee	USA	100
11585	25.90	Kol Israel,Tel Aviv	Israel	100
11595	25.87	Thessaloniki	Greece	35
11600	25.86	R.Beijing	P. Rep. of China	--
11605	25.85	Kol Israel,Tel Aviv	Israel	50
11610	25.84	R.Beijing	P. Rep. of China	--
11615	25.83	R.Pakistan	Pakistan	50/250
11620	25.82	AIR,Delhi/Aligarh	India	50/250
11625	25.81	SBS,Adhra	Syria	500
11630	25.80	CPBS,Beijing	P. Rep. of China	15
		R.Moscow/RPP	USSR	240
11635	25.78	R.Pakistan	Pakistan	250
11640	25.77	R.Hargeisa	Somalia	10
		R.Pakistan	Pakistan	50/250
11645	25.76	Athens	Greece	100
11650	25.75	R.Beijing,Xi'an	P. Rep. of China	20
		R.Moscow/RPP	USSR	240
11655	25.74	Kol Israel,Tel Aviv	Israel	300
		R.Moscow,Alm-Ata	USSR	50
11660	25.73	ORF,Moosbrunn	Austria	100
		R.Moscow/RPP	USSR	500
		RTBF,Wavre	Belgium	100
		R.Beijing	P. Rep. of China	--
11665	25.73	R.Cairo,Abu Zaabal	Egypt	100
		R.Kuwait	Kuwait	500
11670	25.71	R.Moscow/RPP	USSR	--
		RFI,Allouis	France	100
		RFI	French Guiana	500
11675	25.70	R.Moscow/RPP	USSR	100
		R.Beijing,Xi'an	P. Rep. of China	120
		R.Kuwait	Kuwait	250
		R.Pakistan,Islamabad	Pakistan	250
11680	25.69	BBC WS;H.Pol,Por, A,Fr,Sp,EbyR	multiple	

Short wave				
kHz	*metres*	*Station*	*Country*	*Power*
11680	25.69	Pyongyang	Korea(DPR)	100
		R.Moscow	USSR	100
		VOA,Greenville	USA	500
11685	25.67	BSKSA,Riyadh	Saudi Arabia	350
		R.Beijing	P. Rep. of China	120
		R.Prague	Czechoslovakia	--
11690	25.66	R.Moscow/RPP	USSR	100/200
		RFI,Allouis	France	500
11695	25.65	BRTV,Wavre	Belgium	250
		TWR,Monte Carlo	Monaco	100
		R.Beijing	P. Rep. of China	120/240
		VOA,Greenville	USA	250
		KUSW,Utah	USA	100
11700	25.64	Santo Domingo	Dominican Rep.	50
		RFI	multiple	100/500
		R.Moscow/RPP	USSR	240
		Vatican Radio	Vatican	100
		AWR,Agat	Guam	100
		KNLS	Alaska	100
11705	25.64	RFI	multiple	500
		DW	Montserrat	50
		RBI	East Germany	50
		VOA,Kavália	Greece	250
		WRNO,New Orleans	USA	100
		R.Moscow/RPP	USSR	240
		RA,Carnarvon	Australia	100
		RSI,Karlsborg/Hørby	Sweden	350
		Ankara	Turkey	250
11710	25.62	VOA,Woofferton	UK	300
		VOA	Sri Lanka	35
		VOA,Tangier	Morocco	100
		VOA,Monrovia	Liberia	250
		RCI,Sackville	Canada	250
		R.Nacional/RAE	Argentina	100
		R.Veritas,Malolos	Philippines	100
		R.Moscow/RPP	USSR	240
11715	25.61	RNW Bonaire	Neth. Antilles	300
		R.Cairo	Egypt	250
		VOA,Greenville	USA	500
		VOA,Monrovia	Liberia	250
		VOA	Philippines	250
		Algiers	Algeria	50
		AIT,Delhi	India	250
		TWR,Merizo	Guam	100
		R.Moscow/RPP	USSR	240
		Vatican Radio	Vatican	100
		R.Beijing,Xi'an	P. Rep. of China	300
		WYFR,Okeechobee	USA	100
		RNW,Bonaire	Neth. Antilles	300
11720	25.60	R.Sofia	Bulgaria	150/250

Short wave				
kHz	*metres*	*Station*	*Country*	*Power*
11720	25.60	BBC WS;A,Fr,Pe	Cyprus/UK	250
		RA,Shepparton	Australia	100
		CBC,Sackville	Canada	100
		FEBC,Mahé	Seychelles	25
		R.Moscow/RPP	USSR	100/500
		R.RSA,Meyerton	South Africa	250
		R.Sofia	Bulgaria	150/250
11725	25.59	Vatican Radio	Vatican	100
		RFE/RL	West Germany	100
		RFE/RL,Lisbon	Portugal	250
		R.Habana,Havana	Cuba	50
		VOA	Philippines	250
		R.Beijing	P. Rep. of China	120
		R.Korea	Korea(Rep)	250
11730	25.58	RNW,Flevo	Holland	500
		DW,Kigali	Rwanda	250
		REE,Noblejas	Spain	350
		BSKSA,Riyadh	Saudi Arabia	350
		Dubai	UAE	300
		AIR,Delhi	India	100
		RA,Darwin	Australia	250
		US military,Delano	USA	250
		R.RSA,Meyerton	South Africa	250
11734	25.57	R.Tanzania	Tanzania	50
11735	25.56	Belgrade	Jugoslavia	100
		RNW,Talata	Madagascar	300
		TWR,Merizo	Guam	100
		R.Monte Carlo,M'video	Uruguay	1.5
		R.Moscow/RPP	USSR	240
		R.Sofia	Bulgaria	500
		RNI,Kvitsøy	Norway	500
		Pyongyang	Korea(DPR)	400
		KCBI	USA	50
		KGEI	USA	250
11740	25.55	R.Korea	Korean(Rep)	10/250
		RNW Flevo	Netherlands	500
		BBC WS;A,Hi,Pa,U	Oman/Cyprus	100
		R.Moscow/RPP	USSR	50/100
		Vatican Radio	Vatican	100
		VOA	USA	250
		VOA,Kaválla	Greece	250
		VOA	Philippines	50
		RDP,Lisbon	Portugal	100
		R.Baghdad	Iraq	--
		CPBS,Beijing	P. Rep. of China	50
		VFC,Okeechobee	USA	100
		VO Andes,Quito	Ecuador	100
11745	25.54	R.Moscow/RPP	USSR	500
		VFC,T'ai-pei	Taiwan	--
		R.Nacional,Brasilia	Brazil	250

Short wave				
kHz	*metres*	*Station*	*Country*	*Power*
11745	25.54	R.RSA,Meyerton	South Africa	250
11750	25.53	BBC WS	Cyprus/Singapore	125/250
		US military,Tokyo	Japan	10
		R.Moscow/RPP	USSR	240/500
		R.Sofia	Bulgaria	500
		RBI,Leipzig	East Germany	100
		DW	West Germany	500
		DW,Sines	Portugal	250
		R.Cairo,Abu Zaabal	Egypt	100
		VOA,Tangier	Morocco	100
		R.Baghdad	Iraq	500
11755	25.52	R.Nacional,Bs Aires	Argentina	7.5
		R.Moscow/RPP	USSR	100/240
		FEBA,Mahé	Seychelles	100
		R.Finland,Pori	Finland	500
		Kabul relay	USSR	--
		Havana relay	USSR	120
		R.Beijing	P. Rep. of China	120
		R.Veritas	Philippines	250
11760	25.51	BBC WS	Cyprus	250
		VOA,Kaválla/Rhodes	Greece	250/50
		VOA	Philippines	50
		VOA,Monrovia	Liberia	250
		VOA,Greenville	USA	250
		R.Moscow/RPP	USSR	100
		R.Habana,Havana	Cuba	250
		FEBA,Mahé	Seychelles	25
		Vatican Radio	Vatican	100
		ORF,Moosbrunn	Austria	500
		R.Baghdad	Iraq	500
		Rarotonga	Cook Islands	1
		RNI,Kvitsøy	Norway	500
11765	25.50	R.Moscow/RPP	USSR	100
		AIR,Delhi	India	100
		DW	West Germany	100
		R.Sofia	Bulgaria	250
		R.Beijing	P. Rep. of China	120
		RA,Carnarvon	Australia	300
		R.Nacional,Brasilia	Brazil	250
11770	25.49	RFE/RL	West Germany	250
		RFE/RL,Pals	Spain	250
		Ikorodu	Nigeria	100
		RRI,Jakarta	Indonesia	100
		Mexico City	Mexico	10
		WHRI,Noblesville	USA	100
11775	25.48	R.Bucharest	Romania	250
		BBC WS	Hong Kong,Antigua	250
		VOA,Woofferton	UK	300
		VOA	Philippines	250
		VOA,Kaválla	Greece	250

Short wave				
kHz	*metres*	*Station*	*Country*	*Power*
11775	25.48	RCI	UK	300
		R.Moscow/RPP	USSR	240/500
		CBS,T'ai-pei	Taiwan	100
		REE,Noblejas	Spain	350
		R.RSA,Meyerton	South Africa	500
		VO Andes,Quito	Ecuador	100
11780	25.47	BBC WS;Bu,Fr,Ru, SC,Se,EbyR	multiple	--
		R.Belgrano,Bs Aires	Argentina	7.5
		NHK,Yamata	Japan	100
		R.Moscow/RPP/R.Kiev	USSR	100/240
		R.Nacional,Brasilia	Brazil	250
		R.Pyongyang	Korea(DPR)	200
		VOA,Kaválla	Greece	250
		VOA,Tangier	Morocco	35
		Vatican Radio	Vatican	100
		Ankara	Turkey	250
		RNZ,Wellington	New Zealand	7.5
11785	25.46	DW	West Germany	500
		DW	Antigua	250
		DW,Cyclops	Malta	250
		R.Moscow/RPP	USSR	100/240
		RBI	East Germany	500
		Porto Alegre	Brazil	7.5
		R.Cairo	Egypt	50/250
11788	25.45	RRI,Jakarta	Indonesia	100
11790	25.45	RFI,Allouis	France	100
		FEBA,Mahé	Seychelles	100
		VOA,Tangier	Morocco	100
		WHRI,Noblesville	USA	100
		R.Moscow/RPP/Kiev	USSR	240
		R.Bucharest	Romania	250
		REE,Arganda	Spain	100
		R.Baghdad	Iraq	500
		IRIB,Tehran	Iran	500
		AIR,Delhi	India	250
		BBC WS;Fi,Ru	multiple	250
11795	25.43	DW	West Germany	100
		DW,Cyclops	Malta	250
		DW	Antigua	250
		AIR,Delhi	India	100
		R.Moscow/RPP	USSR	100
		SRI/Red CCBS	Switzerland	150
		R.Habana,Havana	Cuba	250
		VO Andes,Quito	Ecuador	100
11800	25.42	SLBC,Colombo	Sri Lanka	100
		NHK,Moyabi	Gabon	500
		RTV Italiana,Rome	Italy	100
		R.Moscow/RPP/Kiev	USSR	100/500
		RDP,Lisbon	Portugal	250

Short wave				
kHz	*metres*	*Station*	*Country*	*Power*
11800	25.42	RA,Shepparton/Darwin	Australia	250
11805	25.41	VOA	West Germany	100
		VOA,Kaválla	Greece	250
		VOA	Philippines	250
		VOA,Woofferton	UK	300
		R.Moscow/RPP	USSR	50/500
		R.Globo,R. de Janeiro	Brazil	10
		RFI,Allouis	France	100
		R.Kabul	Afghanistan	100
11810	25.40	FEBA	Seychelles	100
		DW	West Germany	100/500
		DW,Kigali	Rwanda	250
		DW	Antigua	250
		AIR,Delhi	India	100
		R.Moscow/RPP	USSR	50/100
		RTV Italiana,Rome	Italy	100
		Vatican Radio	Vatican	100/500
		RBI	East Germany	50
		R.Baghdad	Iraq	--
11815	25.39	R.Polonia,Warsaw	Poland	100
		RBC	Brazil	7.5
		RFE/RL	West Germany	100
		RFE/RL,Lisbon	Portugal	250
		NHK,Yamata	Japan	300
		AIR,Delhi	India	100
		R.Moscow/Khabarovsk	USSR	100
		Tripoli	Libya	500
		Ankara	Turkey	500
		R.Habana,Havana	Cuba	250
		TWR,Bonaire	Neth. Antilles	50
11820	25.38	Maputo	Mozambique	120
		BBC WS;Por,Sp,EbyR	Ascension/HK/USA	125
		R.Moscow/RPP	USSR	50/500
		DW	West Germany	100/500
		QBS	Qatar	250
		R.Veritas,Malolos	Philippines	100
		KNLS,Alaska	USA	100
		R.RSA,Meyerton	South Africa	250
11825	25.37	Papeete	Tahiti	25
		RFE/RL	West Germany	250
		RFE/RL,Lisbon	Portugal	250
		VFC,T'ai-pei	Taiwan	250
		ORF,Moosbrunn	Austria	300
		BSKSA,Riyadh	Saudi Arabia	350
		WYFR,Okeechobee	USA	100
11830	25.36	WYFR,Okeechobee	USA	100
		AIR,Bombay/Delhi	India	100
		R.Moscow/RPP	USSR	240
		R.Bucharest	Romania	250
		Vatican Radio	Vatican	100

Short wave				
kHz	*metres*	*Station*	*Country*	*Power*
11830	25.36	R.ELWA,Monrovia	Liberia	50
		R.Pyongyang	Korea(DPR)	100
11835	26.43	VOA,Monrovia	Liberia	250
		VOA,Woofferton	UK	250
		VOA,Kaválla	Greece	250
		NHK,Mayabi	Gabon	500
		SLBC,Colombo	Sri Lanka	35
		R.Moscow/RPP	USSR	100/500
		VO Andes,Quito	Ecuador	100
		BBC WS;Russian,EbyR	Oman	100
		R.Tirana	Albania	100
		R.Sofia	Bulgaria	250
		Montevideo	Uruguay	5
11840	35.34	RDP,Lisbon	Portugal	100
		R.Polonia,Warsaw	Poland	100
		VOA,Monrovia	Liberia	250
		NHK,Yamata	Japan	300
		VOA	Philippines	35
		R.Bucharest	Romania	250
		TWR,Merizo	Guam	100
		R.Sofia	Bulgaria	250
		R.Moscow/RPP,Havana	Cuba	100
		R.Moscow	USSR	50/100
		RCI	UK	300
		REE,Noblejas	Spain	350
		R.Baghdad	Iraq	500
11845	25.33	RSI,Hörby	Sweden	500
		BBC WS;Russian,EbyR	Cyprus	20
		VOA,Kaválla	Greece	250
		VOA,Tangier	Morocco	35
		R.Moscow/RPP	USSR	100
		RFI,Allouis	France	100
		Vatican Radio	Vatican	100
		RCI,Sackville	Canada	250
		AIR,Delhi	India	100
		R.Denmark,Copenhagen	Denmark	50
11850	25.32	BBC WS;Be,Bu,HI	Singapore	250
		AIR,Delhi	India	100
		RNI,Fredrikstad/Sveio	Norway	350
		R.Moscow/RPP	USSR	200/500
		DW	West Germany	500
		TWR,Merizo	Guam	100
		R.Habana relay	USSR	--
		VOA,Monrovia	Liberia	250
		VOA,Tangier	Morocco	50
		FEBC,Bocaue	Philippines	50
		R.Finland,Pori	Finland	500
11855	25.31	VOA,Tangier	Morocco	100
		VOA,Woofferton	UK	300
		WYFR,Okeechobee	USA	50/100

Short wave				
kHz	*metres*	*Station*	*Country*	*Power*
11855	25.31	Ulan Bator	Mongolia	25
		RCI,Sackville	Canada	250
		R.Prague	Czechoslovakia	120
		RFE/RL	West Germany	100
		RFE/RL,Lisbon	Portugal	250
		RFE/RL,Pals	Spain	250
		DW	West Germany	500
		RA,Carnarvon	Australia	100
		R.Aparecida	Brazil	7.5
11860	25.30	FEBA,Mahé	Seychelles	25/100
		BBC WS	Ascension	125/250
		R.Moscow/RPP/Kiev Yerevan/Vilnius	USSR	100/500
		VFC,T'ai-pei	Taiwan	--
		R.Beijing	P. Rep. of China	500
		R.Sofia	Bulgaria	250
		FEBC	Philippines	100
		Ankara	Turkey	250
		KNLS,Alaska	USA	100
11865	25.28	FEBA,Mahé	Seychelles	25/100
		BBC WS;Cz,Hu,Pol,Ru	UK	--
		RRI,Jayapura	Indonesia	25
		DW,Sines	Portugal	100
		DW	West Germany	250
		DW,Cyclops	Malta	50
		FEBC,Bocaue	Philippines	50
		FEBA,Mahé	Seychelles	100
		R.Moscow	USSR	100
		AIR,Delhi	India	100
		RNI,Fredrikstad	Norway	350
		VOA,Woofferton	UK	300
11870	25.27	FEBA,Mahé	Seychelles	100
		RDP,Lisbon	Portugal	100
		R.Moscow/RPP	USSR	240
		AIR,Aligarh	India	250
		R.Sofia	Bulgaria	250/500
		R.Tirana	Albania	100
		Laos National R.	USSR	240
		NHK,Yamata	Japan	100
11875	25.26	RFE/RL	West Germany	100
		VOA,Kaválla	Greece	250
		VOA,Woofferton	UK	300
		NHK,Yamata	Japan	100
		R.Cairo	Egypt	250
11880	25.25	R.RSA Meyerton	South Africa	250/500
		Lusaka	Zambia	50
		R.Moscow	USSR	240
		REE,Noblejas	Spain	350
11885	25.24	RFE/RL	West Germany	250
		RFE/RL,Lisbon	Portugal	250

Short wave				
kHz	*metres*	*Station*	*Country*	*Power*
11885	25.24	RFE/RL,Pals	Spain	250
		Kajang	Malaysia	50
		WYFR,Okeechobee	USA	100
11890	25.23	RBI	East Germany	100
		VOA	USA	250/500
		R.Moscow/RPP	USSR	240
		Radio Oman,Sib	Oman	50
11895	25.22	AIR,Delhi	India	100
		RFE/RL	West Germany	250
		RFE/RL,Lisbon	Portugal	250
		R.Pampa,Porto Alegre	Brazil	1
		FEBA,Mahé	Seychelles	100
		VOA,Greenville	USA	500
11900	25.21	R.RSA, Meyerton	South Africa	250/500
		BBC WS; Russian	UK	--
		R.Moscow/RPP	USSR	100/500
		Kajang	Malaysia	100
		VO Andes,Quito	Ecuador	100
		R.Sofia	Bulgaria	250
		KYOI,Saipan Island	Northern Marianas	100
11905	25.20	CBS,T'ai-pei	Taiwan	100
		DW	West Germany	100/500
		DW,Sines	Portugal	250
		DW	Sri Lanka	250
		RTV Italiana,Rome	Italy	100
		R.Moscow/RPP	USSR	100
		Pathumthani	Thailand	50
		R.Tirana	Albania	100
		R.Beijing	P. Rep. of China	120
		R.Cairo	Egypt	250
		R.Universo	Brazil	7.5
		BBC WS;Persian	Cyprus	--
11910	25.19	R.Budapest	Hungary	20/250
		R.Moscow	USSR	100
		VO Andes,Quito	Ecuador	100
		BSKSA,Riyadh	Saudi Arabia	350
		DW	West Germany	100
		RA,Shepparton	Australia	100
		VOA	Philippines	50
11915	25.18	FEBA	Seychelles	100
		R.Moscow/RPP	USSR	100
		Porto Alegre	Brazil	7.5
		VOA,Monrovia	Liberia	50
		VOA,Greenville	USA	250
		VFC,T'ai-pei	Taiwan	--
		BSKSA,Riyadh	Saudi Arabia	350
		RCI,Sines	Portugal	250
		ORF,Moosbrunn	Austria	100
11920	25.17	BBC WS;Pashto	Singapore	--
		VOA,Monrovia	Liberia	250

Short wave				
kHz	*metres*	*Station*	*Country*	*Power*
11885	25.24	RFE/RL,Pals	Spain	250
		Kajang	Malaysia	50
		WYFR,Okeechobee	100	
11890	25.23	RBI	East Germany	100
		VOA	USA	250/500
		R.Moscow/RPP	USSR	240
		Radio Oman,Sib	Oman	50
11895	25.22	AIR,Delhi	India	100
		RFE/RL	West Germany	250
		RFE/RL,Lisbon	Portugal	250
		R.Pampa,Porto Alegre	Brazil	1
		FEBA,Mahé	Seychelles	100
		VOA,Greenville	USA	500
11900	25.21	R.RSA, Meyerton	South Africa	250/500
		BBC WS; Russian	UK	--
		R.Moscow/RPP	USSR	100/500
		Kajang	Malaysia	100
		VO Andes,Quito	Ecuador	100
		R.Sofia	Bulgaria	250
		KYOI,Saipan Island	Northern Marianas	100
11905	25.20	CBS,T'ai-pei	Taiwan	100
		DW	West Germany	100/500
		DW,Sines	Portugal	250
		DW	Sri Lanka	250
		RTV Italiana,Rome	Italy	100
		R.Moscow/RPP	USSR	100
		Pathumthani	Thailand	50
		R.Tirana	Albania	100
		R.Beijing	P. Rep. of China	120
		R.Cairo	Egypt	250
		R.Universo	Brazil	7.5
		BBC WS;Persian	Cyprus	--
11910	25.19	R.Budapest	Hungary	20/250
		R.Moscow	USSR	100
		VO Andes,Quito	Ecuador	100
		BSKSA,Riyadh	Saudi Arabia	350
		DW	West Germany	100
		RA,Shepparton	Australia	100
		VOA	Philippines	50
11915	25.18	FEBA	Seychelles	100
		R.Moscow/RPP	USSR	100
		Porto Alegre	Brazil	7.5
		VOA,Monrovia	Liberia	50
		VOA,Greenville	USA	250
		VFC,T'ai-pei	Taiwan	--
		BSKSA,Riyadh	Saudi Arabia	350
		RCI,Sines	Portugal	250
		ORF,Moosbrunn	Austria	100
11920	25.17	BBC WS;Pashto	Singapore	--
		VOA,Monrovia	Liberia	250

Short wave				
kHz	*metres*	*Station*	*Country*	*Power*
11920	25.17	VOA	Philippines	250
		REE,Noblejas	Spain	350
		R.Moscow/RPP	USSR	500
		Abidjan	Ivory Coast	100
		Amman	Jordan	100
		RTM,Tangier	Morocco	50
11925	25.16	BBC WS;Cz,Gr,Hu,T	UK	250
		R.Moscow/RPP	USSR	500
		VOA,Kaválla	Greece	250
		VOA,Woofferton	UK	300
		VOA	Philippines	250
		RB,Sao Paulo	Brazil	10
		VO Andes,Quito	Ecuador	100
		RFE/RL	West Germany	100
		RFE/RL,Lisbon	Portugal	250
		SRI/RCBS	Switzerland	150
		CPBS,Beijing	P. Rep. of China	50
		RSI,Varberg (s.s.b.)	Sweden	100
11930	25.15	R.Moscow/RPP	USSR	100/500
		RNW Flevo	Netherlands	500
		RFI,Allouis	France	500
		VOA	Philippines	250
		R.Cairo	Egypt	100
		KNLS,Alaska	USA	100
11935	25.14	RNW Flevo	Netherlands	500
		SRI/RCBS	Switzerland	150
		RCI,Daventry	UK	300
		RFE/RL	West Germany	100
		RFE/RL,Lisbon	Portugal	250
		VOA,Pals	Spain	250
		AIR,Delhi	India	20
		R.Clube Paranaense	Brazil	7.5
		R.Tirana	Albania	100
11938	25.13	VO People,Phnom Penh	Kampuchea	50
11940	25.13	R.Bucharest	Romania	250
		RCI,Sackville	Canada	250
		AIR,Aligarh	India	250
		SBC,Seletar	Singapore	50
		RSI,Hörby	Sweden	350
		Africa 1,Moyabi	Gabon	250
11945	25.12	BBC WS;Cz,Hu,Pol,Ru, T,EbyR	UK	250
		BBC WS	Hong Kong	--
		DW	West Germany	500
		DW	Sri Lanka	250
		R.Beijing	P. Rep. of China	240
		RCI,Sackville	Canada	250
		REE,Noblejas	Spain	350
		VOA,Kaválla	Greece	250
		VOA	Philippines	250

Short wave				
kHz	*metres*	*Station*	*Country*	*Power*
11945	25.12	R.Finland,Pori	Finland	500
		RA,Shepparton	Australia	100
11950	25.11	RNW Flevo	Netherlands	500
		RNW	Madagascar	300
		BSKSA,Diriyah	Saudi Arabia	50
		R.Moscow/RPP/Kazakh R	USSR	100/240
		Rio de Janeiro	Brazil	7.5
		R.Habana,Havana	Cuba	100
		DW,Cyclops	Malta	250
		RSI,Varberg(s.s.b.)	Sweden	100
		VOA,Dixon	USA	250
11955	25.09	RSI,Hörby	Sweden	500
		SRI/RCBS	Switzerland	250
		BBC WS;I,Man,V,EbyR	Singapore	250
		BBC WS	Oman,Singapore	250
		R.Moscow/RPP	USSR	240
		RFI,Allouis	France	500
		R.Nacional,Luanda	Angola	100
		Ankara	Turkey	100
		RCI,Sackville	Canada	250
		Dubai	UAE	300
		R.ELWA,Monrovia	Liberia	50
		IRIB,Tehran	Iran	100
		DW	West Germany	100
11960	25.08	VOA	West Germany	100
		VOA,Rhodes	Greece	50
		VOA,Tangier	Morocco	35
		R.Moscow/RPP	USSR	240
		VO Andes,Quito	Ecuador	100
		RCI,Sackville	Canada	250
		R.Tirana	Albania	100
11965	25.07	R.Pakistan	Pakistan	50/250
		RFI,Allouis	France	100
		VOA	Philippines	250
		R.Record,Sao Paulo	Brazil	7.5
		AWR,Agat	Guam	100
		WRNO	USA	100
11970	25.06	R.Beijing	P. Rep. of China	240
		RFE/RL	West Germany	100
		RFE/RL,Lisbon	Portugal	250
		RFE/RL,Pals	Spain	250
		R.Habana,Havana	Cuba	250
		R.Moscow/RPP	USSR	240
11975	25.05	R.Cairo,Abu Zaabal	Egypt	100
		R.Moscow/RPP	USSR	240
11980	25.04	BRT,Wavre	Belgium	250
		R.Beijing	P. Rep. of China	240
		R.Moscow/RPP	USSR	240/500
		AWR,Agat	Guam	100
		KNLS,Alaska	USA	100

Short wave				
kHz	*metres*	*Station*	*Country*	*Power*
11980	25.04	WHRI,Noblesville	USA	100
11985	25.03	R.Tirana	Albania	100
		R.Moscow	USSR	--
11990	25.02	R.Prague	Czechoslovakia	250
		R.Moscow/RPP	USSR	100
		R.Kuwait	Kuwait	500
11995	25.01	RFI,Allouis	France	100
		R.Pakistan	Pakistan	50/250
		Byelorussian Radio	USSR	100
12000	25.00	R.Budapest	Hungary	250
		R.Moscow/RPP	USSR	--
12005	24.99	R.Pakistan	Pakistan	50/250
		R.Moscow/RPP/Minsk	USSR	100
		Sfax	Tunisia	100
12010	24.98	R.Moscow/RPP	USSR	--
12015	24.97	ORF,Moosbrunn	Austria	100
		R.Moscow/RPP	USSR	--
		R.Beijing,Xi'an	P. Rep. of China	120
		Ulan Bator	Mongolia	250
		R.Pakistan	Pakistan	50/250
12020	24.96	R.Moscow/RPP	USSR	--
		Hanoi	Vietnam	30
12025	24.95	FEBC	Philippines	100
12030	24.94	SRI,Sottens	Switzerland	250
		R.Moscow/RPP	USSR	240
12035	24.93	SRI/RCBS	Switzerland	250
		Hanoi	Vietnam	30
12040	24.92	BBC WS;Cz,Hu,Ru,Pol, Sk,Fr	multiple	250/500
		R.Moscow/RPP	USSR	50
12050	24.90	R.Cairo	Egypt	250
		R.Moscow/RPP	USSR	240
12055	24.89	R.Moscow/RPP	USSR	--
12060	24.88	R.Moscow/RPP	USSR	--
12065	24.87	R.Moscow/RPP	USSR	--
12070	24.86	R.Moscow/RPP	USSR	--
12077	24.84	R.Moscow/RPP	USSR	--
		Kol Israel,Tel Aviv	Israel	50
12085	24.82	SBC,Adra	Syria	500
12095	24.80	BBC WS	UK	250/300
12200	24.59	CPBS,Beijing	P. Rep. of China	15
13605	22.05	R.Moscow/RPP	USSR	--
13625	22.02	R.Moscow/RPP	USSR	--
		Kol Israel,Tel Aviv	Israel	50
13636	22.00	R.Moscow/RPP	USSR	--
13645	21.99	R.Moscow/RPP	USSR	--
		Kiev	USSR	--
13650	21.98	R.Pyongyang	Korea(DPR)	100
		R.Baghdad	Iraq	--
13655	21.97	R.Moscow/RPP	USSR	--

Short wave				
kHz	*metres*	*Station*	*Country*	*Power*
13660	21.96	R.Moscow/RPP	USSR	--
13665	21.95	R.Pakistan	Pakistan	50/250
		R.Moscow/RPP	USSR	--
13670	21.95	R.Korea	Korean (Rep)	10/250
13675	21.94	R.Pakistan	Pakistan	50/250
13680	21.93	R.Moscow/RPP	USSR	--
13695	21.91	WYFR,Okeechobee	USA	100
13700	21.90	RNW Flevo	Netherlands	500
		R.Baghdad	Iraq	--
13705	21.89	R.Moscow/RPP	USSR	--
13715	21.87	R.Prague	Czechoslovakia	120
13725	21.86	Kol Israel,Tel Aviv	Israel	20
13750	21.82	Kol Israel,Tel Aviv	Israel	20
		R.Pyongyang	Korea(DPR)	200
13759	21.80	Reyjavik	Iceland	10
13760	21.80	WYFR,Okeechobee	USA	100
		WCSN,Maine	USA	500
13770	21.79	RNW Flevo	Netherlands	500
		R.Moscow/RPP	USSR	--
13780	21.77	R.Moscow/RPP	USSR	--
13965	21.48	WYFR,Okeechobee	USA	100
14500	20.69	UN Radio	Switzerland	15
14670	20.45	CHU(SF),Ottawa	Canada	3
14802	20.27	Betio	Kiribati	10
14996	20.01	RWM(SF),Moscow	USSR	8
15000	20.00	RTA(SF),Novosibirsk	USSR	5
		BPM(SF),Lintong	P. Rep. of China	10
		BSF(SF)	Taiwan	5
		ATA(SF),New Delhi	India	8
		JJY(SF),Tokyo	Japan	2
		WWVH(SF)Kekaha	Hawaii	10
		WWV(SF),Fort Collins	USA	10
		LOL(SF)	Argentina	2
15004	19.99	RID(SF),Irkutsk	USSR	1
15010	19.99	VO Vietnam	Vietnam	30
15020	19.97	Adra	Syria	500
15030	19.96	R.Beijing	P. Rep. of China	--
15055	19.93	WYFR	Taiwan	250
15060	19.92	BSKSA,Riyadh	Saudi Arabia	350
15070	19.91	BBC WS	UK	300
15084	19.89	IRIB,Tehran	Iran	250
15090	19.88	Vatican Radio	Vatican	100
		R.Pakistan	Pakistan	50/250
15095	19.87	Kol Israel,Tel Aviv	Israel	150
15100	19.87	R.Beijing	P. Rep. of China	240
15105	19.86	BBC WS;Fr,Ha,Por	Ascension	250
		DW	West Germany	100/500
		DW	Sri Lanka	250
		DW	Antigua	250
		DW,Cyclops	Malta	250

Short wave				
kHz	*metres*	*Station*	*Country*	*Power*
15105	19.86	R.Veritas,Malolos	Philippines	50
		RTVM,Tangier	Morocco	50
		Ankara	Turkey	250
		WHRI	USA	100
15110	19.85	R.Moscow/RPP	USSR	500
		R.Prague	Czechoslovakia	250
		AIR,Delhi	India	250
		R.Baghdad	Iraq	--
15115	19.85	R.Pakistan	Pakistan	50/250
		FEBA	Seychelles	100
		BBC WS;Fr,EbyR	UK	100
		VO Andes,Quito	Ecuador	100
		RFE/RL,Lisbon	Portugal	250
		RFE/RL	West Germany	100
		Vatican Radio	Vatican	100
		R.Finland,Pori	Finland	500
15120	19.84	RNW Bonaire	Neth. Antilles	300
		R.Beijing,Xi'an	P. Rep. of China	150
		DW	West Germany	500
		VOA,Woofferton	UK	300
		VOA	USA	250
		VOA,Kaválla	Greece	250
		R.Polonia,Warsaw	Poland	100
		FEBA,Mahé	Seychelles	100
		SLBC,Colombo	Sri Lanka	35/100
		Vatican Radio	Vatican	100
		Ikorodu	Nigeria	100
		R.Pyongyang	Korea(DPR)	400
15125	19.83	R.Moscow/RPP	USSR	240
		REE,Noblejas	Spain	350
		R.RSA Meyerton	South Africa	250/500
		AWR,Agat	Guam	100
		BBC WS;I,J	Singapore	--
15130	19.83	RFE/RL,Lisbon	Portugal	250
		RFE/RL,Pals	Spain	500
		WYFR,Okeechobee	USA	100
15135	19.82	R.Pakistan	Pakistan	50/250
		SRI,Beijing	P. Rep. of China	120
		DW	West Germany	500
		R.Record,Sao Paulo	Brazil	7.5
		RFI,Allouis	France	100
		R.Veritas,Malolos	Philippines	100
		VOA,Greenville	USA	500
		R.Moscow,Sofia	Bulgaria	500
15140	19.82	R.Moscow/RPP	USSR	240
		RCI,Sackville	Canada	250
		R.Nacional,Santiago	Chile	100
		RA,Carnarvon	Australia	300
		AIR,Aligarh	India	100
		R.Pyongyang	Korea(DPR)	400

Short wave				
kHz	*metres*	*Station*	*Country*	*Power*
15145	19.81	WINB	USA	50
		RBI,Nauen	East Germany	500
		RFE/RL,Lisbon	Portugal	250
15150	19.80	RRI,Jakarta	Indonesia	100
		RNZ,Wellington	New Zealand	7.5
		R.Moscow/RPP	USSR	100/500
		RCI,Sackville	Canada	250
		VOA,Rhodes	Greece	50
15155	19.80	VO Andes,Quito	Ecuador	100
		R.Cairo,Abu Zaabal	Egypt	100
		RFI,Allouis	France	100
		VOA	Philippines	50
		R.Moscow/RPP	USSR	250
		R.Prague	Czechoslovakia	250
15160	19.79	R.Budapest	Hungary	20
		RTV Algerienne	Algeria	100
		RA,Shepparton	Australia	100
		VO Andes,Quito	Ecuador	100
		VOA	USA	250
		VOA	Philippines	250
		VOA,Kaválla	Greece	250
		R.Budapest	Hungary	20
		AIR,Delhi	India	100
		DW,Sines	Portugal	250
		Ankara	Turkey	250
		R.Pyongyang	Korea(DPR)	400
		Mexico City	Mexico	10
15165	19.78	R.Beijing,Xi'an	P. Rep. of China	150
		R.Denmark,Copenhagen	Denmark	50
		AIR,Bombay	India	100
		RNI,Kvitsøy/Sveio	Norway	500
15170	19.78	Papeete	Tahiti	20
		RFE/RL,Lisbon	Portugal	250
		WYFR,Okeechobee	USA	100
		RBI	East Germany	50/500
		BSKSA,Jeddah	Saudi Arabia	50
15175	19.77	R.Cairo,Abu Zaabal	Egypt	100
		AIR,Aligarh/Delhi	India	100/250
		R.Moscow/RPP	USSR	500
15180	19.76	R.Beijing	P. Rep. of China	240
		BBC WS; Arabic	UK	--
		RNI,Kvitsøy	Norway	500
		R.Moscow/RPP	USSR	100
		Kiev	USSR	--
		RA,Shepparton	Australia	100
		RFI,Allouis	France	500
		RCI,Daventry	UK	300
		R.Pyongyang	Korea(DPR)	200
15185	19.76	DW	West Germany	100/500
		DW,Cyclops	Malta	300

Short wave				
kHz	*metres*	*Station*	*Country*	*Power*
15185	19.76	DW	Sri Lanka	300
		Ikorodu	Nigeria	100
		VOA,Greenville	USA	500
		VOA	Philippines	250
		R.RSA,Meyerton	South Africa	250
		WINB	USA	50
		R.Moscow/RPP	USSR	240
		R.Tirana	Albania	100
		R.Finland,Pori	Finland	500
		R.RSA,Meyerton	South Africa	250
15190	19.75	R.Pakistan	Pakistan	50/250
		R.Moscow/RPP	USSR	100
		Vatican Radio	Vatican	500
		Belo Horizonte	Brazil	25
		Brazzaville	Congo	50
		RFI,Allouis	France	500
		RNI,Kvitsøy	Norway	500
15195	19.74	R.Pakistan	Pakistan	50/250
		R.Beijing	P. Rep. of China	120
		NHK,Yamata	Japan	100
		VOA,Greenville/Dixon	USA	250/500
		VOA,Tangier	Morocco	100
		VOA,Rhodes	Greece	50
		RFI,Allouis	France	100
15200	19.74	R.Beijing	P. Rep. of China	120
		RFI	French Guiana	500
		Africa-1,Moyabi	Gabon	250
		R.Moscow/RPP	USSR	240
		Kol Israel,Tel Aviv	Israel	20
15205	19.73	FEBA	Seychelles	100
		DW	West Germany	100
		DW	Antigua	250
		VOA,Kaválla	Greece	250
		VOA,Woofferton	UK	300
		VOA,Greenville	USA	500
		VOA,Tangier	Morocco	35/100
		Algiers	Algeria	100
15210	19.72	R.Cairo,Abu Zaabal	Egypt	100
		DW	West Germany	250
		R.Moscow/RPP	USSR	240
		VOA	Philippines	250
15215	19.72	RFE/RL,lisbon	Portugal	250
		WYFR,Okeechobee	USA	100
		Sao Luiz	Brazil	2.5
		R.Veritas,Malolos	Philippines	50
		VOA	Philippines	250
		Algiers	Algeria	100
15220	19.71	R.Budapest	Hungary	3/250
		R.Cairo,Abis	Egypt	250
		R.RSA,Meyerton	South Africa	250

Short wave				
kHz	*metres*	*Station*	*Country*	*Power*
15220	19.71	RNI,Kvitsøy	Norway	500
		Ankara	Turkey	500
		R.Moscow/RPP	USSR	500
		VO Andes,Quito	Ecuador	100
15225	19.70	R.RSA Meyerton	South Africa	250/500
		VOA,Woofferton	UK	250
		R.Beijing	P. Rep. of China	--
		RDP,Lisbon	Portugal	100
		WYFR,Okeechobee	USA	50/100
		BBC WS;Russian	UK	--
		KUSW,Utah	USA	100
15230	19.70	R.Habana,Havana	Cuba	250
		R.Habana relay	USSR	120
		AIR,Delhi	India	100
		NHK relay,Moyabi	Gabon	250
		R.Moscow/RPP,Alma-Ata	USSR	100
		R.Nacional,Brasilia	Brazil	250
15235	19.69	BBC WS;Se,Arabian	UK/Oman	100/250
		Tripoli	Libya	500
		VOA,Tangier	Morocco	100
		VOA,Woofferton	UK	300
		RCI	UK	300
		NHK,Yamata	Japan	100
		RNI,Sveio	Norway	500
15240	19.69	R.RSA Meyerton	South Africa	250/500
		RA,Shepparton	Australia	100
		RBI	East Germany	500
		AIR,Delhi	India	100
		Belgrade	Jugoslavia	100
		R.Veritas,Malolos	Philippines	250
		TWR,Merizo	Guam	100
15245	19.68	BBC WS;Ru,Be,Hi	Singapore	--
		RDP,Lisbon	Portugal	100
		VOA,Greenville	USA	50
		VOA,Woofferton	UK	300
		VOA,Tangier	Morocco	100
		RTV Italiana,Rome	Italy	100
		DW,Sines	Portugal	250
		DW	West Germany	250
		R.Moscow/RPP	USSR	120
		Kinshasa	Zaire	100
		R.Finland,Pori	Finland	500
		BSKSA,Riyadh	Saudi Arabia	350
		AIR,Delhi	India	100
		R.RSA,Meyerton	South Africa	250
15250	19.67	FEBA	Seychelles	25
		R.Bucharest	Romania	250
		VOA	Philippines	250
		VOA	Sri Lanka	35
		AIR,Delhi	India	100

Short wave				
kHz	*metres*	*Station*	*Country*	*Power*
15250	19.67	RDP,Lisbon	Portugal	100
		VO Andes,Quito	Ecuador	250
15255	19.67	RBI,Nauen	East Germany	500
		RFE/RL,Lisbon	Portugal	250
		R.Afghanistan relay	USSR	--
		R.Cairo,Abu Zaabal	Egypt	100
		R.Veritas,Malolos	Philippines	50
15260	19.66	BBC WS	Asc./Canada	100/250
		R.Moscow/RPP,Baku	USSR	240
		VOA,Kaválla	Greece	250
		RCI,Sackville	Canada	250
		R.Beijing,Xi'an	P. Rep. of China	150
15265	19.65	Doha	Qatar	250
		VOA,Greenville	USA	500
		VOA	Philippines	250
		R.Moscow/RPP,Chita	USSR	100
		US military	West Germany	100
		RDP,Lisbon	Portugal	100
		R.Nacional,Brasilia	Brazil	250
		RNI,Kvitsøy	Norway	500
15270	19.65	BBC WS;Russian,EbyR	Cyprus	100
		VFC,T'ai-pei	Taiwan	100
		VOA,Woofferton	UK	300
		VOA,Tangier	Morocco	300
		ORF,Moosbrunn	Austria	500
		Vo Andes,Quito	Ecuador	500
		R.Bucharest	Romania	250
		DW,Kigali	Rwanda	250
		R.Veritas,Malolos	Philippines	50
		WCSN,Maine	USA	500
15275	19.64	R.RSA Meyerton	South Africa	250/500
		DW	West Germany	500
		DW	Antigua	250
		R.Veritas,Malolos	Philippines	100
15280	19.63	RNW Flevo	Netherlands	500
		VOA,Woofferton	UK	250
		BBC WS	Hong Kong	250
		KGEI,Ca	USA	50
		R.Moscow/RPP	USSR	240/500
		AIR,Bombay	India	100
		RNI,Kvitsøy	Norway	500
		R.Beijing	P. Rep. of China	120
		WCSN,Maine	USA	500
		NHK,Yamata	Japan	100
15285	19.63	RDP,Lisbon	Portugal	100
		R.Moscow/RPP	USSR	100/240
		BBC WS;Pa,U,Por,Sp	Ascension	250
		R.Cairo,Abu Zaabal	Egypt	100
		VOA	Ascension	250
15290	19.62	R.Nacional,B.Aires	Argentina	1

Short wave				
kHz	*metres*	*Station*	*Country*	*Power*
15290	19.62	VOA	Philippines	250
		RFE/RL,Pals	Spain	250
		RFE/RL,Lisbon	Portugal	250
15295	19.61	WINB	USA	50
		R.Pakistan	Pakistan	50/250
		Kajang	Malaysia	500
		R.Moscow/RPP,Voronezh	USSR	240
		VO Andes,Quito	Ecuador	100
15300	19.61	FEBA,Mahé	Seychelles	100
		R.Habana,Havana	Cuba	50
		RFI,Allouis	France	500
		RFI	French Guiana	250
		NHK,Yamata	Japan	300
		Dubai	UAE	300
		R.Moscow/RPP	USSR	500
		WCSN,Maine	USA	500
15305	19.60	VOA,Rhodes	Greece	250
		VOA	Philippines	250
		AIR,Delhi	India	100
		Ulan Bator	Mongolia	250
		R.Moscow,Voronezh	USSR	100
15310	19.60	R.Sofia	Bulgaria	250
		RNI,Fredrikstad/ Kvitsøy/Sveio	Norway	350/500
		BBC WS	Oman	100
		Conakry	Guinea	100
15315	19.59	RNW, Bonaire	Neth. Antilles	300
		RFI,Allouis	France	100
		IRIB,Tehran	Iran	100
		VOA,Monrovia	Liberia	250
		VOA	Philippines	250
		RCI,Sines	Portugal	250
		RA,Shepparton	Australia	100
		BBC WS;Finnish	UK	--
15320	19.58	RA,Shepparton	Australia	100
		ORF,Moosbrunn	Austria	100
		DW	West Germany	100
		AIR,Delhi/Aligarh	India	100/250
		VOA,Monrovia	Liberia	250
		Dubai	UAE	300
15325	19.54	FEBA,Mahé	Seychelles	100
		RCI,Sackville	Canada	250
		VOA	Philippines	250
		Dubai	UAE	300
		RNI,Sveio	Norway	500
		R.Gazeta	Brazil	1
15330	19.57	RNW Talata	Madagascar	300
		R.Beijing	P. Rep. of China	150
		DW	West Germany	100
		VOA	Philippines	250

Short wave				
kHz	*metres*	*Station*	*Country*	*Power*
15330	19.57	VOA,Monrovia	Liberia	250
		RTV Italiana,Rome	Italy	100
		Tangier	Morocco	50
		US military,Ohio	USA	175
		R.Moscow/RPP,Kursk/ Tashkent	USSR	100/500
15335	19.56	R.Cairo,Abis	Egypt	250
		AIR,Madras/Aligarh	India	100/250
		Tangier	Morocco	100
		R.Bucharest	Romania	250
		FEBC,Bocaue	Philippines	50
15340	19.56	RFE/RL	West Germany	100
		RFE/RL,Lisbon	Portugal	250
		R.Pyongyang	Korea(DPR)	200
		R.Bucharest	Romania	250
15345	19.55	RSI,Hörby	Sweden	500
		RAE/R.Nacional,B.A.	Argentina	100
		R.Kuwait	Kuwait	250
		VFC,T'ai-pei	Taiwan	250
		US military,CA	USA	100
		BSKSA,Riyadh	Saudi Arabia	350
15350	19.54	NHK,Yamata	Japan	300
		FEBC,Bocaue	Philippines	50
		RL,Junglinster	Luxembourg	10
		R.Moscow/RPP	USSR	240
15355	19.54	DW	Antigua	250
		TWR,Bonaire	Neth. Antilles	250
		RFE/RL,Lisbon	Portugal	100/250
		RTV Italiana	Rome	Italy100
		WYFR,Okeechobee	USA	50/100
15360	19.53	BBC WS; EbyR	Singapore	250
		BBC WS	Singapore	250
		RFI,Allouis	France	100
		Tangier	Morocco	50
		R.Moscow/RPP,Moscow	USSR	240
15365	19.52	RA,Darwin	Australia	250
		REE,Tenerife	Canary Islands	50
		RFI,Allouis	France	100
		AIR,Aligarh	India	250
		R.Bucharest	Romania	250
15370	19.52	RFE/RL	West Germany	250
		RFE/RL,Lisbon	Portugal	250
		RFE/RL,Pals	Spain	250
		R.Moscow/RPP	USSR	500
		BSKSA,Riyadh	Saudi Arabia	350
		VFC,T'ai-pei	Taiwan	50
15375	19.51	R.RSA, Meyerton	South Africa	250/500
		R.Korea	Korea(Rep)	10/250
		R.Cairo,Abu Zaabal	Egypt	100
		R/Moscow/RPP,Kenga	USSR	100

Short wave				
kHz	*metres*	*Station*	*Country*	*Power*
15375	19.51	REE,Noblejas	Spain	350
		VOA,Dixon CA	USA	250
		WYFR,Okeechobee	USA	50/100
15380	19.51	BBC WS;Be,Hi	Singapore	250
		BBC WS	Singapore	250
		R.Bucharest	Romania	250
		RFE/RL,Pals	Spain	250
		RFE/RL,Lisbon	Portugal	250
		RA,Carnarvon	Australia	250
		REE,Noblejas	Spain	350
15385	19.50	R.Sofia	Bulgaria	500
		R.Beijing,Xi'an	P. Rep. of China	150
		RTV Italiana,Rome	Italy	100
		TWR,Bonaire	Neth. Antilles	50
		R.Oman,Thumrait	Oman	100
15390	19.49	RSI,Hörby	Sweden	500
		BBC WS;Bu,Gr,Hu,Pol, SC,Sk,Se,T,EbyR	Cyprus	--
		WCSN,Maine	USA	500
15395	19.49	RA,Carnarvon	Australia	250
		REE,Arganda	Spain	100
		VOA	Philippines	250
		VOA	Sri Lanka	35
		R.Moscow/RPP	USSR	100/240
		QBS,Doha	Qatar	250
		WCSN,Maine	SA	500
15400	19.48	BBC WS;Portuguese	Ascension	250
		BBC WS	Ascension	250
		R.Finland,Pori	Finland	500
		VOA,Greenville	USA	250
		VOA,Monrovia	Liberia	250
		DW	West Germany	100
		WINB	USA	50
15405	19.47	FEBA,Mahé	Seychelles	100
		R.Moscow/RPP	USSR	100/500
		R.Tirana	Albania	100
		Vatican Radio	Vatican	500
		DW	West Germany	100
		DW,Cyclops	Malta	250
		KYOI,Saipan Island	Northern Marianas	100
		Ankara	Turkey	250
15410	19.47	ORF,Moosbrunn	Austria	100
		FEBC,Bocaue	Philippines	50
		VOA	Philippines	250
		VOA,Greenville	USA	500
		DW,Kigali	Rwanda	250
		DW	Antigua	250
15415	19.46	FEBA,Mahé	Seychelles	100
		Belgrade	Jugoslavia	100
		Ribeirao Prêto	Brazil	1

Short wave				
kHz	*metres*	*Station*	*Country*	*Power*
15415	19.46	R.Moscow/RPP,Kenga	USSR	500
		Tripoli	Libya	500
		RA,Carnarvon	Australia	250
15420	19.46	SRI,Varberg	Switzerland	250
		R.Cairo,Abu Zaabal	Egypt	100
		BBC WS;So,Sw,	Cyprus	250
		BBC WS	Cyprus	250
		TWR,Merizo	Guam	100
		R.Moscow/RPP	USSR	100/500
		WRNO,New Orleans	USA	100
15425	19.45	ABC,Perth	Australia	50
		RFI,Allouis	France	100
		DW	West Germany	500
		R.Moscow/RPP	USSR	100/500
		SLBC,Colombo	Sri Lanka	100
		VOA	Philippines	250
15430	19.44	FEBA,Mahé	Seychelles	45
		SRI/RCBS	Switzerland	500
		VOA	Philippines	250
		Mexico City	Mexico	50
		US military,Ohio	USA	250
		RSI,Varberg	Sweden	500
15435	19.44	VOA,Kaválla	Greece	250
		R.Moscow/RPP	USSR	240/500
		RFI,Montsinery	French Guiana	500
		SRI,Varberg(s.s.b.)	Sweden	100
		R.Beijing	P. Rep. of China	240
		BBC WS;Russian,EbyR	UK	500
		BBC WS	Hong Kong	250
		BSKSA,Jeddah	Saudi Arabia	50
		DW	Sri Lanka	250
		R.Afghanistan relay	USSR	--
15440	19.43	RCI,Sackville	Canada	250
		WYFR,Okeechobee	USA	100
		R.Moscow/RPP,Riazan	USSR	120
		R.Baghdad	Iraq	500
		R.Beijing	P. Rep. of China	120
15445	19.42	RFE/RL	West Germany	100
		RFE/RL,Lisbon	Portugal	250
		RFE/RL,Pals	Spain	250
		VOA,Monrovia	Liberia	250
		FEBC,Bocaue	Philippines	50
		R.Beijing	P. Rep. of China	500
		BBC WS;So,Sw	Cyprus	--
		BBC WS	Cyprus	--
15450	19.42	R.Moscow/RPP	USSR	100
		Karachi	Pakistan	50
		Sfax	Tunisia	100
		Tripoli	Libya	500
15455	19.41	R.Moscow/RPP	USSR	--

Short wave				
kHz	*metres*	*Station*	*Country*	*Power*
15455	19.41	FEBC,Bocaue	Philippines	50
15460	19.48	R.Moscow/RPP	USSR	100
		RFI,Allouis	France	100
		AWR	Costa Rica	5
15465	19.40	R.Moscow/RPP	USSR	--
15470	19.39	R.Moscow/RPP	USSR	--
15474	19.39	RNASG	Antarctica	1
15475	19.39	Africa-1,Moyabi	Gabon	250
		R.Moscow/RPP	USSR	--
15480	19.38	R.Moscow/RPP	USSR	--
15485	19.37	Kol Israel,Tel Aviv	Israel	300
		R.Moscow/RPP	USSR	--
15490	19.37	R.Moscow/RPP	USSR	--
15495	19.36	R.Kuwait	Kuwait	500
		R.Moscow/RPP	USSR	--
15500	19.35	R.Beijing	P. Rep. of China	120
		R.Moscow/RPP	USSR	--
15505	19.35	R.Kuwait	Kuwait	500
		R.Moscow/RPP	USSR	--
15510	19.34	BRT,Wavre	Belgium	250
		R.Moscow/RPP	USSR	--
15515	19.34	BRT,Wavre	Belgium	250
		R.Moscow/RPP	USSR	--
15520	19.33	R.Kabul relay	USSR	--
		R.Moscow/RPP	USSR	--
15525	19.32	SRI/RCBS	Switzerland	500
		Dhaka	Bangladesh	250
		R.Moscow/RPP	USSR	--
15530	19.32	R.Moscow/RPP	USSR	--
15535	19.31	R.Moscow/RPP	USSR	--
15540	19.31	RTBF,Wavre	Belgium	100
		R.Moscow/RPP	USSR	--
15545	19.31	R.Moscow/RPP	USSR	--
15550	19.29	CPBS,Beijing	P. Rep. of China	15
		R.Moscow/RPP	USSR	--
15560	19.28	RNW Flevo	Netherlands	500
		RNW,Bonaire	Neth. Antilles	300
		R.Moscow/RPP	USSR	--
15565	19.27	R.Pakistan,Islamabad	Pakistan	50/250
15566	19.27	WYFR,Okeechobee	USA	100
15570	19.27	RNW Talata	Madagascar	300
		SRI/RCBS,Sottens	Switzerland	500
		R.Moscow/RPP	USSR	--
15575	19.26	R.Korea	Korean (Rep)	10/250
15580	19.26	R.Pakistan	Pakistan	50/250
		VOA,Greenville	USA	250
15585	19.25	Kol Israel,Tel Aviv	Israel	300
		R.Moscow/RPP	USSR	--
15590	19.24	BRT,Wavre	Belgium	250
		CPBS,Beijing	P. Rep. of China	--

Short wave				
kHz	*metres*	*Station*	*Country*	*Power*
15595	19.24	R.Pakistan,Islamabad	Pakistan	250
		R.Moscow/RPP	USSR	--
15600	19.23	R.Beijing	P. Rep. of China	--
		VOA,Monrovia	Liberia	250
		R.Moscow	USSR	--
15605	19.22	R.Pakistan,Islamabad	Pakistan	250
15615	19.21	Kol Israel,Tel Aviv	Israel	300
15630	19.19	Athens	Greece	100
15640	19.18	Kol Israel,Tel Aviv	Israel	300
15650	19.17	Kol Israel,Tel Aviv	Israel	300
15670	19.15	CPBS,Kunming	P. Rep. of China	50
		KUSW,Utah	USA	100
15710	19.10	CPBS,Beijing	P. Rep. of China	--
15880	18.89	CPBS,Beijing	P. Rep. of China	--
		KUSW,Utah	USA	100
16230	18.48	R.Tirana	Albania	50
17387	17.25	AIR,Delhi	India	100
17550	17.09	LQC20(time),B. Aires	Argentina	5
17555	17.09	Kol Israel,Tel Aviv	Israel	500
17565	16.99	Athens	Greece	100
17570	17.08	SRI/RCBS	Switzerland	500
17575	17.07	RNW, Talara	Madagascar	300
		RNW,Flevo	Netherlands	500
		Kol Israel,Tel Aviv	Israel	300
17595	17.05	BRT,Wavre	Belgium	250
17605	17.04	RNW,Bonaire	Neth. Antilles	300
		RNW,Flevo	Netherlands	500
		CPBS,Beijing	P. Rep. of China	--
17612	17.03	WYFR,Okeechobee	USA	100
17620	17.03	RFI,Allouis	France	500
17630	17.02	R.Baghdad	Iraq	--
		Kol Israel,Tel Aviv	Israel	300
17640	17.01	R.Pakistan	Pakistan	50/250
		VOA,Greenville	USA	500
		WCSN,Maine	USA	500
		WYFR,Okeechobee	USA	100
17650	17.00	R.Beijing,Kunming	P. Rep. of China	50
17655	16.99	R.Kabul relay	USSR	--
17660	16.99	R.Pakistan	Pakistan	50/250
17670	16.98	R.Cairo,Abu Zaabal	Egypt	100
17675	16.97	RTBF,Wavre	Belgium	250
		R.Cairo,Abis	Egypt	250
		R.Moscow/RPP	USSR	--
17680	16.97	RTBF,Wavre	Belgium	250
		R.Beijing	P. Rep. of China	500
		R.Moscow/RPP	USSR	500
17690	16.96	R.Cairo,\abis	Egypt	250
17695	16.95	BBC WS;Ru,T,EbyR	UK	300
17700	16.95	CPBS,Beijing	P. Rep. of China	50
17705	16.94	BBC WS	UK	500

Short wave				
kHz	*metres*	*Station*	*Country*	*Power*
17705	16.94	R.Prague	Czechoslovakia	250
		VOA,Monrovia	Liberia	250
		AIR,Delhi	India	50
		R.Habana relay	USSR	500
		RNZ,Wellington	New Zealand	7.5
17710	16.94	R.Budapest	Hungary	3/250
		Kol Israel,Tel Aviv	Israel	300
		VOA,Greenville	USA	250
17715	16.93	DW	West Germany	100
		DW	Antigua	250
		BBC WS;Gr,A,	Cyprus	250
		RTV Italiana,Rome	Italy	100
		RA,Darwin/Carnarvon	Australia	300
17720	16.93	R.Afghanistan relay	USSR	--
		RFI,Allouis	France	500
		R.Bucharest	Romania	250
		R.Moscow/RPP	USSR	100
		R.Cairo,Abis	Egypt	250
		VFC,T'ai-pei	Taiwan	100
		RFI,Montsinery	French Guiana	500
17725	16.93	R.Pakistan	Pakistan	50/250
		RFE/RL,Lisbon	Portugal	250
		RFE/RL,Pals	Spain	500
		R.Beijing	P. Rep. of China	--
17730	16.92	Vatican Radio	Vatican	100
		R.Moscow/RPP,Irkutsk	USSR	240
		WYFR,Okeechobee	USA	50
17735	16.92	RFE/RL,Lisbon	Portugal	250
		VOA	Philippines	250
		R.Moscow/RPP	USSR	240
17740	16.91	BBC WS;So,Sw,EbyR	Cyprus	--
		BBC WS	Cyprus	--
		VOA,Greenville	USA	250
		VOA,Monrovia	Liberia	250
		VOA	Philippines	250
		BSKSA,Riyadh	Saudi Arabia	350
		R.Moscow/RPP	USSR	100
		Vatican Radio	Vatican	100
17745	16.91	R.Cairo,Abis	Egypt	100
		R.Bucharest	Romania	250
		R.Moscow,Kursk	USSR	240
17750	16.90	RFE/RL	West Germany	250
		RFE/RL,Lisbon	Portugal	250
		WYFR,Okeechobee	USA	100
		RA,Darwin	Australia	250
17755	16.90	R.Suriname Intl relay	Brazil	250
		RBI	East Germany	50
		NHK,Moyabi	Gabon	500
		R.RSA,Meyerton	South Africa	250/500
17760	16.89	RFE/RL	West Germany	100

Short wave				
kHz	*metres*	*Station*	*Country*	*Power*
17760	16.89	Ankara	Turkey	500
		BBC WS	UK	--
17765	16.89	DW	West Germany	100
		VOA,Dixon	USA	250
		R.Moscow/RPP,Tula	USSR	500
		Mexico City	Mexico	100
17770	16.88	RFE/RL,Lisbon	Portugal	250
		RFE/RL,Pals	Spain	250
		REE,Noblejas	Spain	350
		RSI,Varberg(s.s.b.)	Sweden	100
		R.Cairo,Abis	Egypt	250
17775	16.88	Dubai	UAE	300
		R.Beijing	P. Rep. of China	--
		VOA,Greenville	USA	250
		R.Moscow/RPP	USSR	100/500
		KVOH	USA	50
17780	16.87	BBC WS;Gr,Russian	Cyprus	--
		VOA,Tangier	Morocco	35
		VOA,Woofferton	UK	300
		AIR,Aligarh	India	100
		R.RSA,Meyerton	South Africa	500
		RNI,Sveio	Norway	500
		DW	West Germany	100
		KYOI,Saipan Island	Northern Marianas	100
		RTV Italiana,Rome	Italy	100
		FEBA,Mahé	Seychelles	100
		R.Budapest	Hungary	3/250
17785	16.87	R.Cairo,Abis	Egypt	250
		RFI,Allouis	France	500
		AIR,Aligarh	India	250
		VOA,Philippines	USA	250
		VOA,Greenville	USA	250
		FEBA,Mahé	Seychelles	25/100
		R.RSA,Meyerton	South Africa	250/500
17790	16.86	VO Andes/R,Nacional, Quito	Ecuador	500
		BBC WS	Ascension/Oman	250
		R.Bucharest	Romania	250
		R.RSA,Meyerton	South Africa	250
17795	16.86	RFI,Allouis	France	100
		RTV Italiana,Rome	Italy	100
		RA,Shepparton	Australia	100
		R.RSA,Meyerton	South Africa	250
17800	16.85	VOA,Ohio	USA	250
		DW,Kigali	Rwanda	250
		RFI,Allouis	France	100
		R.Cairo,Abis	Egypt	250
		R.Pakistan	Pakistan	50/250
17805	16.85	R.Moscow/RPP,Tbilisi	USSR	500
		AIR,Aligarh	India	250

Short wave				
kHz	*metres*	*Station*	*Country*	*Power*
17805	16.85	RFE/RL,Lisbon	Portugal	250
		RFE/RL	West Germany	100
		R.Bucharest	Romania	250
		WYFR,Okeechobee	USA	100
17810	16.84	DW	West Germany	500
		DW	Antigua	250
		BBC WS;Fr,Ha,Por,Sp	Ascension/UK	250
		NHK,Yamata	Japan	300
		VOA,Ohio	USA	250
		VOA	Ascension	250
17815	16.84	R.Cultura,Sao Paulo	Brazil	7.5
		R.Moscow/RPP,Frunze	USSR	100
		Kol Israel,Tel Aviv	Israel	250
		Tangier	Morocco	50
		R.Cairo,Abis	Egypt	250
17820	16.84	R.Moscow/RPP,Kiev/ Novosibirsk	USSR	250/500
		RCI,Sackville	Canada	250
		VOA	Philippines	100
17825	16.83	NHK,Yamata	Japan	200
		DW	West Germany	100/500
		DW,Cyclops	Malta	250
		DW	Sri Lanka	250
17830	16.83	SRI/RCBS	Switzerland	250
		BBC WS	Singapore	250
		VOA,Kaválla	Greece	250
		VOA	Ascension	250
		AIR,Delhi	India	100
		Dubai	UAE	300
17835	16.82	R.RSA Meyerton	South Africa	250/500
		RFE/RL,Lisbon	Portugal	250
		R.Moscow/RPP	USSR	240
		NHK,Yamata	Japan	100
17840	16.82	R.Prague	Czechoslovakia	250
		RNI,Kvitsøy	Norway	500
		Vatican Radio	Vatican	100
17845	16.81	RFI,Allouis	France	500
		WYFR,Okeechobee	USA	100
		DW	West Germany	100/500
		REE,Noblejas	Spain	350
		NHK,Yamata	Japan	100
		RFE/RL,Pals	Spain	250
17850	16.81	RFI,Allouis	France	500
		R.Moscow/RPP	USSR	100
		R.Kuwait	Kuwait	250
		SLBS,Colombo	Sri Lanka	36
17855	16.80	FEBA,Mahé	Seychelles	100
		VOA,Woofferton	UK	500
		VOA,Tangier	Morocco	100
		AIR,Aligarh	India	250

Short wave				
kHz	*metres*	*Station*	*Country*	*Power*
17855	16.80	AWR,Agat	Guam	100
17860	16.80	VOA,Monrovia	Liberia	250
		DW,Kigali	Rwanda	250
		R.Finland,Pori	Finland	500
17865	16.79	VOA,Kaválla	Greece	250
		VOA	Philippines	250
		RFE/RL,Lisbon	Portugal	250
		RFE/RL,Pals	Spain	250
		Vatican Radio	Vatican	100
		AWR,Agat	Guam	100
17870	16.80	VOA,Monrovia	Liberia	250
		Vatican Radio	Vatican	100
		R.Moscow/RPP,Chita	USSR	500
		Dhaka	Bangladesh	250
17875	16.78	RCI,Sackville	Canada	250
		DW	West Germany	500
		DW,Sines	Portugal	250
		DW	Sri Lanka	250
		Rio de Janeiro	Brazil	7.5
		R.Moscow/RPP,Vinnitsa	USSR	100
		AIR,Aligarh	India	250
		FEBA,Mahé	Seychelles	100
		R.Cairo,Abis	Egypt	250
17880	16.78	BBC WS;Portuguese	Ascension	250
		BBC WS;	Ascension	250
		R.Moscow/RPP,Irkutsk	USSR	500
		Ankara	Turkey	500
17885	16.77	BBC WS	Ascension,Cyprus	250
		R.Kuwait	Kuwait	250
17890	16.77	R.Pakistan,Islamabad	Pakistan	50/250
		VO Andes,Quito	Ecuador	100
		REE,Noblejas	Spain	350
17895	16.76	RFE/RL,Pals	Spain	250
		RFE/RL,Lisbon	Portugal	250
		R.Zambia,Lusaka	Zambia	50
		BSKSA,Riyadh	Saudi Arabia	360
		R.Kuwait	Kuwait	500
18050	16.62	R.Pakistan,Islamabad	Pakistan	50/250
18080	16.59	BBC WS;So,Sw,Pe	multiple	250
18195	16.49	R.Moscow,Moscow	USSR	20
20000	15.00	WWV(SF),Fort Collins	USA	2.5
21465	13.98	R.Cairo,Abis	Egypt	250
		RBI,Leipzig	East Germany	100
21470	13.97	BBC WS	UK	500
21475	13.97	R.Pakistan,Islamabad	Pakistan	50/250
21480	13.97	RNW Talata	Madagascar	300
21485	13.96	RNW Talata	Madagascar	300
		Vatican Radio	Vatican	100
		VOA,Monrovia	Liberia	250
21495	13.96	BSKSA,Riyadh	Saudi Arabia	350

Short wave				
kHz	*metres*	*Station*	*Country*	*Power*
21500	13.95	RFE/RL,Lisbon	Portugal	250
		VOA,Woofferton	UK	300
		VOA,Monrovia	Liberia	50
21505	13.95	R.Prague	Czechoslovakia	250
21510	13.95	RFE/RL	West Germany	250
		RFE/RL,Lisbon	Portugal	250
21520	13.94	VOA,Woofferton	UK	300
		VOA,Kaválla	Greece	250
21525	13.93	R.Budapest	Hungary	3/2
		WYFR.Okeechobee	USA	50/100
21530	13.93	RFE/RL,Lisbon	Portugal	250
21535	13.93	R.RSA,Meyerton	South Africa	500
21540	13.93	RNW Bonaire	Neth. Antilles	300
		RBI,Nauen	East Germany	500
		VOA	Philippines	250
		DW	Sri Lanka	300
21550	13.92	VOA,Monrovia	Liberia	250
21555	13.92	RSI,Varberg(s.s.b.)	Sweden	100
21560	13.92	DW	West Germany	250
		VOA,Dixon	USA	250
21565	13.91	RNI,Fredrikstad	Norway	350
21575	13.90	REE,Noblejas	Spain	350
21580	13.90	RFI,Allouis	France	500
		VOA,Greenville	USA	250
21585	13.92	R.Moscow/RPP,Dushanbé	USSR	100
21590	13.90	R.RSA Meyerton	South Africa	250/500
		VOA,Ohio	USA	250
21595	13.89	R.RSA Meyerton	South Africa	250/500
21600	13.89	DW	West Germany	100
21605	13.89	Dubai	UAE	300
21610	13.88	RTV Italiana,Rome	Italy	100
		VOA,Greenville	USA	500
		NHK,Yamata	Japan	300
21615	13.88	RTV Italiana,Rome	Italy	100
		WYFR,Okeechobee	USA	50/100
21620	13.88	RFI,Allouis	France	100
21625	13.87	Kol Israel,Tel Aviv	Israel	300
21640	13.86	BBC WS French,Hausa	Ascension	250/500
		WCSN,Maine	USA	500
21645	13.86	Tripoli	Libya	500
21650	13.86	DW	West Germany	100
		DW,Cyclops	Malta	250
		VOA,Tangier	Morocco	35
		Kol Israel,Tel Aviv	Israel	300
21665	13.85	R.Budapest	Hungary	250
		RFE/RL,Lisbon	Portugal	250
		R.Bucharest	Romania	250
21675	13.84	Kol Israel,Tel Aviv	Israel	300
21680	13.84	DW	West Germany	500
		R.Moscow/RPP,Baku	USSR	100

Short wave				
kHz	*metres*	*Station*	*Country*	*Power*
21680	13.84	RNW,Bonaire	Neth. Antilles	300
21685	13.83	RNW Bonaire	Neth. Antilles	300
21690	13.83	RSI,Hörby	Sweden	500
21695	13.83	SRI/RCBS	Switzerland	250
		NHK,Moyabi	Gabon	100
21700	13.82	RDP,Lisbon	Portugal	100
		Dubai	UAE	300
		RNI,Kvitsøy/ Fredrikstad	Norway	350/500
		NHK,Moyabi	Gabon	500
21705	13.82	R.Prague	Czechoslovakia	250
		RNI,Kvitsøy	Norway	500
21710	13.82	BBC WS;	UK	500
21720	13.81	RFE/RL,Lisbon	Portugal	100
21725	13.81	Vatican Radio	Vatican	100
21730	13.81	RNI,Kvitsøy	Norway	500
21735	13.80	RFE/RL,Lisbon	Portugal	250
21745	13.80	RFE/RL,Lisbon	Portugal	50
21810	13.76	BRT,Wavre	Belgium	200
25640	11.70	Kol Israel,Tel Aviv	Israel	20/500
25730	11.66	RNI,Fredrikstad	Norway	350

6 Short wave stations of the world – geographically

Afghanistan

6085	9635	9665	11805	15255	15435
17720					

Albania

639	648	864	963	972	990
981	1026	1089	1098	1161	1287
1305	1422	1548	5057	6080	6125
6170	6185	6200	7065	7080	7090
7105	7120	7155	7165	7170	7205
7235	7300	7310	9375	9430	9480
9500	9600	9750	9760	10510	11835
11870	11905	11938	11960	11985	15185
15405	16230				

Algeria

531	549	576	666	693	738
783	837	873	891	909	927
981	1026	1089	1098	1161	1287
1305	1422	1548	6145	6160	7145
7245	9640	11715	15160	15205	15215

Andorra

819

Angola

3355	3375	4770	4820	4860	4885
4895	4970	5060	5192	5405	6150
6175	7170	7215	7245	9535	9720
11955					

Antarctica

6012	15474

Antigua

6040	6045	6085	6120	6166	6175
9510	9590	9605	9640	9690	11775
11785	11795	11810	15105	15205	15275
15355	15410	17715	17810		

Argentina

5000	6060	6090	6120	6180	8167.5
9690	9710	10000	11710	11755	11780
15000	15290	15345	17550		

Ascension

6020	6155	7105	9515	9560	9600
11820	11860	15105	15285	15400	17790
17810	17830	17880	17885	21640	

Australia

2310	2325	2485	4835	4910	4920
5025	5995	6035	6060	6080	6140
7120	7135	7205	7215	7265	9505
9580	9610	9620	9645	9655	9660
9710	9720	9760	9770	11705	11720
11730	11765	11800	11855	11910	11945
15140	15160	15180	15240	15315	15320
15365	15380	15395	15415	15425	17715
17750	17795				

Austria

585	774	1026	1476	1602	5035
5945	6000	6155	9550	9580	9655
9725	11660	11760	11825	11915	12015
15270	15320	15410			

Azores

683	837	909	1260	1395	1566

Bangladesh

4880	6240	7105	7505	9640	9775
9945	15525	17870			

Belgium

540	621	927	1125	1188	1233
1305	1512	5910	6035	6050	7140
9675	7860	9880	9905	9925	11660
11695	11980	15510	15515	15540	15590
17595	17675	17680	21810		

Benin

4870	5025	7190			

Bhutan

6035					

Bolivia

4682	4740	4765	4775	4785	4795
4830	4845	4876	4936	4945	4965
4975	4980	4990	4991	5005	5020
5954	5965	5975	5995	6015	6080
6105	6140	6155	9715		

Botswana

3355	4820	5955	7255		

Brazil

2310	2340	2380	2420	3245	3285
4755	4765	4785	4795	4805	4815
4825	4835	4845	4855	4865	4875
4885	4895	4904	4915	4925	4936
4945	4955	4965	4975	4985	5015
5025	5035	5045	5055	5955	5970

Brazil

5980	5990	6000	6010	6020	6030
6050	5070	6105	6120	6135	6150
6160	6170	6180	9505	9550	9585
9615	9630	9645	9655	9665	9685
9695	7905	9725	9760	11745	11765
11780	11785	11805	11815	11855	11895
11905	11915	11925	11935	11950	11965
15135	15190	15215	15230	15265	15325
15415	17755	17815	17875		

Bulgaria

576	595	648	747	774	828
864	873	945	963	1017	1161
1224	1296	1377	6035	6070	6085
6115	6135	6160	7115	7135	7150
7155	7215	7255	7280	7670	9560
9595	9700	9740	9745	9755	11720
11735	11750	11765	11835	11840	11860
11870	11900	15135	15310	15385	

Burkina Faso

4815	7230

Burma

4725	5985	7185	9730

Burundi

3300	6140

Cameroon

3970	4000	4750	4795	4850	4971
5010	5955	6005	7150	7205	7240
9745					

Canada

5960	5965	6045	6065	6070	6120
6130	6140	6195	6335	9510	9535
9590	9605	9625	9650	9660	9750
9755	9760	11710	11720	11845	11855
11940	11945	11955	11960	14670	15140
15150	15260	15325	15440	17820	17875

Canary Islands

621	648	720	747	837	882
1008	1269	1341	15365		

Cape Verde

3931

Central African Republic

5035	7220

Chad

4904	7120				

Chile

6135	9510	9550	9630	15140	

Colombia

4785	4815	4845	4865	4875	4885
4915	4945	4975	5050	5095	5975
6035	6065	6085	6095	6150	6160
6170	9635				

Comoros

3330	7260				

Congo

6115	15190				

Cook Islands

11760					

Costa Rica

4832	5055	6005	6105	6150	6175
9645	15460				

Cuba

4765	5965	6060	6090	6120	6140
9525	9550	9600	9655	9730	9770
11725	11760	11795	11815	11840	11950
11970	15230	15300			

Cyprus

548	603	639	693	720	918
981	1044	1089	1098	1233	1314
1323	1503	6030	6050	6070	6120
6125	7135	9580	9590	9600	9610
9625	9660	11720	11740	11750	11760
11845	11905	15210	15390	15420	15445
17715	17740	17780	17885		

Czechoslovakia

281	558	567	621	634	702
774	792	837	846	864	900
927	954	981	1017	1071	1098
1233	1287	1332	1485	1521	1593
5930	6055	7345	9505	9600	9605
9630	9740	11685	11855	11990	13715
15110	15155	17705	17840	21505	21705

Denmark

245	1062	6150	9730	9740	9745
11845	15165				

Djibouti

4780

Dominican Rep.

11700

Ecuador

3220	3380	3395	4762	4795	4800
4810	4840	4850	4870	4890	4900
4910	4920	4960	4990	5015	5025
5050	5055	5060	6050	6075	6080
6130	6205	6230	9715	9745	9765
9845	9860	9870	11740	11775	11795
11835	11900	11910	11925	11960	15115
15155	15160	15220	15250	15270	15295
17790	17890				

Egypt

558	621	702	711	756	774
819	864	873	882	918	936
981	990	1008	1062	1080	1107
1143	1161	1179	1197	1278	1305
1314	1341	1350	1422	1476	1485
1503	1521	1539	1575	1584	1593
1602	7150	9455	9475	9620	9670
9675	9700	9740	9755	9770	9805
9850	9900	11665	11715	11750	11785
11875	11905	11930	11975	12050	15155
15175	15210	15220	15255	15285	15335
15375	15420	17670	17675	17690	17720
17745	17770	17785	17800	17815	17875
21465					

Eire

531	567	612	729	891	963
1305	1143	1188	1251	1278	1404
6930					

Equatorial Guinea

4926	6250	9553

Ethiopia

7110	7165	9560	9595

Falklands

2380	3958

Finland

254	540	558	963	1242	1404
6120	9530	9560	9605	9635	9655
11755	11850	11945	15115	15185	15245
15400	17860				

France

162	585	603	675	711	792
864	945	963	1071	1161	1206
1242	1278	1350	1377	1404	1485
1495	1557	1584	3965	5950	5990
5995	6040	6045	6055	6115	6150
6175	7120	7135	7145	7235	7280
9535	9550	9575	9605	9715	9745
9790	9805	9810	9860	11670	99690
11790	11805	11845	11930	11955	11965
11995	15135	15155	15180	15190	15195
15300	15315	15360	15365	15425	15460
17620	17720	17785	17795	17800	17845
1780	21580	21620			

French Guiana

5055	6055	6170	6175	9535	9790
11670	15200	15300	15435	17720	

Gabon

4777	4830	4890	7135	7160	7200
7270	9570	9630	9645	11800	11835
11940	15200	15230	15475	17755	21695
21700					

Germany (East)

180	254	531	558	576	657
693	729	783	882	891	999
1017	1044	1116	1170	1188	1323
1341	1359	1431	1458	1575	1584
1602	5965	6010	6140	6070	6080
6105	6115	6165	7105	7115	7165
7170	7185	7260	7295	9560	9620
9645	9665	9715	9730	9770	11705
11750	11785	11810	11890	15145	15170
15240	15255	17755	21465	21540	

Germany (West)

153	180	207	549	567	576
595	630	666	684	702	711
720	756	774	801	810	828
855	873	936	972	990	1017
1143	1197	1269	1413	1422	1449
1485	1539	1593	3960	3970	3980
3985	3990	3995	4465	5955	5960
5970	5985	5990	5995	6000	6010
6020	6025	6030	6035	6040	6045
6050	6060	6065	6070	6075	6085
6090	6095	6100	6105	6115	6120
6130	6135	6140	6145	6150	6170
6185	6190	7110	7115	7120	7130
7135	7145	7150	7155	7160	7165
7175	7180	7190	7200	7220	7225
7235	7240	7245	7255	7265	7270

Germany (West)

7275	7280	7285	7295	9505	9520
9540	9545	9555	9565	9570	9575
9585	9595	9605	9610	9615	9625
9640	9645	9650	9660	9670	9680
9690	9700	9705	9715	97256	9735
9745	9750	9765	9770	10380	11725
11750	11765	11770	11785	11795	11805
11810	11815	11820	11825	11850	11855
11865	11875	11885	11895	11905	11910
11925	11935	11945	11955	11960	11970
15105	15115	15120	15135	15185	151205
15210	15245	15265	15275	15320	15330
15340	15370	15400	15405	15425	15445
17715	17750	17769	17765	17780	17805
17810	17825	17845	17875	21510	21560
21600	21650	21680			

Ghana

3350	3365	4915	6130	7295

Greece

666	724	765	792	927	945
981	1008	1044	1080	1116	1179
1260	1278	1314	1350	1386	1404
1485	1494	1512	1539	1584	1602
5955	5965	5985	6015	6060	6080
6085	6105	6140	6145	6150	6160
6180	7105	7125	7130	7135	7145
7170	7205	7210	7265	7270	7280
7295	7430	9395	9420	9425	9530
9540	9565	9580	9615	9635	9670
9680	9690	9695	9700	9705	9715
9740	9855	9935	11595	11645	11705
11740	11760	11775	11780	11805	11835
11845	11875	11925	11945	11960	15120
15150	15160	15195	15205	15260	15305
15435	15630	17565	17830	17865	21520

Greenland

3999

Guam

7365	9465	9515	9530	9585	9590
9675	9750	9820	9830	9840	9870
11700	11715	11735	11840	11850	11965
11980	15125	15240	15420	17855	17865

Guatemala

2360	2390	3300	4825	4835	5955
6090	6180				

Guyana

5950

Haiti

4930

Hawaii

2500 5000 10000 15000

Honduras

4820 6075

Hong Kong

3915 7180 11775 11945 15280 15435

Hungary

540 873 1116 1188 1251 1341
1350 6025 6110 7155 7220 9520
9585 9835 11910 12000 15160 15220
17710 17780 21525 21665

Iceland

207 666 3400 9595 9985 13759

India

3235 3268 3275 3295 3305 3315
3345 3355 3365 3375 3905 3925
4778 4800 4820 4840 4850 4860
4895 4920 4960 5050 5960 5970
5990 6010 6020 6035 6045 6050
6065 6105 6110 6120 6140 6145
6155 6160 6190 7110 7120 7140
7150 7160 7170 7210 7215 7225
7235 7240 7250 7255 7260 7265
7280 7295 7410 9515 9525 9545
9550 9610 9615 9630 9665 9675
9730 9750 9755 9910 9950 10000
10335 11620 11715 11730 11765 11790
11795 11810 11815 11830 11845 11850
11865 11870 11895 11935 11940 15000
15110 15140 15160 15165 15175 15230
15240 15245 15250 15280 15305 15320
15335 15365 17387 17705 17780 17785
17805 17830 17855 17875

Indonesia

2307 2360 2419 2435 2901 3000
3215 3250 3265 3305 3325 3345
3385 3395 3905 3935 3945 3995
4000 4003 4340 4700 4719 4753
4764 4775 4790 4805 4835 4855
4875 4900 4910 4920 4927 4955
5056 5257 5886 5894 5970 5983
6045 6070 6135 6190 7098 7210
7270 7295 9680 11770 11788 11865
15150

Iran

684	702	711	720	747	765
837	990	1026	1080	1098	1116
1152	1188	1278	1332	1386	1422
1449	1457	1503	1539	1566	1593
7215	7230	9022	11790	11955	15084
15315					

Iraq

603	684	693	756	846	909
1035	1116	1197	1224	1359	1377
1431	6190	7120	9635	9665	9690
9745	9770	9875	11740	11750	11760
11790	11810	11840	13650	13700	15110
15440	17630				

Israel

531	576	657	711	738	846
882	1026	1224	1287	1305	1368
1458	9010	9385	9435	9930	11585
11605	11655	12077	13625	13725	13750
15045	15200	15485	15585	15615	15640
15650	17555	17575	17630	17710	17815
21625	21650	21675	25640		

Italy

189	207	567	657	814	846
900	936	981	999	1017	1035
1062	1098	1107	1116	1188	1301
1305	1314	1332	1368	1431	1449
1485	1512	1575	1602	3995	5000
5990	6050	6060	7105	7175	7235
7275	7290	7295	9515	9575	9585
9710	11800	11810	11905	15245	15330
15335	14385	17715	17780	17795	21610
21615					

Ivory Coast

4940	6015	7215	11920

Japan

3910	3925	3945	3970	5965	5990
6055	6080	6115	6130	6155	6175
6190	7140	7155	7210	7260	7280
9505	9525	9535	9570	9580	9595
9695	9760	10000	11750	11780	11815
11840	11870	11875	15000	15195	15235
15280	15300	15350	17810	17825	17835
17845	21610				

Java

2350	2377	2390

Jordan

207	612	801	855	7155	9530
9560	11920				

Jugoslavia

531	549	558	567	576	595
612	630	639	648	666	675
684	693	702	711	729	738
747	756	765	774	783	792
810	828	837	864	882	891
918	936	945	963	972	981
990	999	1008	1026	1035	1044
1062	1071	1089	1107	1134	1143
1170	1179	1197	1206	1215	1224
1233	1242	1251	1269	1287	1296
1305	1314	1323	1332	1341	1350
1359	1368	1377	1386	1395	1413
1431	1440	1449	1458	1467	1485
1503	1512	1530	1539	1557	1566
1584	1602	5980	6100	7200	7240
9505	9620	11735	15240	15415	

Kampuchea

6090	6143	9695	11938

Kenya

4885	4915	4950	6045	6075	6100
6150	7125	7140	7150	7240	7270

Kiribati

14802

Korea(DPR)

2300	2350	2400	2850	3250	3960
6180	6250	6400	6540	6576	6600
7150	7200	7230	7290	9220	9325
9345	9505	9530	9555	9600	9650
9665	9940	9977	11680	11735	11780
11830	13650	13750	15120	15140	15160
15180	15340				

Korea(Rep)

3930	5975	6015	6060	6135	6165
6480	7275	7550	9515	9570	9640
9750	9870	11725	11740	13670	15375
11575					

Kuwait

6055	7120	9750	9840	9880	11665
11675	11990	15345	15495	15505	17850
17885	17895				

Laos

5660	6130	6660	7112	7385

Lebanon
963 6215 6280

Lesotho
3255 4800 6190 9515

Liberia
3220 3255 3975 3990 4760 6025
6045 6070 6090 6180 7135 7175
7195 7265 7280 9540 9550 9605
9620 9750 9775 11710 11715 11760
11830 11835 11840 11850 11915 11920
11955 15315 15320 15330 15400 15445
15600 17705 17740 17860 17870 21485
21500 21550

Libya
234 648 675 695 711 792
828 909 1053 1080 1125 1251
1440 1449 6155 6185 7245 9890
11815 15235 15415 15450 21645

Lithuania
6100 7165 9710

Luxembourg
234 1440 6090 15350

Madagascar
3288 5010 6020 6135 7285 9505
9515 9540 9590 9690 9715 11735
11950 15330 15570 17575 21480 21485

Malawi
3380 5995

Malaysia
4845 4895 4950 4970 5030 5965
6025 6050 6060 6100 6175 7130
7145 7160 7270 7295 9515 9665
9750 11885 11900 15295

Mali
4783 4835 5995 7285 9636

Malta
756 999 1485 1557 6000 6025
6085 6110 6130 6185 7130 7235
7265 9505 9545 9565 9585 9605
9616 9625 9650 9670 9700 9735
11785 11795 11865 11950 15105 15185
15405 17825 21650

Marshall Islands

4940	6070				

Mauretania

4845	7245	9610			

Mauritius

4855					

Mexico

2390	5980	6045	6105	6115	6165
6185	9515	9555	9600	9705	11770
15160	15430	17765			

Monaco

216	1467	5920	5945	6230	7105
7205	7495	9610	11695		

Mongolia

3960	4080	4750	4850	4865	4895
4995	5960	6383	7260	9575	11855
12015	15305				

Morocco

171	207	540	595	612	656
702	711	774	819	828	864
904	936	972	999	1017	1026
1044	1053	1080	1116	1152	1188
1197	1233	1296	1323	1485	1593
5995	6040	6090	6095	6150	6180
7190	9530	9540	9575	9605	9615
9635	9645	9650	9715	9760	9770
11710	11750	11780	11790	11845	11850
11855	11920	11960	15105	15195	15205
15235	15245	15270	15330	15335	15360
17780	17815	17855	21650		

Mozambique

3280	3370	4865	6025	6115	7110
7240	9525	9618	9635	11820	

Namibia

3270	3290	4930	4965		

Nepal

3230	5005	7165			

Neth. Antilles

6020	6040	6145	6165	6180	9535
9590	9630	9650	9665	9685	9715
9770	9775	11715	11815	15120	15315
15355	15385	15560	17605	21540	21680
21685					

Netherlands

675 747 891 1008 1116 1251
5955 5990 6020 6110 7110 7295
9610 9715 9775 9840 9850 9860
9845 9899 11730 11740 11930 11935
11450 13700 13770 15280 15560 17575
17605

New Caledonia

3355 7170

Nicaragua

6015 6100 6120

Niger

3260 5020 6060 7155 9705

Nigeria

3325 4770 4990 5965 6025 6050
6145 6195 7145 7255 7285 11770
15120 15185

Northern Marianas

9465 9495 9520 9670 9685 9745
11900 15405 17780

Norway

153 216 630 675 702 1314
6010 6035 7215 9560 9590 9605
9615 9620 9655 11735 11760 11850
11865 15165 15180 15190 15220 15235
15265 15280 15310 15325 17780 17840
21565 21700 21705 21730 25730

Oman

702 1035 1242 1413 5965 6030
6085 7140 7160 7270 9535 9570
9735 9740 11740 11835 11890 11955
15235 15310 15385 17790

P. Rep. of China

2310 2340 2430 2445 2460 2475
2490 2560 3200 3260 3300 3310
3535 3960 3990 4020 4045 4130
4200 4250 4330 4460 4500 4620
4735 4760 4770 4785 4800 5815
4830 4840 4865 4883 4905 4915
4925 4940 4960 4970 4975 4990
5010 5020 5030 5040 5050 5060
5075 5090 5125 5145 5163 5220
5240 5250 5295 5320 5420 5770
5800 5850 5860 5880 5900 5915
5950 5960 5970 5975 6000 6005
6015 6045 6070 6075 6080 6095

P. Rep. of China

6100	6120	6125	6140	6150	6155
6165	6175	6185	6190	6225	6260
6400	6500	6765	6790	6825	6860
6890	6920	6937	6955	6974	6995
7010	7035	7050	7055	7065	7080
7120	7165	7185	7190	7210	7225
7235	7275	7285	7295	7315	7335
7360	7375	7385	7440	7470	7480
7505	7516	7525	7590	7620	7660
7700	7775	7800	7820	7935	8007
8260	8300	8345	8425	8450	8490
8566	8660	9020	9030	9064	9080
9170	9290	9335	9365	9380	9440
9455	9457	9480	9505	9530	9535
9550	9560	9570	9580	9585	9590
9595	9605	9645	9670	9700	9710
9725	9750	9755	9765	9775	9780
9785	9800	9820	9860	9880	9900
9915	9945	9955	10000	10245	10260
11000	11040	11100	11290	11330	11375
11445	11455	11500	11505	11515	11575
11600	11610	11630	11650	11660	11675
11685	11695	11715	11725	11740	11755
11765	11860	11905	11925	11945	11970
11980	12015	12200	15000	15030	15100
15120	15135	15165	15180	15195	15200
15225	15260	15280	15330	15385	15435
15440	15445	15500	15550	15590	15600
15670	15710	15580	17605	17650	17680
17700	17725	17775			

Pakistan

4880	4950	5010	5090	5905	5980
6065	6090	6130	6175	7090	7175
7195	7265	7290	7375	9455	9465
9575	9495	9545	9860	9885	11615
11635	11640	11675	11965	11995	12005
12015	13665	13675	15090	15115	15135
15190	15195	15295	15450	15565	15580
15595	15605	17640	17660	17725	17800
17890	18050	21475			

Papua New Guinea

2419	3235	3245	3290	3305	3325
3335	3345	3385	4890	5985	6020
6040	6080	6140	9520	9575	

Paraguay

6025	9735

Peru

4755	4762	4785	4790	4810	4825
4840	4855	4910	4920	4922	4936

Peru

4950	4960	4970	4975	4990	4995
5010	5015	5030	5040	5045	5050
5060	5198	5325	5950	5955	5970
5995	6010	6020	6045	6060	6115
6140	6200	6243	6280	6725	8065
8930	9485	9520	9655	9675	

Philippines

6015	6030	6065	6100	6120	6130
6145	6160	6170	6185	6200	7105
7120	7130	7200	7210	7225	7230
7240	7255	7260	7275	7285	9505
9510	9540	9545	9550	9555	9560
9575	9595	9605	9610	9615	9621
9630	9645	9650	9660	9665	9670
9675	9680	9700	9710	9715	9725
9730	9740	9760	9770	9800	9830
11710	11715	11725	11740	11755	11760
11775	11805	11820	11840	11850	11860
11865	11910	11920	11925	11930	11945
11965	12025	15105	15135	15155	15160
15185	15210	15215	15240	15250	15255
15265	15270	15275	15290	15305	15315
15325	15330	15335	15350	15395	15410
15425	15430	15445	15455	17735	17740
17785	17820	17865	21540		

Poland

198	738	819	1080	1206	1305
1368	1485	1503	1584	1602	5995
6095	6135	6350	7125	7145	7270
7285	9525	9540	9675	11815	11840
15120					

Portugal

558	567	576	595	630	666
693	720	783	828	891	927
963	1035	1062	1170	1197	1251
1332	1377	1431	1566	1575	1593
5955	5970	5985	6010	6015	6050
6060	6070	6095	6115	6130	6135
6190	7115	7145	7155	7165	7190
7200	7215	7245	7255	7260	7270
7285	9505	9555	9575	9590	9595
9600	9605	9615	9625	9635	9640
9650	9660	9670	9680	9695	9705
9725	9740	11725	11740	11750	11800
11815	11825	11840	11855	11865	11870
11885	11875	11905	11915	11925	11935
11970	15115	15130	15145	15160	15170
15215	15225	15245	15250	15255	15265
15285	15290	15315	15340	15355	5370
15380	15445	17725	17735	17750	17770

Portugal

17805	17835	17875	17895	21500	21510
21530	21665	21700	21720	21735	21745

Qatar

9585	11820	15265	15395

Romania

153	531	558	567	603	630
711	720	756	855	909	945
1053	1152	1179	1314	1323	1332
1404	1422	1458	1530	1593	5990
6155	7145	7195	7225	9510	9570
9590	9625	9685	9690	9750	11775
11790	11830	11840	11940	15250	15270
15335	15340	15365	15380	17720	17745
17790	17805	21665			

Rwanda

3330	6055	7225	9565	9640	9690
9735	11730	11810	15270	15410	17800
17860					

Sao Tomé

4807

Saudi Arabia

549	585	595	648	900	1440
1512	1521	5875	7145	7150	7155
7210	7225	7275	7280	9520	9570
9655	9705	9720	9730	9870	9885
11685	11730	11825	11910	11915	11950
15060	15170	15245	15345	15370	15435
17740	17895	21495			

Senegal

4890	6045	6180	7170	7210

Seychelles

6080	7130	9510	9590	9600	9610
9670	9770	11720	11755	11760	11790
11810	11860	11865	11870	11895	11915
15115	15120	15205	15250	15300	15325
15405	15415	15430	17780	17785	17885
17875					

Sierra Leone

5980

Singapore

5052	5995	6000	6080	6155	6190
7145	7165	7170	7250	9570	9580
9635	9680	9725	9730	9740	11750
11850	11920	11940	11955	15125	15245
15360	15380	17830			

Solomon Islands

5020	9545				

Somalia

6095	7120	7200	11640		

South Africa

3215	3220	3230	3320	3927	3955
4585	4810	4880	4990	5980	6010
6065	6160	7270	7285	7295	9580
9585	9590	9615	9655	9665	11720
11730	11745	11775	11820	11880	11900
15125	15285	15220	15225	15240	15245
15275	15375	17755	17780	17785	17790
17795	17835	21535	21590	21595	

Spain

254	531	558	576	585	621
639	657	684	693	724	738
747	774	792	810	828	837
855	864	873	882	918	936
954	972	990	999	1008	1026
1080	1107	1134	1179	1224	1260
1314	1395	1413	1476	1485	1503
1521	1539	1575	1584	1602	5955
6020	6125	6135	7145	7155	7245
7275	7450	9360	9505	9555	9565
9570	9625	9630	9650	9660	9675
9750	9765	9875	11730	11770	11775
11790	11840	11855	11880	11885	11920
11935	11970	15125	15130	15290	15370
15375	15380	15395	15445	17725	17770
17845	17865	17890	17895	21575	

Sri Lanka

4870	4902	4940	4968	5020	5990
5995	6005	6065	6075	6120	6130
6170	6185	7105	7115	7125	7190
7200	7265	9515	9545	9585	9600
9615	9640	9645	9650	9720	11710
11800	11835	11905	11945	15105	15120
15185	15250	15395	15425	15435	17825
17850	17875	21540			

Sudan

5039	9600				

Swaziland

3200	3205	3240	3275	3365	4760
4980	5055	5955	6070	6155	7385
9540	9550	9600	9640	9725	

Sweden

189	1179	6045	6065	7265	9565
9605	9615	9630	9645	9655	9695
9700	9715	9730	11705	11845	11925
11940	11950	11955	15345	15390	15430
15435	17770	21555	21690		

Switzerland

531	558	765	1485	1566	3985
5965	6035	6135	6165	6190	7210
9535	9560	9625	9680	9725	9885
11795	11925	11935	11955	12030	12035
14500	15420	15430	15525	15570	17570
17830	21695				

Syria

567	612	666	747	783	828
873	918	954	1035	1071	1125
1314	1485	9950	11625	12085	15020

Tahiti

9750	11825	15170

Taiwan

3335	5275	5980	6085	6210	6300
6565	7105	7150	7250	7285	7445
9465	9510	9575	9600	9630	9685
9690	9750	9765	9845	9930	9955
11550	11745	11775	11825	11860	11905
11915	15000	15055	15270	15345	15370

Tanzania

4785	5050	6005	7165	9684	9750
11734					

Thailand

4830	6070	7115	9655	11905

Tibet

4035	4750	5935	5995	7110	7170
9490					

Togo

5047	6155	7265

Tristan da Cunha

3290

Tunisia

585	603	630	720	882	963
1521	1566	7225	7310	11550	12005
15450					

Turkey

162	180	198	245	254	558
595	630	702	765	891	927
954	1017	1062	1179	5955	5960
6155	6900	7135	7215	9560	9660
9670	9730	11705	11780	11815	11860
11955	15105	15160	15220	15405	17760
17880					

Uganda

4976	5027	7195

UK

198	254	585	603	630	648
657	666	693	720	729	756
774	792	801	828	837	855
873	882	909	936	945	990
999	1017	1026	1035	1053	1089
1107	1116	1125	1152	1161	1170
1197	1215	1242	1251	1260	1278
1296	1305	1323	1332	1341	1359
1368	1431	1449	1458	1476	1485
1503	1521	1530	1548	1557	1584
1602	2500	3255	3915	3955	3975
5000	5965	5975	5995	6005	6010
6015	6025	6030	6040	6045	6050
6060	6080	6085	6110	6125	6130
6140	6145	6150	6155	6160	6180
6190	6195	7120	7125	7130	7140
7155	7170	7180	7185	7200	7210
7220	7230	7235	7255	7260	7295
7325	9410	9530	9540	9555	9650
9660	9690	9715	9735	9740	9750
9760	9770	9825	9915	10000	11710
11720	11775	11805	11835	11840	11855
11865	11875	11900	11925	11935	11945
12095	15075	15115	15120	15180	15315
15435	17695	17705	17760	17780	17810
17855	21470	21500	21520	21710	

United Arab Emirates

657	729	810	927	1314	1539
1575	5960	7215	9695	9705	11730
11955	15300	15320	15325	17775	17830
21605	21700				

Uruguay

6045	6140	9595	11735	11835

USA

2500	5000	5950	5960	5980	5985
5995	6000	6005	6015	6020	6030
6040	6055	6065	6080	6085	6095
6100	6105	6125	6130	6135	6140
6150	6155	6160	6175	6185	6190
7355	7365	7400	7651	9185	9455
9465	9495	9505	9520	9525	9530
9535	9540	9550	9555	9565	9575
9580	9605	9615	9630	9640	9650
9660	9670	9680	9700	9705	9715
9750	9755	9770	9775	9815	9840
9850	9870	10000	10060	10380	10454
11580	11680	11695	11705	11715	11730
11735	11740	11760	11770	11790	11820
11825	11830	11855	11860	11890	11895
11915	11930	11950	11965	11980	13695
13760	13965	15000	15105	15120	15130
15135	15145	15160	15170	15185	15195
15205	15215	15225	15245	15265	15270
15280	15295	15300	15330	15345	15355
15375	15390	15400	15410	15420	15430
15440	15566	15580	15670	15880	17612
17640	17710	17730	17740	17750	17765
17775	17785	17800	17805	17810	17845
20000	21525	21560	21580	21590	21610
21615	21640				

USSR

162	171	180	189	198	207
216	234	254	263	281	531
549	567	576	612	648	657
666	675	693	702	711	738
765	774	783	792	801	810
828	837	846	855	864	873
891	900	918	936	945	972
999	1008	1026	1035	1044	1062
1071	1089	1098	1107	1116	1125
1143	1170	1197	1206	1215	1242
1278	1296	1332	1350	1359	1377
1386	1404	1422	1431	1449	1458
1467	1476	1494	1512	1530	1539
1557	1566	1593	2500	3965	3995
4010	4025	4030	4040	4050	4055
4060	4395	4450	4485	4510	4520
4545	4610	4635	4740	4785	4795
4800	4810	4820	4825	4850	4860
4875	4895	4920	4930	4940	4957
4975	4990	5000	5004	5015	5035
5040	5260	5290	5900	5905	5910
5915	5920	5925	5930	5935	5940
5945	5950	5960	5970	5975	5980

USSR

6005 6010 6020 6035 6045 6050
6060 6065 6070 6075 6080 6090
6095 6100 6105 6110 6115 6120
6125 6165 6170 6180 6185 6190
6195 6200 7100 7105 7110 7120
7130 7135 7140 7145 7150 7160
7165 7170 7175 7185 7195 7200
7205 7210 7220 7230 7240 7245
7250 7255 7260 7265 7275 7280
7290 7295 7300 7310 7315 7320
7325 7330 7340 7345 7355 7360
7370 7380 7390 7400 7410 7420
7440 7925 9200 9210 9450 9470
9480 9490 9500 9505 9515 9520
9540 9545 9550 9565 9575 9600
9620 9635 9640 9645 9650 9655
9665 9670 9675 9685 9695 9710
9715 9720 9730 9735 9740 9745
9750 9760 9775 9780 9785 9790
9795 9800 9810 9820 9825 9966
10000 10004 10690 11630 11650 11655
11660 11670 11675 11680 11690 11700
11705 11710 11715 11720 11735 11740
11745 11750 11755 11760 11765 11775
11780 11785 11790 11795 11800 11805
11810 11815 11820 11830 11835 11840
11845 11850 11860 11865 11870 11880
11890 11900 11905 11910 11915 11920
11925 11930 11950 11955 11960 11970
11975 11980 11985 11990 11995 12000
12005 12010 12015 12020 12030 12040
12050 12055 12060 12065 12070 12077
13605 13625 13636 13643 13655 13660
13665 13680 13705 13770 13780 14996
15000 15004 15110 15125 15140 15150
15155 15175 15180 15185 15190 15200
15210 15220 15230 15245 15255 15260
15265 15280 15285 15295 15300 15305
15330 15350 15360 15370 15375 15395
15405 15415 15420 15425 15435 15440
15450 15455 15460 15465 15470 15475
15480 15485 15490 15495 15500 15505
15510 15515 15520 15525 15530 15535
15540 15545 15550 15560 15570 15585
15595 15600 17655 17675 17680 17705
17720 17730 17735 17740 17745 17765
17775 17805 17815 17820 17835 17850
17870 17875 17880 18195 21585 21680

Vanuatu

3945 7260

Vatican

999	1530	1611	6015	6035	6145
6150	6185	6190	6245	7125	7250
9605	9615	9625	9645	9650	9705
9755	11700	11715	11725	11740	11760
11780	11810	11830	11845	15090	15115
15120	15190	15405	17730	17740	17840
17865	17870	21485	21725		

Venezuela

4770	4780	4830	4840	4970	4980
5020	5040	6010	6100	6180	9500
9540	9660				

Vietnam

3999	5920	7420	7430	9840	10010
10060	12020	12035	15010		

Yemen

5970	6135	7190	9780

Zaire

4839	5065	7150	7205	7295	15245

Zambia

3345	4910	6060	6165	7220	7235
9505	11880	17895			

Zimbabwe

3305	3395	5975	6020	6045

7 Standard frequency transmissions

Frequency (kHz)	*Wave-length (m)*	*Station*	*Country*	*Power (kW)*
2500	120	MSF Rugby (SF)	UK	0.5
		WWV (SF) Fort Collins	USA	2.5
		WWVH (SF) Kekaha	Hawaii	5
		ZLF (SF) Wellington	New Zealand	—
		RCH (SF) Tashkent	USSR	1
3330	90.09	CHU (SF) Ottawa	Canada	3
4996	60.05	RWM (SF) Moscow	USSR	5
5000	60	WWV (SF) Fort Collins	USA	10
		WWVH (SF) Kekaha	Hawaii	10
		LOL (SF) Buenos Aires	Argentina	2
		MSF (SF) Rugby	UK	0.5
		IBF (SF) Turin	Italy	5
		RCH (SF) Tashkent	USSR	1
5004	59.95	RID (SF) Irkutsk	USSR	1
7335	4090	CHU (SF) Ottawa	Canada	10
7500	40	VNG (SF) Lyndhurst	Australia	10
8167.5	36.73	LQB9 (SF) Buenos Aires	Argentina	5
9996	30.01	RWM (SF) Moscow	USSR	5
10000	30	WWV (SF) Fort Collins	USA	10
		WWVH (S) Kekaha	Hawaii	10
		LOL (SF) Buenos Aires	Argentina	2
		MSF (SF) Rugby	UK	0.5
		RTA (SF) Novosibirsk	USSR	5
		RCH (SF) Tashkent	USSR	1
1004	29.99	RID (SF) Irkutsk	USSR	1
12000	25	VNG (SF) Lyndhurst	Australia	10
14670	20.45	CHU (SF) Ottawa	Canada	3
14996	20.01	RWM (SF) Moscow	USSR	8
15000	20	WWV (SF) Fort Collins	USA	10
		WWVH (SF) Kekaha	Hawaii	10
		LOL (SF) Buenos Aires	Argentina	2
		RTA (SF) Novosibirsk	USSR	5
15004	19.99	RID (SF) Irkutsk	USSR	1
16384	18.31	Allouis	France	2000
17550	17.09	LQC20 (SF) Buenos Aires	Argentina	5
20000	15	WWV (SF) Fort Collins	USA	2.5

8 Useful information for DXers

Clubs (in the UK)

International Listeners' Association
1 Jersey Street, Hafod
Swansea SA1 2HF

The Association was formed in 1985 to encourage the exchange of information, ideas and techniques between listeners regardless of their affiliations. Membership is £1.50 per year and includes the quarterly 'Newsletter' which covers all interests within the hobby including broadcast, RTTY, fax, air and marine monitoring. There are a number of awards available for broadcast listening within an extensive awards programme.

European DX Council (EDXC)
PO Box 4
St Ives
Huntingdon
Cambridgeshire PE17 4FE

EDXC is the umbrella association of short wave listeners and DXers in Europe with more than thirty member and observer clubs from all over the world. It produces a newsletter and other interesting publications, for example a *QSL* reporting guide in English, French, German etc., a club list with membership and publication details, and a QSL survey. The newsletter, *Euro DX*, is published ten times a year.

For further information send a SAE (UK), 2 IRCs (Europe), 3 IRCs (the rest of the world).

Note: An IRC is an International Reply Coupon. These can be exchanged for stamps abroad, and you can buy them from larger Post Offices in this country. Many advertisers or stations will expect you to send some if you want a reply. One is usually enough for a seamail reply, two or three for airmail. Check when buying them if they are valid in the country you are writing to.

Handicapped Aid Programme (HAP-UK)
c/o EDXC, PO Box 4
St Ives, Huntingdon
Cambridgeshire PE17 4FE

HAP is a voluntary organization which introduces DXing to handicapped people, and helps those already involved in the hobby. It produces many of the tapes mentioned elsewhere. Note that the address is the same as for the

EDXC, but please keep correspondence and orders separate as they are different organizations.

British DX Club (BDXC-UK)
54 Birkhall Road
Catford
London SE6 1TE

The club was founded in 1974 as the Twickenham DX club, but expanded rapidly and became the British DX Club in 1979. It covers most aspects of DXing, except ham radio, citizens band and utility reception. The monthly publication *Communication* is sent to all members, is about twenty pages long, and contains regular features by experienced DXers. The club also publishes an annual guide to *Radio Stations in the UK*, and a *QSL Survey* every two years, and operates a *Tape Circle*. Send return postage with any enquiries.

Medium Wave Circle
137a Hampton Road
Southport
Merseyside PR8 5DY

The prime activity of the club (founded in 1955) is the publication of its newsletter, *Medium Wave News* (MWN), which currently appears eight times per year – monthly during the winter DX season. MWN normally consists of 16 A5 pages of information, news and comment, including a number of regular columns as well as feature articles. These include DX news (latest station information), DX log (what members have recently heard) and the QSL corner (details of members' activities in this sphere). A feature entitled Member-to-member also appears, allowing members to advertise items, request help or ideas and so on. The MWC also organizes a *DX Alarm*, which is an early warning scheme designed to keep members informed of good DX conditions, and operates a *Bulletin Exchange Scheme* with radio clubs worldwide. Additional direct sources of information include the BBC, the IBA and EBU. Further details are available from the Secretary, Harold Emblem.

World DX Club
17 Motspur Drive
Northampton NN2 6LY

World DX Club was founded in 1968, and the membership is spread throughout the English-speaking world.

The club's monthly bulletin *Contact* is stencil duplicated to keep costs low and to provide a very quick turn-round of news and fresh information.

Interest is within the broadcast band side of the hobby and the bulletin provides space for a DX news column, QSL report, QSL ladder, and a fun listing of QSL's received totals – nothing serious! Short wave logbook, medium wave logbook, TV/FM section, members' correspondence column, and original articles are also included.

The World DX Club is a full member of the European DX Council (EDXC) and an associate member of the Association of North American

Radio Clubs (ANARC), the respective umbrella organizations for DX clubs on those continents. Enquiries should be sent to Arthur Ward at the address above.

DX Association of Great Britain
44a Porter Terrace
Murton
Co Durham SR7 9PT

A member of the European DX Council; publishes a monthly newsletter. Membership details from treasurer/editor R. Young.

International Short Wave League
10 Clyde Crescent
Wharton
Winsford
Cheshire CW7 3LA

The ISWL was formed in October 1946. It produces a monthly journal entitled *Monitor* which regularly includes both broadcast and amateur sections. Of 42 pages plus cover, *Monitor* also features articles of short wave interest.

Contests are held throughout the year for amateurs and broadcast band listeners, the winners receiving certificates. There is also an award for the highest total score in any one year, a trophy becoming the permanent possession of the winner.

A whole range of award certificates are free to members obtaining the specified number of QSL cards. A QSL bureau service is available. Nets are held weekly on 3.5, 7.0 and 14 MHz amateur bands.

The ISWL is affiliated to the Radio Society of Great Britain and the European DX Council. Details of membership and a sample copy of *Monitor* are available from the Hon Secretary, Jim May.

Radio Society of Great Britain (RSGB)
Lambda House
Cranbourne Road
Potters Bar
Hertfordshire EN6 3JE

For those listeners who want to become talkers, i.e. two-way amateur radio enthusiasts. The Society publishes many of its own books and runs a comprehensive publications service through its monthly magazine *Radio Communication*.

Note that a worldwide list of clubs is published in the *World Radio TV Handbook*, distributed in the UK by Pitman.

Magazines

Several of these magazines have readers' book services so you can keep up to date with the latest publications. The best magazines will keep you up-to-date with frequency changes.

Practical Wireless
Enefco House
The Quay
Poole
Dorset BH15 1PP

Regular features on VHF, MW, and SW DXing. Monthly.

Radio and Electronics World
Sovereign House
Brentwood
Essex CM14 4SE

Regular features include Medium wave DXing and Short wave news. Monthly.

Ham Radio Today
1 Golden Square
London W1R 3AB

Mostly about amateur radio. Monthly.

Amateur Radio
Sovereign House
Brentwood
Essex CM14 4SE

Construction projects for SWLs occasionally, but mostly for two-way radio enthusiasts. Monthly.

The Shortwave Magazine
Enefco House
The Quay
Poole
Dorset BH15 1PP

Includes a clubs' roundup. Runs a mail order books department. Much improved since its takeover by Practical Wireless. Monthly.

Electronics and Wireless World
Quadrant House
The Quadrant
Sutton
Surrey SM2 5AS

The consulting editor and communications editor have been heavily involved in producing this twentieth edition and the magazine has been connected with the book for forty years. The magazine, however, is now aimed very much at professionals. Monthly.

Radio Communication
The Radio Society of Great Britain
Lambda House
Cranbourne Road
Potters Bar
Herts EN6 3JE

The official RSGB publication for members. Mainly to do with two-way amateur radio. Monthly.

Monitoring Times
140 Dog Branch Road
PO Box 98
Brasstown NC 28902
USA

An American magazine that's worth reading. It is available in the UK from Interbooks, Lynton, Perth, Scotland PH1 4QQ.

In addition to these, various electronics magazines have occasional articles and projects for SWLs. Look out for: *Electronics (The Maplin Magazine); Practical Electronics; Everyday Electronics; Elektor Electronics;* and *Electronics Today International*.

Cassettes

Interesting and useful tape cassettes are available from two UK sources: The Handicapped Aid Programme, PO Box 4, St Ives, Huntingdon, Cambridgeshire PE17 4FE and HS Publications, 7 Epping Close, Derby DE3 4HR. Write to them for details of prices and availability but include stamps or IRCs if you want to be sure of a reply. Some of the more interesting tapes are described below, and are marked as available from HAP or HS.

Identification Signals Tape (HAP)

This recording contains the interval signals and identifications of the majority of the world's international broadcasters. The tape lists the signals in sound order: in other words, all the bell-type signals are grouped together in one section, the bird-like signals are in another section and so on. It includes a large number of Soviet regional stations, many of which can easily baffle the beginner. The tape is always kept fully up-to-date, so as any changes occur in the broadcast scene, you are kept fully aware of current interval signals. A comprehensive guide is included with the tape detailing all the signals on the recording.

Foreign Language Recognition Course (HAP)

This tape consists of spoken examples of fifty-five different languages which can be heard on the short wave bands. Along with these language examples are comments by language expert, author and DXer Dr Richard E. Wood, who gives many helpful guides to pronunciation and recognition of the various language families and also gives many keywords to help in the identification of different languages.

The course, which lasts about eighty minutes, is designed to give the serious SWL and DXer the basic means of recognizing and sorting out the jumble of different languages that can be heard on short wave. Once the language is known, it is that much easier to determine the country.

Unofficial Radio Series (HAP)
Six tapes are included in this series. *Secret local radio* examines the clandestine radio scene around the world over the past decade, with the background to these stations and extracts from some of their broadcasts. In a two-part documentary running some two hours, *The London underground* explores the alternative broadcasting media in the British capital. In *Famous radio hoaxes* there are transmitter hijacks, with actual studio recordings and extracts from programmes: such items as London Mono Radio's interview with Dr David Strange of Radio Strange. A second two-part documentary, *SW pirates* examines the SW hobby pirate scene in Europe. It includes European Music Radio, Radio Utopia, Empire Radio and others, with interviews and programme extracts which explain just why they're on the air.

Long Live Short Wave! (HAP)
This is dedicated to the short wave stations of the world and to the men and women working behind the scenes. It is an introduction to short wave: frequencies; propagation; the radio spectrum; identifications of facsimile telegraphy; RTTY; slow scan television; WWHV and much more. There is a talk by Henry Hatch whose experience dates back over fifty years; his career began at the BBC's monitoring receiving station and later he was promoted to become a senior engineer responsible to the Chief Engineer of External Services. Henry's voice is well-known from the days of the BBC World Service 'World Radio Club'. Also available as an LP record.

World on the Air (HS)
This cassette tape includes the following stations: Finnish Broadcasting Corporation; WAPA; Radio Tabajara; Voice of America; Radio Cordac; American Forces Radio; Radio Clarin; Far East Broadcasting Co.; KGEI; La Voz Evangelica; Radio Hong Kong; Family Radio; Capital Radio; Radio Tonga; Radio Los Andes; Radio Botswana; Radio New Zealand; Radio Canada; Deutsche Welle; Radio Prague; HCJB; TWR; Radio Nederland; BBC and many more (total of ninety stations). The tape lasts about sixty-five minutes, and was produced in Finland a few years ago, so you will need a good radio and a time warp to hear some of them today. Good fun, nevertheless.

USA on the Air (HS)
Also from Finland. Programme excerpts from forty-three US and Canadian stations plus some catchy commercials. This cassette also features a word-by-word text booklet, so it is possible to practise writing reception reports. After playing the tape, the listener is able to make a trial report, and check it with the cassette's 100 per cent report.

Latin America on the Air (HS)
This Finnish cassette tape is for all radio DXers interested in Latin American stations. The tape includes excerpts from fifty stations and covers twenty-three Latin American and Caribbean countries. It is supplied with a 24-page guide book with useful information on Latin American DXing. The guide

also includes a transcription of everything on the tape so that it will be easier for the enthusiast to follow the Spanish language programme excerpts. The guide book is available only with the cassette tape.

Other tapes
HS also distribute four West German tapes giving examples of stations in Argentina, Uruguay, USA and the UK (local FM).

Two sources of tapes from abroad may be useful, if you can speak German. The ADXB in Vienna has probably the world's largest collection of interval signal tapes, announced in German. A DX language and Morse course is also available. Send three IRCs (international reply coupons) for full details to Orbit Postfach 29, Vienna A-1111 Austria.

A tape of modulation types is available from Joerg Klingenfuss, Hagenloher Strasse 14, Hagelloch, Tuebingen D-7000, West Germany. It gives examples of various types of emission, for identification and checking purposes: speech, Morse, teletype, facsimile, etc.

Guide to broadcasting
Two C-90 cassettes containing local recordings of South African FM and AM stations have recently become available. The recordings made in 1987 and 1988, contain recordings of national stations (Radio South Africa, Radio 2000, etc.) and regional stations (Radio Good Hope, Radio Jakaranda, etc.) The second tape is a collection of ethnic stations such as Radio Zulu, Radio Xhosa, etc. The tapes are available in US dollars at $7.00 each surface mail/$10.00 airmail, or both for $10.00 surface/$15.00 airmail. Rough equivalents in other currencies or IRC's are also welcome. Orders to: Mr Vashek Korinek, PO Box 910, Edenvale, 1610, South Africa.

Computers
According to the EDXC Computer Survey (conducted in the winter of 1985–86), few home computers are being used to their full potential in connection with short wave radio – most are employed simply for the keeping of listening logs and for use as word processors when writing to clubs and stations. Only a very small proportion of microcomputers are presently being used in conjunction with receivers for computerized control and memory functions. However, a new computer system has been developed in The Netherlands for short wave radio listeners. Known as INFODUTCH (**INFO**rmation of **D**irect **U**se **T**o **C**omputer **H**obbyists) it provides a service to listeners having a home computer and a telephone line with modem to access the Radio Netherlands computer and obtain information including a regularly updated *Propagation Report*, tests on receivers and other DX-related news.

If you have a computer and a suitable modem connected to the telephone, you can now call up any of their data sheets, frequency schedules, or even advanced programme news on the screen. By dialling 31, the country code for Holland, and then 3545395 you can reach the NOS Radio – Radio Nederland on-line computer. Your modem needs to be capable of decoding CCITT tones (standard in Europe) and their computer will automatically switch to either 300/300, 1200/1200 or 1200/75 baud.

This computer is also part of the FIDO net, rapidly expanding in Europe and North America. The computer is in Net 500, and it is node number 202. In this way you can ask for Radio Nederland data via your local FIDO node. The new database operates 24 hours a day, and you can choose from either Dutch or English instructions. The password for beginners on the system is BASICODE, and users should fill in their first name as 'NOS' and last name 'HOBBYSCOPE'.

Regular reading of the recommended magazines will keep you up-to-date with other available computer software and services.

Radio Nederland's *Infodutch bulletin* contains up-to-date information on available software, hardware and bulletin boards, etc. Write for a copy to:

Media Network
English Section
Radio Nederland Wereldomroep
PO Box 222
1200 JG Hilversum
The Netherlands

QSL addresses

This selected list was kindly provided by Trevor Morgan, GW4OXB, of the International Listeners' Association. 'QSL' is one of the Q-code abbreviations in Morse, meaning 'Can you acknowledge receipt?' or 'I will acknowledge receipt'. Broadcasting stations use QSL cards for verification.

Alaska	3910 Seward Highway, Anchorage 99503
Albania	Rue Ismail Quemal, Tirana
Algeria	21 Boulevard des Martyrs, Algiers
Angola	CP 1329 Luanda
Antarctica	AFAN McMurdo, US Naval Support Force, Antarctica, Fleet PO, San Francisco, California 96601, USA
Argentina	PO Box 555, Buenos Aires 1000
Ascension Island	BBC Atlantic Relay Station, English Bay
Australia	PO Box 428G, GPO Melbourne 3001
Austria	PO Box 200, A-1043, Vienna
Bangladesh	20 Green Road, Dacca 5
Belgium	PO Box 26, 1000 Brussels
Botswana	Private Bag 0060, Gaborone
Brazil	PO Box 1620, Brasilia
Bulgaria	4BB Dragan Tsankov, Sofia
Burma	GPO Box 1432, Rangoon
Canada	PO Box 6000, Montreal, H3C 3A8
Chile	PO Box 244V, Santiago
China	Fu Hsin Men, Beijing
Colombia	Via del Aeropuerto, El Dorado, Bogota (Radio Nacional)
Colombia	Aereo 7170, Bogota (Radio Sutatenza)
Cuba	Apartado 7062, La Havana

Cyprus	PO Box 4824, Nicosia
Czechoslovakia	12099 Vinohradska, Praha 2
Denmark	Radio House, Rosenorns Alle 22, 1999 Copenhagen
Ecuador	Casilla 691, Quito (Radio HCJB)
Egypt	PO Box 1186, Cairo
Finland	Kesakatu 2, 00260 Helsinki 26
France	BP 9516, 75762 Paris, Cedex 16
Gabon	BP 10150 Libreville
Germany (East)	Nalepastrasse 18–50, Berlin 116 (Radio Berlin International)
Germany (West)	PO Box 100444, D-5000 Koln 1 (Radio Deutsche Welle)
Ghana	PO Box 1633, Accra
Greece	PO Box 19, Aghia Paraskevi, Athens
Guam	PO Box 368 Agana
Holland	PO Box 222, 1200JG, Hilversum (Radio Nederland)
Hong Kong	Broadcast Drive, PO Box 70200, Kowloon
Hungary	Brody Sandor 5–7, H-1800 Budapest
India	Post Box 500, New Delhi, 110001
Indonesia	PO Box 157, Jakarta
Iran	PO Box 41–3456 Tehran
Iraq	Salihiya Baghdad
Israel	PO Box 7139, Jerusalem
Italy	Casella Postale 320, Roma
Jamaica	PO Box 100, Kingston 10
Japan	NHK Center, 2–2–1 Jinnan, Shibuya-ku, Tokyo
Kenya	PO Box 30456, Nairobi
Korea	Korean Central Broadcasting Committee, Pyongyang
Korea	1–51 Yeoido-Dong, Yeongdeunngpo-Gu, Seoul
Kuwait	PO Box 397, Kuwait
Lebanon	Radio Lebanon, Beirut
Libya	PO Box 3731, Tripoli
Luxembourg	Villa Louvigny, Luxembourg
Malawi	PO Box 30133, Chichiri, Blantyre 3
Malaysia	PO Box 1074, Kuala Lumpur
Malta	PO Box 2, Valletta, Malta
Monaco	BP 128, Monte Carlo
Morocco	1 Rue El Brihi, Rabat
Netherlands	PO Box 10, 1200 JB Hilversum

New Zealand	PO Box 2092, Wellington
Nicaragua	Ministerio del Interior, Minagua
Nigeria	Voice of Nigeria, Lagos
Norway	Bj. Bjornsons Plass 1, Oslo 3
Pakistan	PO Box 443, Karachi
Panama	Apartado 1628, Panama 1
Papua	Box 1359, Boroko
Peru	Av 28 de Julio 800, Lima 1
Philippines	Box 2041, Manila (FEBC)
Philippines	PO Box 939, Manila (Radio Veritas)
Poland	Al Niepodleglosci 75/77, Warsaw
Portugal	Rua do Quelhas 21, Lisboa 2
Puerto Rico	PO Box Q, Hato Rey
Romania	PO Box 111, Bucharest
Saudi Arabia	PO Box 570, Riyadh
Seychelles	Box 234 Mahe
Singapore	PO Box 1902, Singapore
South Africa	PO Box 4559, Johannesburg
Spain	Apartado 150039, Madrid 24
Sri Lanka	PO Box 574, Torrington Square, Columbo 7
Sweden	S-10510, Stockholm
Switzerland	Giacomettistrasse 1, CH-3000, Berne 15
Taiwan	53 Jen Ai Road, Section 3, Taipei City 106
Turkey	PO Box 333, Ankara
Trans World Radio	PO Box 98, Chatham, New Jersey 07928, USA
UAE	PO Box 1695, Dubai, United Arab Emirates
UK	Bush House, Strand, London WC2B 4PH
UN	United Nations Radio, New York, NY 10017
Uruguay	Fernandez Crespo 1534, Montevideo
USA	Voice of America, Washington DC 20547
USA	AFRTS, 1016 North McCaddem Place, Los Angeles, CA 90038
USA	WYFR, 290 Hegenberger Road, Oakland, California 94621
USSR	Piatnitskaya ulitza 25, Moscow
Vatican	Vatican City, Italy
Vietnam	58 Quan Su Street, Hanoi
Yugoslavia	2 Hilendarska, Beograd
Zambia	PO Box 50015, Lusaka

* Some countries have a number of stations operating under separate control. Listen for information at the beginning or end of broadcasts to make sure you have ALL the details.

Listeners' services

Radio Nederland has sent out free pamphlets of interest to SWLs for over twenty-five years. Write to the English Section for a catalogue of what's currently available. The address is given in the Computers section. Perhaps the most useful is the 32-page 'booklist' which is updated regularly and includes a selection of recommended books, magazines, tapes and addresses.

The BBC External Services give away a variety of technical information sheets, mainly aimed at overseas listeners to the BBC World Service, with details of languages (they broadcast in thirty-six), programmes, and frequency schedules. Other leaflets include regular reviews of receivers, transcribed from their 'Waveguide' programme. *London Calling* is the programme journal of the BBC World Service (English Language), and is available in all parts of the world. For a free copy and a subscription form write to London Calling, PO Box 76, Bush House, Strand, London WC2B 4PH. Other enquiries should go to the Engineering Department or the Publicity Department at the same address. If you live in London drop into the BBC World Information Centre and Shop at Bush House in the Strand or write for a mail-order book list. The Independent Broadcasting Authority has an Engineering Information Service at Crawley Court, Winchester, Hants SO21 2QA, where there's a library, and 70 Brompton Road, London SW3 1EY.

You will soon get to know which other stations run helpful services by listening to them, particularly to their programmes for DXers (listed elsewhere in this book).

The BBC Monitoring Service publishes every day from Monday to Saturday the *Summary of World Broadcasts* (SWB) covering foreign broadcast (and printed) sources. This is issued in four parts: 1 The USSR; 2 Eastern Europe; 3 The Far East (including the Sub-Continent and South-East Asia); 4 The Middle East, Africa and Latin America.

Some items, such as major government or party statements, communiqués, press or radio commentaries, etc., may be given word for word; others are published in part, or summarized, or reported briefly. Each part has an introduction which highlights main points, and these introductions are combined in a separate publication called the *Monitoring Report*. Each of the four parts publishes a *Weekly Economic Report* containing economic, technical and scientific information. A section on Space Research, compiled largely from Soviet broadcasts, is also published as and when material becomes available.

Note that these summaries are fairly expensive, so it's probably best to find a library that takes them, if you are interested. Further details are available from the Subscriptions Office, News and Publications, BBC Monitoring Service, Caversham Park, Reading RG4 8TZ, England. You could have listened to *Six Continents*, the Radio 3 programme, for the most interesting parts of the week's broadcasts, but this excellent programme has now been chopped by the BBC.

Wavelength/frequency conversion charts

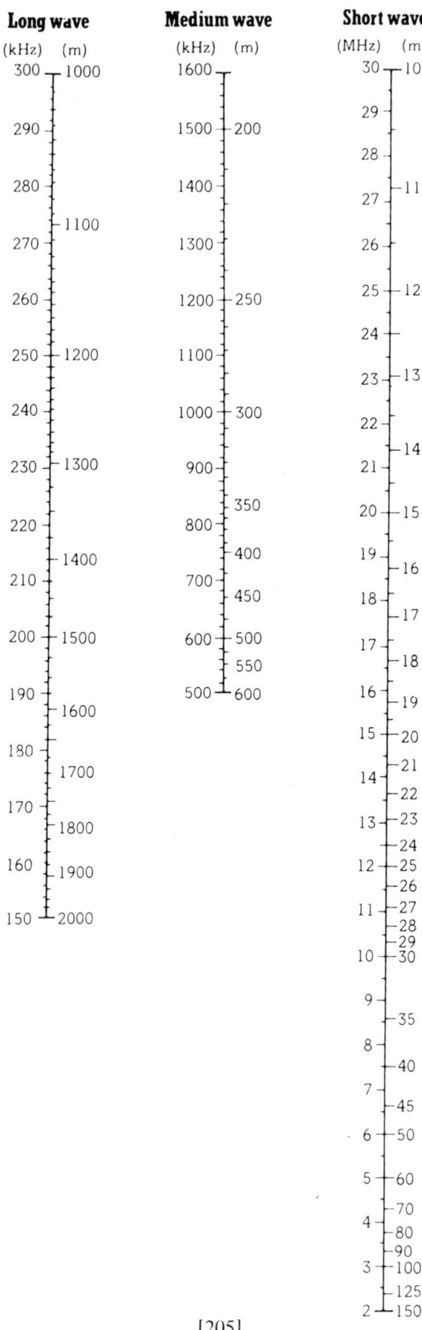

World time chart

Difference between local time and Greenwich mean time
The differences marked + indicate the number of hours ahead of GMT. Differences marked – indicate the number of hours behind GMT. Note that GMT, UTC (co-ordinated Universal Time), and Z (Zulu) are in effect the same. UTC is probably the one most commonly used outside the UK.

	Normal time	*Summer time*
Afars and Issas	+3	+3
Afghanistan	+4½	+4½
Alaska		
Juneau	–8	–8
General	–10	–10
Nome and Aleutians	–11	–11
Albania	+1	+1
Algeria	GMT	GMT
Andorra	+1	+1
Angola	+1	+1
Argentina	–4	–3
Ascension Islands	GMT	GMT
Australia		
Victoria		
New South Wales		
Queensland	+10	+10
Tasmania	+10	+11
North Territory		
South Australia	+9½	+9½
West Australia	+8	+8
Austria	+1	+1
Azores	–1	–1
Bahamas	–5	–5
Bahrain	+4	+4
Bangladesh	+6	+6
Barbados	–4	–4
Belgium	+1	+1
Bermuda	–4	–4
Bolivia	–4	–4
Botswana	+2	+2
Brazil		
Eastern and Coastal	–3	–2
Manaos	–4	–3
Acre	–5	–4
Brunei	+8	+8
Bulgaria	+2	+2
Burma	+6½	+6½
Burundi	+2	+2
Cambodia	+7	+7
Cameroon	+1	+1

	Normal time	*Summer time*
Canada		
Newfoundland	–3½	–2½
Atlantic	–4	–3
Eastern	–5	–4
Central	–6	–5
(Alberta)	–7	–6
Pacific	–8	–7
Yukon	–9	–8
Canary Islands	GMT	GMT
Cape Verde Islands	–2	–2
Central African Republic	+1	+1
Chad	+1	+1
Chile	–4	–4
China		
General	+8	+8
Tibet and Urumchi	+6	+6
Colombia	–5	–5
Comoro Islands	+3	+3
Congo (Brazzaville)	+1	+1
Costa Rica	–6	–6
Cuba	–5	–5
Cyprus	+2	+2
Czechoslovakia	+1	+1
Dahomey	+1	+1
Denmark	+1	+1
Dominican Republic	–5	–4
Ecuador	–5	–5
Egypt	+2	+3
El Salvador	–6	–6
Ethiopia	+3	+3
Falkland Islands	–4	–3
Faeroe Islands	GMT	GMT
Fiji Islands	+12	+12
Finland	+2	+2
France	+1	+1
Gabon	+1	+1
Gambia	GMT	GMT
Germany	+1	+1
Ghana	GMT	GMT
Gibraltar	+1	+1
Gilbert Islands	+12	+12
Great Britain	GMT	+1
Greece	+2	+2
Greenland	–3	–3
Guadeloupe	–4	–4
Guam	+10	+10
Guatemala	–6	–6

	Normal time	*Summer time*
Guiana	−3¾	−3¾
Guiana (French)	−3	−3
Guinea	GMT	GMT
Guinea Equatorial	+1	+1
Guinea Bissau	−1	−1
Haiti	−5	−5
Hawaii	−10	−10
Holland	+1	+1
Honduras	−5	−6
Honduras (Belize)	−6	−5½
Hong Kong	+8	+9
Hungary	+1	+1
Iceland	−1	GMT
India	+5½	+5½
Indonesia		
Java, Sumatra	+7	+7
Borneo, Celebes, Bali	+8	+8
Moluccas, West Irian	+9	+9
Iran	+3½	+3½
Iraq	+3	+3
Ireland	GMT	+1
Israel	+2	+2
Italy	+1	+2
Ivory Coast	GMT	GMT
Jamaica	−5	−5
Japan	+9	+9
Jordan	+2	+2
Kenya	+3	+3
Korea	+9	+9
Kuwait	+3	+3
Laos	+7	+7
Lebanon	+2	+2
Leeward Islands	−4	−4
Lesotho	+2	+2
Liberia	−¾	−¾
Luxembourg	+1	+1
Libya	+2	+2
Macao	+8	+8
Madagascar	+3	+3
Madeira	GMT	GMT
Malawi	+2	+2
Malaysia	+7½	+7½
Maldive Island	+5½	+5½
Mali	GMT	GMT
Mauritania	GMT	GMT

	Normal time	Summer time
Malta	+1	+1
Marshall Islands	+12	+12
Martinique	–4	–4
Mauritius	+4	+4
Mexico		
Generally	–6	–6
Mongolia	+8	+8
Morocco	GMT	GMT
Mozambique	+2	+2
Nauru	+11½	+11½
Nepal	+5.40	+5.40
Neth. Antilles	–4	–4
New Caledonia	+11	+11
New Guinea	+10	+10
New Hebrides	+11	+11
New Zealand	+12	+12
Nicaragua	–6	–6
Niger	+1	+1
Nigeria	+1	+1
Norway	+1	+1
Oman	+4	+4
Pakistan	+5	+5
Panama	–5	–5
Papua	+10	+10
Paraguay	–4	–4
Peru	–5	–5
Phillipines	+8	+8
Poland	+1	+1
Portugal	+1	+1
Qatar	+4	+4
Reunion	+4	+4
Rhodesia	+2	+2
Rumania	+2	+2
Rwanda	+2	+2
Sabah	+8	+8
Samoa Islands	–11	–11
St Pierro	–3	–3
S Tomé	GMT	GMT
Sarawak	+8	+8
Saudi Arabia	+3	+3
Senegal	GMT	GMT
Seychelles	+4	+4
Sierra Leone	GMT	GMT
Singapore	+8	+8

	Normal time	*Summer time*
Solomon Islands	+11	+11
Somalia	+3	+3
South Africa	+2	+2
South Yemen	+3	+3
Spain	+1	+1
Sri Lanka	+5½	+5½
Sudan	+2	+2
Surinam	−3½	−3½
Swaziland	+2	+2
Sweden	+1	+1
Switzerland	+1	+1
Syria	+2	+3
Tahiti	−10	−10
Taiwan	+8	+9
Tanzania	+3	+3
Tasmania	+10	+11
Thailand	+7	+7
Timor	+8	+8
Togo	GMT	GMT
Tonga Islands	+13	+13
Trinidad	−4	−4
Trucial States	+4	+4
Tunisia	+1	+1
Turkey	+2	+2
Uganda	+3	+3
Upper Volta	GMT	GMT
Uruguay	−3	−3
USA		
Eastern Zone	−5	−4
Central Zone	−6	−5
Mountain Zone	−7	−6
Pacific Zone	−8	−7
USSR		
Moscow		
Leningrad	+3	+3
Baku	+4	+4
Sverdlosk	+5	+5
Tashkent	+6	+6
Novosibirsk	+7	+7
Irkutsk	+8	+8
Yakutsk	+9	+9
Khabarovsk	+10	+10
Magadan	+11	+11
Petropavlovsk	+12	+12
Anadyr	+13	+13
Venezuela	−4	−4
Vietnam	+7	+7

	Normal time	*Summer time*
Virgin Islands	–4	–4
Windward Islands	–4	–4
Yemen	+3	+3
Yugoslavia	+1	+1
Zaire		
Kinshasa	+1	+1
Lumumbashi	+2	+2
Zambia	+2	+2

9 Programmes in English directed to the United Kingdom

Richard Lambley

Usually the broadcasts listed below are receivable at good strength in the UK and north-west Europe on one or more of the frequencies given. However, many stations broadcast in English to other target areas at other times, and you may well find that you can pick up some of these transmissions just as reliably. Among the possibilities are broadcasts from Europe to North America, which can be heard after midnight in the lower-frequency short wave bands.

Bear in mind that most stations alter their schedules several times a year to match the expected radio propagation conditions. Some alter programme timings by one hour to take into account local summer time in the target country. Forthcoming changes are normally announced on the air and published in advance in the station's schedule leaflet or magazine. This list is mainly compiled from schedules current in the third and fourth quarters of 1988.

Because the short wave spectrum does not contain enough channels for all the stations that want to broadcast, each channel is shared by stations in different parts of the world. As they enter each new season with their revised schedules, broadcasters sometimes discover that the changed patterns of interference do not match their predictions; and often their engineers may be driven to altering certain frequencies again, even quite soon after the published changes have come into effect. If you cannot find the signal you want, be prepared to search nearby frequencies.

Times are expressed in Greenwich Mean Time (GMT). British Summer Time is one hour ahead of GMT; Central European Time (CET) is GMT + 1 in winter, GMT + 2 in summer. Universal Co-ordinated Time (UTC) is equivalent to GMT. To set your clock accurately by the familiar six-pip radio time signal, remember that the exact minute is marked by the start of the final pip (with the Greenwich signal from the BBC, the long pip). Transmitters which receive their programme feeds by satellite link will of course radiate time signals which are noticeably late, because of the delay due to the long journey to and from the satellite.

Frequencies are given in kilohertz (thousands of cycles per second): 1000 kHz equals 1 MHz (one megahertz).

Albania

Radio Tirana, Tirana.

0530–0600: 7300, 9500
1730–1800: 1395, 7155, 9480
2130–2200: 1395, 7065, 9480

Australia
Radio Australia, GPO Box 428G, Melbourne, Victoria 3001.
0700–1000: 9655
1530–2030: 6035, 7205

Austria
Radio Austria International (Radio Österreich International), A-1136 Wien.
0430–0500: 6155
0630–0700: 6000, 6155
0830–0900: 6000, 6155, 7210
1230–1300: 6000, 6155
1530–1600: 6000, 6155, 11780
1830–1900: 6000
2130–2200: 5945, 6000

Bangladesh
National Broadcasting Authority, External Services, Shahbag Avenue, Dhaka.
Radio Bangladesh.
1230–1300: 15195, 17710
1815–1915: 6240, 7505, 9525

Belgium
BRT International Service, Postbus 26, B-1000 Brussel.
1730–1755: 1512, 5910, 11695
2100–2125: 1512, 5910, 9925
2330–2355: 9925, 11695

Brazil
Radiobrás – Empresa Brasileira de Radiodifusâo Rádio Nacional do Brasil, PO Box 04–0340, 70 000 – Brasilia – DF.
1800–1900: 15265

Bulgaria
Radio Sofia.
0630–0700: 9700, 11720
1830–1900: 6070, 9700, 11720
2030–2100: 6070, 7115, 9700
2130–2200: 9700, 11720
2300–2400: 9700, 11720

Canada
Radio Canada International, PO Box 6000, Montreal, Quebec H3C 3A8.
0515–0600 (Mon–Fri only): 6050, 6140, 7295, 9750
1830–1900 (Mon–Fri only): 9555, 7325, 11945, 15325, 17875
2000–2030 (Sat, Sun, –2100): 6030, 9555, 11945, 15325, 17820, 17875
2100–2200 (Mon–Fri only): 11945, 15325

China, People's Republic
Radio Beijing, Beijing.
1900–2000: 9470
2100–2200: 6860, 9470

Cuba
Radio Habana Cuba, Apartado de Correos 7026, La Habana.
1700–1800: 15295
1830–2000: 11795
2200–2300: 7150

Czechoslovakia
Radio Prague, Vinohradska 12, Praha 2.
0530–0545: 1287, 6055, 9505, 11990
1630–1657: 5930, 7345
1900–1927: 5930, 7345
2000–2027: 5930, 7345
2130–2200: 1287, 6055

Dubai
UAE Radio and Television, External Services, PO Box 1695, Dubai.
UAE Radio.
1030: 11955, 15435, 17865, 21605
1330: 11955, 15435, 17865, 21605
1600: 11730, 11955, 15320, 17865

Ecuador
HCJB, Casilla 691, Quito.
0645–0830: 9610
1900–2000: 17790
2130–2200: 17790

Equatorial Guinea
Radio Africa: Pierce International Communications, 10201 Torre Avenue, Suite 320, Cupertino, California 95014, USA.
1800–2400: 9555

Finland
Radio Finland, PO Box 95, SF-00251 Helsinki.
0515–0530: 254, 558, 963, 6120
0730–0755: 254, 558, 963, 6120, 9560, 11755
1930–1955: 254, 558, 963, 6120, 9530, 11755
2200–2225: 254, 558, 963, 6120, 9670, 11755

France
Radio France Internationale, BP 95, 16 Paris.
0315–0330: 738, 3965, 6175, 7135, 7175, 9550, 9790, 9800, 11670, 11700, 11995
1245–1255: 9805, 11670, 15155, 15195, 15365, 17720, 21645
1600–1654: 738, 6175, 11705, 15360, 17620, 17795

Germany, Federal Republic
Deutschlandfunk – DLF, Postfach 51 06 40, D-5000 Köln 51.
1915–2000: 1269
Programmes in English for countries outside Europe are radiated by a sister station, Deutsche Welle, PO Box 10 04 44, D-5000 Köln 1.

German Democratic Republic
Radio Berlin International, 1160 Berlin, GDR.
0500–0545: 5965, 6115
0745–0830: 6115, 6040, 7185, 9730
0945–1030: 6115
1100–1145: 6115, 9665, 17775
1300–1345: 6115
1345–1430: 9730
1545–1630: 7295, 9730
1745–1830: 7260, 7295, 9730
1945–2030: 1359, 6115
2145–2230: 5965

Greece
Elliniki Radiophonia Tileorasi, PO Box 19, Aghia Paraskevi, Attikis, Athens.
The Voice of Greece.
1920–1930: 9395, 7430, 9425

Hungary
Radio Budapest, Bródy Sándor u. 5–7, Budapest 1800.
1045 (Sun): 7220, 9585, 9835, 11910, 15160, 15220
1130 (Sat): 7220, 9585, 9835, 11910, 15160, 15220
1615 (Mon, Thu): 7220, 9585, 9835, 11910, 15160, 15220
1930: 6110, 7220, 9585, 9835, 11910, 15160
2100: 6110, 7220, 9585, 9835, 11910, 15160

India
All-India Radio, External Services Division, PO Box 500, New Delhi.
General Overseas Service.
1845–2230: 7412, 11620
2000–2230: 9910

Indonesia
Radio Republik Indonesia, PO Box 157, Jakarta.
Voice of Indonesia
2000–2100: 7125, 11790, 15150

Iran
Islamic Republic of Iran Broadcasting, PO Box 3333, Tehran.
Voice of the Islamic Republic of Iran.
1930–2030: 9022

Iraq

Radio Baghdad, PO Box 8145, Baghdad.
2000–2200: 9770, 15230

Ireland

Radio Tara (working title)
0600–1900: 252
This station, owned jointly by Radio Telefis Eireann and Radio-Télé Luxembourg was due to begin operation in September 1989.

Israel

Kol Israel, External Services, PO Box 1082, 91 010 Jerusalem.
Israel Radio Short Wave Service.
0000–0030: 7460, 9435, 9855
0100–0125: 7460, 9435, 9855
0200–0225: 7460, 9435, 9855
0500–0515: 7460, 9435, 11585, 11590, 11655, 17590
1100–1130: 11585, 17575, 17630, 21660, 21675
1800–1815: 9930, 11585, 11655, 13750
2000–2030: 9435, 9460, 9855, 11605, 11960
2230–2255: 9010, 9435, 9460, 9855, 11605, 11960

Italy

RAI-Radiotelevisione Italiana, Casella Postale 320, Centro Corrispondenza, 00100 Roma.
Radio Roma.
1935–1955: 7275, 9710, 11800

Japan

Radio Japan, Tokyo 150.
0700–0800: 15325, 21695
1500–1600: 21700
2300–2400: 11800

Jordan

Radio Jordan, PO Box 909, Amman.
1500–1730: 9560

Korea, North

Radio Pyongyang.
1500–1550: 11740
1700–1750: 11740

Korea, South

KBS, Seoul, Korea.
Radio Korea.
0800–0900: 7550, 13670
1800–1900: 15575
2020–2130: 6480, 15575

Kuwait
Radio Kuwait, Ministry of Information, PO Box 397, 13004 Safat, Kuwait.
1800–2100: 11665

Libya
Radio Jamaheriya, PO Box 333, Tripoli.
Voice of the Socialist People's Libyan Arab Jamaheriya.
1800–1900: 15450
2230–2400: 7245

Luxembourg
Radio-Télé Luxembourg: Radio Luxembourg (London) Ltd, 38 Hertford Street, London W1Y 8BA.
0000–0300: 1440, 6090
1900–2400: 1440

Malta
Radio Mediterranean, PO Box 2, Valletta.
2230–2330: 1557, 6100

Monaco
Trans World Radio, PO Box 349, MC98007, Monte Carlo.
0725–0935 (–1010, Mon; –1025, Sat; –1100, Sun): 7105

Netherlands
Radio Nederland Wereldomroep, Postbus 222, 1200JG, Hilversum.
Radio Netherlands.
1130–1225: 5955, 9715, 17605
1430–1525: 5955
1830–1925: 6020

Norway
NRK Radio Norway, 0340 Oslo 3.
Radio Norway International.
1000–1100 (Sunday): 15235
1300–1400 (Sunday): 6035, 9590
1600–1700 (Sunday): 1314
1700–1800 (Sunday): 9655
1900–2100 (Sunday): 9590

Pakistan
Pakistan Broadcasting Corporation, Constitution Avenue, Islamabad.
Radio Pakistan.
1100–1120: 15606, 17660
1718–1800: 11570, 15270

Poland

Radio Polonia, Al. Niepodleglosci 77/85, 00–950 Warszawa.
0630–0700: 6135, 7270, 15120
1200–1225: 6095, 7285
1400–1430: 6095, 7285
1600–1630: 6135, 9540
1830–1855: 1503, 5995, 6135, 7285
2230–2300: 1503, 5995, 6135, 7125, 7270
2305–2355: 738, 1206, 1503, 5995, 6135, 7125, 7145, 7270
Radio Polonia also transmits concerts of Chopin's music, 1130–1200, on 1503, 5995, 6095 and 7285.

Portugal

Radiodifusâo Portuguesa, Rua do Quelhas 21, 1200 Lisboa.
RDP International Service.
2030–2100 (Mon–Fri only): 9740, 1174

Romania

Radioteleviziunea Românâ, Str. Nuferilor Nr 62, Bucuresti.
Radio Bucharest.
1300–1400: 9690, 11940, 15270, 15365
1930–2030: 7145, 9750, 9690, 11940
2100–2130: 7145, 9750, 9690, 11940

Saudi Arabia

Ministry of Information, PO Box 61718, Riyadh 11575.
1600–2100: 9705, 9720

South Africa

Radio RSA, PO Box 4559, Johannesburg 2000, Republic of South Africa.
1100–1156: 15220, 21590
1300–1556 (Sat, Sun): 7270, 15220, 21590
1800–1856: 5980, 7270, 9685

Spain

Radio Exterior de Espana, Apartado 156.202, 28080 Madrid.
1900–2000: 9765, 11790
2100–2200: 9765, 11790

Sweden

Radio Sweden, S-105 10 Stockholm.
0330: 11705
1530: 15240
1800: 1179, 6065, 7265
2100: 1179, 6065, 9655
2230: 1179, 11925 (s.s.b.)
Radio Sweden's European schedule is available via teletext to viewers who can receive Sky Television.

Switzerland
Swiss Radio International, CH-3000 Bern 15.
0730–0800: 3985, 6165, 9535
1300–1330: 6165, 9535, 12030
1800–1830: 3985, 6165, 9535

Syria
Radio Damascus.
2005: 12085, 15095

Taiwan (Republic of China)
Broadcasting Corporation of China, PO Box 24–38, Taipei.
Voice of Free China.
2200–2300: 9455, 9955, 15370

Turkey
TRT, PO Box 333–06443, Yenisehir, Ankara.
The Voice of Turkey.
2000–2100: 9825
2200–2300: 9685

United Kingdom
BBC World Service, Bush House, Strand, London WC2B 4PH.
24-hour service using many short wave frequencies, including (at various times) 3955, 5975, 6195, 7325, 9410 and 12095 kHz. Transmissions are from sites in the UK and abroad. A long wave channel, 198 kHz, is used during the night (approx. 0045–0445 local time). A special medium wave service called BBC648 (648 kHz) mostly relays mainstream World Service in English for western Europe; however, at certain times it carries alternative programmes including some in French and German (0430–0700; 1130–1200; 1715–2000). Daily programme listings are carried in many British newspapers.

United Arab Emirates
UAE Radio and Television, PO Box 1695, Dubai.
1030–1100: 11955, 15435, 17865, 21605
1330–1400: 11955, 15435, 17865, 21605
1600–1645: 9550, 11730, 11955, 15320

United States of America
Voice of America, Washington, DC 20547.
0300–0330: 6040, 7170, 7200, 9715
0400–0430: 5995, 6040, 7170, 7200, 9670, 9770, 11925, 15205
0430–0500: 3980, 5995, 6040, 7170, 7200, 9670, 9770, 11925, 15205
0500–0600: 3980, 5995, 6040, 7170, 7200, 9670, 9770, 11925, 15205
0600–0700: 3980, 5955, 5965, 5995, 6040, 6060, 7170, 7200, 7325, 9635, 9670, 9715, 11805
1500–1600: 9700, 15205, 15260
1600–1630: 1197, 3980, 9700, 15205, 15260
1630–1700: 1197, 9700, 15205, 15260

1700–1800: 6040, 9700, 9760, 11760, 15205, 15260
1800–2100: 6040, 9700, 9760, 11760, 15205
2100–2200: 6040, 7205, 9700, 9760, 11760, 15205

VOA-Europe (times are Central European Time):
0800–1800 (1400– Sun): 1197 Munich; and by cable on 92.2 MHz (Coventry), 104.0 MHz (Croydon)

KNLS, Anchor Point, Alaska 99556.
1600–1700: 7355, 9750

KUSW, PO Box 7040, Salt Lake City, Utah 84107.
0000–0100 (not Sun): 15580
0100–0300 (not Sun): 11695
0300–0500 (not Sun): 9815
0500–0700: 6155
0700–1100: 6135
1100–1600: 9850
1600–1900 (–1800 Sun): 15225
1900–2200 (not Sun): 15690
2200–2400 (not Sun): 15580

WCSN, Scotts Corner, Maine.
World Service of *The Christian Science Monitor*, PO Box 860, Boston, MA 02123; Herald of Christian Science, PO Box 58, Boston, MA 02123.
0600–0800 (Sat, Sun –0715): 9495
1400–1515: 13760
2000–2200 (Sun –2115): 15390

WINB, Box 88, Red Lion, PA17356.
1602–2000: 15295
2003–2245: 15185
2248–2345: 15145

WRNO Worldwide, PO Box 100, New Orleans, Louisiana 70181.
0000–0400: 7355
0400–0600: 6185
1400–1700: 11965
1700–2100: 15420
2200–2400: 13760
For up-to-date technical information you can contact the station engineers during transmission hours by telephone on 010 1 504 889 2424.

WYFR Family Radio Network, 290 Hegenburger Road, Oakland, California 94621.
0500–0600: 11580
0600–0700: 7355, 9852.5

NDXE Global Radio, PO Box 569, Opelika, Alabama 36801.
Not yet on the air at the time of writing; plans are for a.m. stereo transmissions (Kahn system) as follows:
1400–1800: 17 MHz, 21 MHz bands
0000–0300: 9 MHz, 11 MHz bands

Radio Earth, 1724 Sherman Avenue, Evanston, Illinois 60201.
'Worldwide commercial radio'

Winter, Tuesdays 0300–0400: 7400, 9870
Summer, Tuesdays 0300–0400: 7400, 7355

USSR
Radio Moscow, Moscow.
2000–2100:
(spring 1989) 1143, 7240, 7250, 9450, 9685, 9740
. . . and around the clock on many Radio Moscow World Service frequencies.
Radio Station 'Peace and Progress', Moscow, USSR.
2200–2230: 1323, 4060, 5905, 6145, 7250, 7340, 7360
Radio Kiev, Kiev, Ukrainian SSR.
1800–1830: 6010, 6090, 6165, 7240
Lithuania
Lietuvos Radijas, 232674 Lietuvos TSR, Vilnius.
Radio Vilnius
2130: 666, 6100
2200: 7165, 7400, 11790, 13645, 15180

Vatican City
Radio Vaticana, 00120 Città del Vaticano.
0600–0620: 1530, 6185, 9645
0700–0710 (weekdays): 1530, 6248, 9645, 11740
1140 (weekdays): 6248, 9645, 11740
1445–1500: 6248, 7250, 9645, 11740
1940–2000: 1530, 6248, 9645
2050–2110: 1530, 6190, 7250, 9645
2300: 1530, 6185

Trans World Radio
45 London Road, Biggleswade, Bedfordshire SG18 8ED.
Transmissions from Monaco.
0625–0840 (Sat, Sun –1000): 7100
2130–2230 (Sun, Tue –2245): 1467

Special programmes for radio enthusiasts
Many stations broadcast programmes of special interest to short wave hobbyists, or DXers as they are often called. These may include such material as technical advice, receiver reviews, ionospheric forecasts and news of the international broadcasting scene.

Programmes listed below are in English, for listeners in Europe; some stations may transmit them at other times to different target areas. In most cases, feature programmes will follow a regular news bulletin or current affairs sequence and so may begin somewhat later than the times given.

Times are for the winter schedule. Note that many European stations alter their transmission times to suit local summer time in Britain.

Sunday
0630 DX Corner (Radio RSA)
0715 DX Postbag (FEBA)

0750 Waveguide (BBC World Service)
0800 World of Radio (WRNO Worldwide)
0830 Shortwave (Radio Korea)
0900 Austrian Shortwave Panorama
0926 DX Corner (Radio Japan)
1030 Mailbag (RTV Dubai, UAE)
1045 Calling DXers and Radio Amateurs (Radio Budapest)
1126 DX Corner (Radio Japan)
1230 Austrian Shortwave Panorama
1330 Mailbag (RTV Dubai, UAE)
1430 Austrian Shortwave Panorama
1600 Mailbag (RTV Dubai, UAE)
1805 Austrian Shortwave Panorama
1830 Shortwave (Radio Korea)
1900 DX Corner with Ben Dalfen (Kol Israel)
1915 DX Programme: Radio España Exterior
2100 Shortwave (Radio Korea)
2130 DX Corner with Ben Dalfen (Kol Israel)
2300 DX Corner with Ben Dalfen (Kol Israel)
2326 DX Corner (Radio Japan)
2345 DX Programme: Radio España Exterior

Monday
0430 Austrian Shortwave Panorama
0450 Waveguide (BBC World Service)
1615 Calling DXers and Radio Amateurs (Radio Budapest)
RBI DX Club alternating with DX-tra (Radio Berlin International), in programmes beginning at 0500, 0745, 0945, 1100, 1300, 1345, 1545, 1745, 1945 and 2145.

Tuesday
1115 Waveguide (BBC World Service)
1600 DX-Club (Radio Polonia)
1700 Sweden Calling DXers
1730 VOA's Worldwide Shortwave Spectrum (in the Magazine Show)
1830 Sweden Calling DXers
1930 The Special Programme for Radio Amateurs (Radio Bucharest)
2015 DX programme (This is Germany, Deutschlandfunk)
2100 Sweden Calling DXers
2230 DX-Club (Radio Polonia)
2300 Sweden Calling DXers
2305 DX-Club (Radio Polonia)

Wednesday
0630 DX-Club (Radio Polonia)
0800 Ham Radio Today (HCJB)
1030 Ham Radio Today (HCJB)
1130 Sweden Calling DXers
1206 Ham Radio Today (HCJB)
1300 The Special Programme for Radio Amateurs (Radio Bucharest)
1400 DX-Club (Radio Polonia)

1830 DX-Club (Radio Polonia)
1900 DX-Chat (Radio Prague)
1930 DX Mailbag (Radio Bucharest)
2130 DX-Chat (Radio Prague)
2130 Ham Radio Today (HCJB)

Thursday
0130 Waveguide (BBC World Service)
0230 Ham Radio Today (HCJB)
0630 Ham Radio Today (HCJB)
1150 Media Network (Radio Netherlands)
1300 DX Corner (Radio RSA)
1300 DX Mailbag (Radio Bucharest)
1450 Media Network (Radio Netherlands)
1615 Calling DXers and Radio Amateurs (Radio Budapest)
1850 Media Network (Radio Netherlands)

Friday
1930 DX (RDP Internacional, Portugal); alternates with Mailbag, Philately

Saturday
0300 World of Radio (WRNO Worldwide)
0630 Swiss Shortwave Merry-Go-Round
0900 Deutsche Welle DXer's Desk (3rd Sat.; for Asia, Australasia)
1030 Mailbag (RTV Dubai, UAE)
1130 Calling DXers and Radio Amateurs (Radio Budapest)
1200 Swiss Shortwave Merry-Go-Round
1330 Mailbag (RTV Dubai, UAE)
1600 Mailbag (RTV Dubai, UAE)
1700 Swiss Shortwave Merry-Go-Round
1730 Radio World (BRT Brussels Calling)
1930 DX (RDP International Service, Portugal)
2005 SWL Digest (Radio Canada International)
2100 Radio World (BRT Brussels Calling)
2100 DX Corner (The Voice of Turkey)
2100 Deutsche Welle DXer's Desk (3rd Sat; for Asia, Australasia)
2130 DX Party Line (HCJB, Ecuador)
2300 DX Corner (The Voice of Turkey)
2330 World of Radio (WRNO Worldwide)

Information from Radio Netherlands' *Media Network* programme, including an introduction to DXing, news about radio, propagation forecasts and receiver reviews, is available to computer users direct from a dial-up computer bulletin board in Hilversum, telephone (010 31 35) 45395, at 300, 1200 or 2400 bit/s, 8–N–1 format (or FidoNet 500, Node 202). There is no charge to callers, other than for the telephone connection.

10 The software connection

Jonathan Marks
Radio Nederland Wereldomroep

With the growing use of home computers in North America, Europe, and Asia, it is interesting to note how quite a number of users want to use this piece of equipment in their radio listening activities. Standard programs exist for most home computers to allow word-processing or the building up of a database for names and addresses. But the potential uses extend far beyond this.

Shortwave broadcasting is quite a technical business! Unlike local transmissions on AM or FM, it involves the use of a layer in the earth's atmosphere to 'reflect' (more correctly, refract) signals, thus being able to reach over the horizon. This layer, the so called 'ionosphere', is far from being a perfect reflector, and is constantly changing. So there are some times when no matter how much power you may have at the transmitting end, the signal will not be heard in the target area at all. There is a section on propagation elsewhere in this book. Computers can be used to examine all these variable factors, and thus tell you the best time, and best part of the dial, to listen for certain stations.

You may also want to use a computer to help design a new antenna or some other kind of accessory. If you have the space for a directional short wave antenna, you may find a range and bearing program useful, to make sure it is pointing in the right direction.

The bad news

Some people use a computer to help write reception reports to a radio station. Whilst this may speed up the time taken to write a letter, check that you include as much 'station specific' information as possible. If you simply use the computer to print out a reception report form, your letter may get very impersonal. The people who open your letter may put it into the 'chain' letter category, i.e. someone who is more interested in collecting material as fast as possible than listening to the station's programmes.

Whilst computers and short wave radio go together, they shouldn't get too close. Each home computer contains a microprocessor of one type or another, and this is a potential source of radio-frequency interference. So is the TV monitor, printer cable, and modem. Early models of some computers (e.g. Apple II+, Dragon, Vic 20 etc.) would produce a terrible buzzing sound on any short wave radio within a few metres from it. Manufacturers have certainly improved on this, but the level to which the microprocessor is screened is still rather variable. Make sure that the cables at the back of the computer are well screened too, and keep the aerial lead for your short wave receiver as far away as possible. Active antennae are especially prone to any computer noise within a few hundred metres! You can try reducing the radiation of printer cables by good shielding and the use of ferrite beads around the leads as they emerge from both the computer and the peripheral device, e.g. a printer.

Paint pitfalls

You can buy spray conducting paint in hobby and electronics stores. If your computer is producing too much radio noise, then it might be worth spraying this paint onto the inside of the computer's plastic case, and then grounding the resulting thin metal screen. This, in effect, produces a Faraday Cage around the interference source and stops it from radiating. However, don't immediately embark on such a project, for if the spray paint doesn't stick properly to the plastic you could have problems. In an experiment conducted by Radio Nederland we noted that because the inside of the computer got warm (due to power supplies, ICs etc.) the paint layer is subjected to varying temperatures. You need to be certain that the paint will not start to flake off for small pieces of paint falling onto the printed circuit board of the computer could cause very expensive short-circuits. Likewise do not attempt to spray the inside of the case if printed circuit boards are in the vicinity. Even a fine spray is enough to cause short circuits.

Software or hardware

Many household items already have built-in microprocessors inside them. This extends to radio receivers, TV's, and even washing machines. The difference between these microprocessors and the one in your home computer, is that the latter is usually more versatile. Simply by loading different software into the computer, you can make it behave as a typewriter, address book, or games machine.

In some aspects of radio listening you will get a choice. Let us consider the hobby of decoding radio teletype (RTTY) signals. Such stations can be found on a short wave radio, but in order to be able to convert the audio tones into the text being transmitted, you need some kind of decoder unit. For several years so called 'RTTY decoders' have been on sale, mostly via amateur radio outlets. These contain a microprocessor, and a built-in program that it needs. Alternatively, you can now buy programs to load into your home computer, and some sort of interface unit/card to fit between your short wave radio and the computer. Since RTTY decoders have been specifically designed for that task, they are often better than using a home computer. This because they contain filters to make them less prone to reading errors due to short wave interference. RTTY programs for home computers, however, tend to be much less expensive and their quality is reasonable.

The garage computer company

Writing software for radio applications is rather specialized. The majority of companies in this field are therefore rather small, often one person. They may be doing it for commercial gain, or purely as a hobby. This has both advantages and disadvantages.

Small software companies tend to have quite a high standard of achievement. They have more personal experience with radio, and therefore programs are versatile and creative. On the other hand, there are those one-person companies where the founder finds he/she has started something beyond their capabilities. Writing a computer program is one thing, managing a business is another. Check details before you order, and enclose return postage with any enquiry.

Hardware/software for radio use

The following is a list of some of the radio software sources available in January 1989. Note that it does not pretend to be a complete listing. Note that telephone numbers, where known, begin with the international dialling code for that country in brackets e.g. (44) is used for the UK. If you are phoning from inside that particular country, you may have to dial an '0' instead. Check your local telephone directory or ask the operator.

Interface units

Apart from modems (see below), there are some other interfaces to connect between your short wave radio and the computer. In early 1984, the Japanese company of ICOM launched their ICOM ICR-71A/D/E receiver. Part of the specifications include a computer interface. Since then the Yaesu FRG-8800, Kenwood R-5000, and NRD-525 all offer the possibility of computer control. In theory, any computer with a RS232 interface can be used to program frequency and mode details into this short wave receiver. But it took receiver manufacturers a long time to realize that good software was also important. Here is a selection of what is currently available.

'PC & R7000'. This is a German language computer package designed for the Icom ICR-7000 receiver owner. It allows you to search the memories in the receiver, or simply scan the bands for signals of a particular criteria (e.g. SSB mode). It also draws a graph of frequency occupancy over a user determined period. The package comes with its own interface unit for the Icom receiver, and costs DM 498 including postage within Federal Republic of Germany. Further details from IBC Computertechnik, Postfach 1334, D-5657 Haan 1, Federal Republic of Germany.

'Seeker'. At press time a new version of the popular Seeker program was being developed for the IBM PC/AT and close compatibles. It will allow control of the Kenwood R-5000 or ICOM ICR-71. Older versions for the Commodore 64 and ICOM ICR-71 combination are still available. The program is a database for the short wave listener, giving an instant overview of the frequencies in the receivers memory, and allowing control of the receiver through the computer keyboard. Further details from Seeker, AF Systems, PO Box 9145-Z, Waukegan, Illinois, 60079-9145 USA. The demo diskette and owners manual costs US $10.00.

'Short wave navigator'. Jim Frimmel of Texas USA has made one of the best graphic connections we have seen so far between the computer and the radio. He has developed a computer program for the Apple Macintosh that not only stores station schedules and puts them up onto the screen, it has some 30 interval signals digitally stored in the computer. Further information from SW Navigator, 232 Squaw Creek Road, Willowpark, TX 76087 USA.

'SWL – A PC to Kenwood R-5000 control program', is a Short Wave Listener's control, logging, and memory program for the R-5000 receiver. Backs up memory information to disk and even allows multiple groups of 100 memories. Works with the IBM PC XT or AT (or compatibles). Timothy

R. Hickman, 1342 Brook Road, Baltimore, MD 21228, USA. Tel: 1 301–744–7526. Available through several US dealers for US $49.95. In order to connect to the R-5000, you will need the IF232C controller (US $89.95) and the IC-10 chip set (US $31.95) from Kenwood.

'Utility logbook version 2.0'. This is a database and reporting system specifically designed for the utility DXer. The program operates on the IBM PC/XT/AT and close compatibles. A hard disk is preferred, but not required. The program requires 384 K RAM after DOS and TSR programs have been loaded. All monitor (mono, CGA, EGA, VGA) types are supported. Price: US $20, payable in US funds by cheque or money order from: TRS Consultants, PO Box 2275, Vincentown, NJ 08088–2275, USA. NJ residents need to add $1.20 sales tax, whilst overseas orders should add US $5 for airmail shipping and handling.

RTTY options

There are several manufacturers of RTTY interface units designed to fit between a short wave radio and a home computer. They are listed here in alphabetical order.

1. Advanced Electronic Applications Inc, PO Box C-2160, Lynnwood, WA 98036 USA (Tel: (1) 206 775 7373) offer a very sophisticated interface called the PK232. You can connect this to any home computer that has provision for a modem (i.e. you only need a communications program on the computer). It is basically designed for packet. The European distributor of AEA equipment is ICS Electronics Ltd, PO Box 2, Arundel, West Sussex BN18 ONX, England (Tel: (44) 24365 590).
2. Kantronics, 1202 East 23rd Street, Lawrence, Kansas 66044, USA. This company offers several interface units at a various price level. The UTU-XT-P works with any computer using an RS-232 terminal. It allows reception of most types of commercial morse and radio-teletype. Distribution of these units seem to be restricted to the North American market. The price is around US $190.
3. MFJ Enterprises Inc, Box 494, Mississippi State, MS 39762 USA (Tel: (1) 601 323 5869) made a unit called the MFJ-1225. This fits the VIC-20, Apple II series, TRS-80C, Atari, TI-99A, and Commodore 64. The software is provided free, the hardware costs US $69.95, excluding postage costs. The unit will handle commercial morse, RTTY and ASCII transmissions.
4. Microlog, 18713 Mooney Drive, Gaithersburg, MD 20879, USA (Tel: (1) 301 258 8400). This company has produced simple units for the Radio-Teletype enthusiast with a Commodore 64. The Microlog C-64 offers computer enhanced detection and software filtering to improve the accuracy of received text. The unit simply plugs into the back of the computer and costs US $64.00.
5. The Commodore Radio Users Group supports all Commodore machines from the PET through to the Amiga. They have a wide range of software available. A frequent magazine is offered for £8.00 a year. Details from CRUG, 22 Whiteford Avenue, Bellsmyre, Dumbarton G82 2JT. Tel: (44) 389 61250.
6. Technical Software is a long established software company that specialize in the BBC B, Spectrum, Commodore 64, and VIC-20. The range includes RTTY/SSTV/CW reception program, and a distant and bear-

ing program. Details from Technical Software, Fron, Upper Llandwrog, Caernarfon LL54 7RF, North Wales. Tel: (44) 286 881886.

7. Universal SW is a US mail-order company that has an excellent reputation in the field of utility and broadcast listening. They have recently released the M-7000 probably the most sophisticated utility monitor on the market. Most of the intelligence is inside the unit, all you need is a computer printer and monitor. Probably the best choice for the advanced user who can appreciate all the features. Price is around US $1000. Details from Universal SW Radio, 1280 Aida Drive, Reynoldsburg, Ohio, 43068 USA.

Further reading

'Amateur Radio Software' by Dr John Morris.
Publisher: RSGB Publications, Cranborne Rd, Potters Bar, Herts EN6 3JW, England.

The book is now out of print, but may be found in libraries. Some of it is still current. It covers programs that would also be of interest to the short wave listener. These include circuit component values, propagation predictions, and satellite tracking.

'BASIC Programming for Electronics' by Mike James.
Publisher: Heinemann Newnes, Halley Court, Jordan Hill, Oxford OX2 8EJ, UK. Price: £6.95 in UK.

This 128 page, softcover, illustrated book is a valuable guide to the electronics constructor. Shows how a home computer can be used to design circuits, plot waveforms, and some rather complex calculations. ISBN: 0 408 01341 9.

'Computer Programs for Amateur Radio' by Wayne Overbeck and James A. Steffen.
Publisher: Hayden Book Company, 50 Essex Street, Rochelle Park, NJ 07662, USA, Tel: (1) 201 843 0550. Price: US $16.95.

This 352 page paperback contains 60 computer programs written for the IBM PC, CP/M machines, Apple, Commodore, and TRS-80 computer families. While intended for the amateur radio community, many are equally useful to the SWL. ISBN 0–8104–0657–8.

'DXers Guide to Computing' edited by George Wood.
Publisher: English Section, Radio Sweden, S-105 10, Stockholm, Sweden. Price: On application.

A 24 page guide to software, hardware, and publications for the short wave listener. Also includes advice and programs, and regular updates. This book is recommended.

'Satellite Tracking Software for the Radio Amateur' by John Branegan.
Publisher: Radio Society of Great Britain (Publication Sales Dept), Lambda House, Cranborne Road, Potters Bar, Herts, EN6 3JW, UK. Price: £4.50 (overseas postage extra, rates on application).

This is a 50 page booklet describing and listing 12 programs for various types of satellite tracking.

Radio related electronic bulletin boards

As the name implies, these are electronic ways of spreading a message. You will need a home computer, a telephone line, and a device to link the two, called a modem. These come in various types, and are now becoming more affordable after being very expensive. If you are planning to call bulletin boards run by hobby groups there are some points to watch when buying:

- **Speeds.** Prestel, Viditel, and other European PTT databases tend to use a system with a split baud rate. They send the information, in the form of pages, at 1200 Baud down the phone. Any replies from you go at a much slower rate, i.e. 75 Baud. Hence you will see 75/1200 Baud. The slow 75 baud speed is fine for short telegram style messages, but it is useless if you want to send lots of data to someone.

  Modem technology is constantly improving, and your modem should at least be capable of operating at 300/300 and 1200/1200 Baud (full duplex). If you plan to call bulletin boards in your area you might think about using 2400/2400 baud too. This is only available on more expensive modems but means that you can save a lot on telephone bills. At the start of 1989, experience shows that you can call within Europe and even in the USA with 1200 Baud. Some transatlantic paths to Canada and the West Coast of the United States tend to be slightly too noisy, but if you get garbage on the screen, just try calling again.
- **Tones.** North America and Europe use different, incompatible, tone systems for bulletin boards. In Europe, the standard is known as CCITT. In America, the BELL system is used. If you want to use bulletin boards on both sides of the Atlantic, you will need a modem with both tone systems. Many modems offer both, but check before you buy.
- **Protocol.** There are different standards of communicating via modem. The standard used by all computer bulletin boards is 8-N-1, i.e. 8 data bits, 1 stop bit, and no parity. If you do not set your modem to this standard you will simply get garbled characters on the screen.

In April 1986, Larry DiGioia, sysop of the 'Neverboard' in Pittsburgh, organized a small group of bulletin boards (BBS) running Fido software into a network to exchange short wave-related messages and files automatically every night. This arrangement not only increased the information available on each BBS, making them more interesting for callers, but callers were able to save on their phone bills by accessing the pool of messages through the node nearest to them. From this small seed grew the FidoNet's SWL Echo Conference. The basic idea remains the same, and the Neverboard is still the unofficial 'hub'. But so many BBSs are involved now, and the number of files and messages transferred nightly is so large, that not all participating boards store the same information. Most of the messages seem to be discussions of equipment, reports of recent DX 'catches', and questions asked and answered. In the course of 1989/90 it is hoped that the number of radio-related software boards will increase in Europe.

While there's a definite similarity to the mix of information one finds in radio clubs, the Echo Conference has no analogue to club newsletters' consolidated lists of loggings, so useful as tuning guides, and Fido's software limits the length – thus the detail – of message texts. But if you are looking for software, then asking on a bulletin board is a good way to start. Here is a list of bulletin boards in the SWL Echo Conference, based on information provided by Kurt Barnhart, Dennis Diaz, Larry DiGioia and David Snyder. They do their best to keep track of who's in the net, although remember since this is a free service, hobbyists are entitled to change things at short notice.

USA (Dial international access code (e.g. 010 in UK) then 1 followed by number below)

Telephone	*Name (Fido node)*	*Location*
309–688–0604	**ANARC Board (280/304)**	**Peoria, IL**
404–546–7857	Athens Forum (18/43)	Athens, GA
412–427–4488	AMRG #101	Pittsburgh, PA
512–852–8194	AMSAT Software Exchange	Texas
414–738–1219	Applegate (139/630)	Appleton, WI
301–574–1984	Berkshire Board (261/204)	Essex, MD
602–742–1551	Bit Bucket (15/20)	Tucson, AZ
312–491–2611	Chicago Business (115/429)	Evanston, IL
716–937–3521	The Comm Centre (260/160)	Alden, NY
312–630–6282	COPH Mail (115/700)	Chicago, IL
301–350–1299	Fido's 1st RBBS (109/652)	Largo, MD
412–243–5880	**Neverboard (129/17)**	**Pittsburgh, PA**
609–859–1910	**Pinelands Bulletin Board**	**Vincentown NJ**
408–251–4926	Tranquility Base #1 (143/31)	San Jose, CA

Holland (Dial international access code (e.g. 010 in UK) then 31 followed by number below)

35–45395	**Radio Nederland BBS**	**Hilversum**

Those boards in **bold** are probably the most comprehensive from the radio point of view.

What can you expect to see?

There is a wide range of bulletin board software in use for radio-related bulletin boards. We called two examples in the list above and recorded some of the conversation material received over the line. We first dialled the Association of North American Radio Clubs board in the USA.

Connect 1200

ANARC BBS
POB 3436
Peoria, Illinois
61614
USA

300/1200/2400 baud

REMEMBER: Capital letters and lower case letters are considered different in your password. You must enter your password exactly as you did at registration.

First Name? Jonathan
Last Name? Marks
Searching User File . . .
Calling From HILVERSUM, HOLLAND
Is this correct? Y
Enter Your Password: *********

TBBS Welcomes JONATHAN MARKS
Calling From HILVERSUM, HOLLAND
Your last time on was 01/07/89 14:09
You have read through message 13370
Current last message is 13480
You have called this system 275 times before

You are caller number 39491

Type P to Pause, S to Stop listing

Welcome to the ANARC BBS. ANARC stands for the 'Association of North American Radio Clubs', which is an organization of 19 member clubs dealing with the radio listening hobby. Please refer to our files section for more information about ANARC, and how to receive the ANARC Newsletter.

Searching Message Base . . .

You have the following waiting:

Msg #: 13383 *MEDIA NETWORK*
07/01/89 02:12:54 (Read 8 Times)
From: CHRISTOPHER HILL
To: JONATHAN MARKS
Subj: REPLY TO MSG   10252 (ENGLISH)

Msg #: 13434 *E-MAIL*
07/01/89 05:51:57
From TOM MCELVY
To: JONATHAN MARKS
Subj: REPLY TO MSG # 13371 (LETTER)

These message(s) are marked for retrieval

Read Now(Y/N)? y

Pause after each msg(Y/N)? n

For reply chains:
<1> Ask on Each
<2> Always follow
<3> Never follow
<?> for help

Which one? 3

Msg #: 13383 *MEDIA NETWORK*
07/06/88 02:12:54 (Read 8 Times)

From: CHRISTOPHER HILL
To: JONATHAN MARKS
Subj: REPLY TO MSG #10252 (ENGLISH)
I have tried the new Eska 33 modified receiver here in the US and find it performs well. Would you like a full user report? Also I'm pleased to note that Radio Netherlands will use 0030 and 0330 UTC in future for North America.

After receiving messages you can explore the Main Menu options. You simply select the letter in brackets to choose the item.

ANARC BBS Main Menu Options

[T]ime [G]oodbye

-----Message Centers-----
[P]rivate mail (EMAIL)
[M]essage Center
[C]omment to the SYSOP
-----Teletext Center-----
[S]hortwave magazine section
[I]nfo-Mat News Magazine

-----Miscellaneous Functions-----
[D]ownload/upload program section
[U]tilities to reconfigure the BBS
[N]ews file at sign-on
[L]ist the recent callers
[$] Search userlog for other users

Command: M

In this case we chose the Message Centre

ANARC BBS Message Center

[T]ime [G]oodbye

[*] Combined read of all message boards
[I]nactivate a message board during combined reading
[+] Echo message boards: Shortwave & Ham Radio

-----ANARC Clubs and Organizations

[A] Association of Clandestine Enthusiasts (ACE)
[B] Association of North American Radio Clubs (ANARC)
[C] NASWA message center
[D] SPEEDX message center

[E] Minnesota DX club message center
[M] Radio Netherland's 'Media Network' message center
[S] General Shortwave section
[V] VHF/UHF Radio Section

[-] Return to previous menu

Cost?
You do not have to pay for the computer time on the ANARC board, but you do have to pay the cost of the phone call. Providing you save everything on disk while you are on the line, for later analysis, you can get a lot worthwhile material with a three minute call.

A European example
After supporting NOS BASICODE, a kind of esperanto for home computers, and adapting the idea for use overseas (e.g. in Britain via the BBC), Radio Netherlands, the Dutch International Service, is now supporting the NOS-FIDO computer net. Radio Netherlands' listeners overseas, with suitable equipment, can now access English language material on the computer in one of two ways. They can either phone the number in Hilversum direct or they can phone their local FIDO computer and ask that the files they need be sent to that local computer through a fast, efficient, and inexpensive electronic mail system. Some 2500 FIDO computers exist on a worldwide basis, and the number is growing daily. Tests show that there is a very large demand for radio related information by computer, especially in North America. Launched in May 1986, it is believed this is the first time a radio station has operated a free on-line computer service for its listeners.

How to access the board directly
First you need to dial your international exchange code. This varies in each country, then dial 31 for Holland, 35 for Hilversum, and then the subscriber number 45395. The computer uses the standard set up for bulletin boards, i.e. 8 data bits-no parity-1 stop bit. You may need to set this up in your computer software. The board answers works at any of these three speeds: 300/1200/2400 Baud. The modem accepts either CCITT (European) or BELL (North America) tones. When you successfully log on, the computer in Hilversum will send acknowledge with

```
Connect 1200
```

If nothing further happens, prompt the Dutch computer by typing in a few RETURNs or ENTER on your computer keyboard. This should lead to the following screen:

```
Fido(tm) Version 11w
FidoNet(tm) Net 500 Node 202
=-=-=-=-=-=-=-=-=-=-=-=-=-=-=-=-=-=-=-=-|
|     N O S Hobbyscoop      >--<      _  |
|     ----------------     /|oo \    ((  |
|     Postbus 1200        (_|  /_)    \\ |
|     1200 BE Hilversum   _`@/_ \     \\ |
|     -----------------   |_hcc_| \    >) |
|    **HCC-Hobbyscoop**   | (#) |  \  //  |
|    **      FIDO     **  |_nos_| / \//   |
|    **   net  500    **   _//|| _\   )   |
|    **  node  202    **  (_/(_|(____/ (jm)|
|    **HCC-Hobbyscoop** 300/300,1200/75   |
|    **              1200/1200, 2400/2400 |
=-*-*-*-*-*-*-*-*-*-*-*-*-*-*-*-*-*-*-*-*-=
| Sysops : Hans Janssen / Joop Engels     |
=-*-*-*-*-*-*-*-*-*-*-*-*-*-*-*-*-*-*-*-*-=
|Zoekt u alleen infor|If you're only inter|
|matie over radio en/|ested in radio/basi |
|of basicode,gebruik |code info, please   |
|dan de volgende naam|use the following   |
| + password :       |name + password :   |
|-----------------------------------------|
| firstname : NOS   lastname : HOBBYSCOOP |
| password  : BASICODE                    |
=-=-=-=-=-=-=-=-=-=-=-=-=-=-=-=-=-=-=-=-|
Your FIRST name: Bob
Your  LAST name: Harris
Bob Harris [Y,n]: y
Wait ...
Password: .........
You last called on 28 Jan 1989  18:42:12

Hello,welcome to our system. This
bulletin board is open 24 hrs a day.
Our speciality is broadcasting.
--------------
You are the 38,319th caller

Wait ...

Main: M F G S B Y C U E V or ? for help: m a 2
```

The dog symbol shown above is that of the FIDO system, after its American developer and inventor. The software is written in English, though some of the opening sequences have been written in both English and Dutch. The first time you call the board you can either enter your real name (and then get allocated a password for future use) or use the 'guest' name of NOS, HOBBYSCOOP, with the password BASICODE. If you have problems call the system with the guest IDs, and leave a message for the SYSOP. In our example, caller Bob Harris now has a number of areas at his disposal. He may select the message area to check for mail. You do this by entering **M A 2** (standing for Message Area 2). The following sequence might then follow:

```
Msg Area #2: Radio Netherlands message area
25 messages, highest is #25, last you read was #7
Want to check for mail? [Y,n]: y


New messages to you:
25, 24, 23,
Old messages to you:
7,
Messages you have entered:
3, 1,
Msg: A L R E K I S G M or ? for help: r

Read messages.


#7   5 27-01-89  12:32:48  (PRIVATE)
From: Wolfgang Meyer
To:   Bob Harris
Subj: Receivers

Dear Bob,:

Thanks for ......
```

etc

In addition to exchanging electronic mail with other listeners or the editors, Radio Netherlands 'Media Network' supports the NOS-FIDO net by providing the following information of interest to both NOS and Radio Netherlands listeners:

1. Texts of consumer tests on communications equipment, i.e. new short wave radios, antennae, and computer interfaces.
2. BASICODE programs received from listeners abroad, and developed by Radio Netherlands.
3. WESTLINK Radio Bulletins, including news from the American headquarters of the Amateur Radio Satellite Corporation in Washington DC.
4. Communications/Broadcasting news. Taken from the Media Network programme on Radio Netherlands.

To get to the file area first return to the main menu (you may have to press **Q** to quit what you're doing) and then type **M** to get to the main menu. Then type in **F A 2 F**. This will list the files available in File Area 2. Here is a look at some of the files available as of January 1st 1989.

```
File Area #2: Radio Netherlands files
File: A L F T G U D S M K or ? for help: f

FRG-8800          9215 Review of this Yaesu receiver
DXING            10307 Intro to DXing
FRG-9600         10467 Review of this Yaesu receiver
RFB.60L           7965 Review of this Panasonic travel radio
NRD-525           9336 Test of Japan Radio Corp Receiver
D2935             9320 Review of this Philips Receiver
HF125             7679 Review of the Lowe HF 125 SW Receiver
GERMANY.BBS      13696 A list of mailboxes in West Germany
USAPCBBS.ARC     35456 PC-devoted Bulletin Boards in the U.S.A.
ATARI.BBS         1024 Atari-devoted Bulletin Boards in Germany
FINBOXIS.ARC      3584 BBSes in Finland
USA.BUL           4095 North American SWL Bulletin Boards
ICF7601           5884 Review of this Sony Travel Portable
NEWSMIR.055       5305 ENGLISH VERSION MIR REPORT FROM SURREY.
AMSAT.250        11392 Amsat North America News January 15th
MN.NEWS           6600 Media Network News January 11. 1989.
```

Any of the files can be selected and downloaded free of charge. The only cost to the caller is that of the telephone connection.

Of course, the new electronic computer service will not replace or diminish the value of letters and telephone calls currently received by Radio Netherlands. Research indicates that this development will reach new potential listeners and help them to discover international broadcasting through computing.

What next?

As well as continuing to provide computer data via the phone, many groups worldwide are looking into ways to link this database type of radio related information into the packet radio system. This is a network of amateur radio transmitters located around the world which permit computer data to be sent over the airwaves to other licensed amateur radio operators. At the moment the material that can be picked up via packet radio has a heavy emphasis on ham radio topics . . . only some of it is relevant to the broadcast listener.

Computer information on the air

Two magazine programmes deal specifically with radio-related computer software topics, as and when news appears:

- **Sweden Calling DXers:** George Wood's excellent Tuesday programme regularly looks at computing topics. This is backed up with the publication 'The DXers Guide to Computing'. This publication is reasonably priced. For details write to DX Editor, Radio Sweden, S-105 10 Stockholm, Sweden.
- **Media Network** is broadcast each Thursday. Further information from 'Media Network', Radio Netherlands, PO Box 222, 1200 JG, Hilversum. The science magazine 'Research File' on Mondays also deals with computer topics.